THE BOOK OF
GRISWOLD & WAGNER

FAVORITE PIQUE - SIDNEY HOLLOW WARE - WAPAK

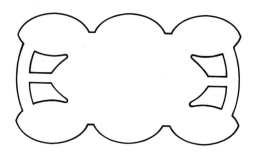

**David G. Smith
& Charles Wafford**

With Revised Price Guide

Revised & Expanded 2nd Edition

Photography by David G. Smith

Schiffer Publishing Ltd®

4880 Lower Valley Road, Atglen, PA 19310 USA

ACKNOWLEDGMENTS

We would like to express our gratitude to those who shared their collections and knowledge, without which this book would not have been possible:

Betsy & Larry Knight; John & Roberta Knoch; Marvin & Paula Fullenkamp; John & Ursula Harris; Joe & Joan Baldini; Jim & Sally Swanson; Joseph Noto; Thomas Todsen; Roger Aschenbach; Brad Schwartling; Merle Henry; Courtney McClendon; Paul & Bunny Baker; James Wiseman; Jack Jenny; Richard Wallace; Jon F. Baker; Theodore G. Boerger; Donald E. Doll; Glen Miller; Shirley A. Propst; Curt Hansen; Jerome Wagner, Jr.; Grant Windsor.

A special thanks to Larry & Sue Foxx for their assistance and support, and to Karl Miller for his special effort with the black & white photo processing.

Revised price guide: 2000
Copyright © 1995 & 2000 by David G. Smith and Charles Wafford.
Library of Congress Catalog Card Number: 99-066927

Designed by Sue

ISBN: 0-7643-0926-9
Printed in China
1 2 3 4

Published by Schiffer Publishing Ltd.
4880 Lower Valley Road
Atglen, PA 19310
Phone: (610) 593-1777; Fax: (610) 593-2002
E-mail: Schifferbk@aol.com
Please visit our website catalog at
www.schifferbooks.com

This book may be purchased from the publisher.
Include $3.95 for shipping. Please try your bookstore first.
We are interested in hearing from authors
with book ideas on related subjects.
You may write for a free printed catalog.

In Europe, Schiffer books are distributed by
Bushwood Books
6 Marksbury Avenue
Kew Gardens
Surrey TW9 4JF England
Phone: 44 (0)208-392-8585; Fax: 44 (0)208-392-9876
E-mail: Bushwd@aol.com

Contents

PART 2—THE WAGNER MANUFACTURING CO.

PART 3—SIDNEY HOLLOW WARE CO.

PART 4—FAVORITE STOVE & RANGE CO.

PART 5—WAPAK HOLLOW WARE CO.

BIBLIOGRAPHY

GRISWOLD PATTERN NUMBERS

INDEX

INTRODUCTION

Historians say that the first casting of metal probably occurred about 4000 B.C. Castings of iron were first made by the Chinese in the sixth century B.C. After spreading eastward, the casting process also spread westward into the Near East, the Mediterranean basin, and into the rest of Europe. In Europe, iron was not generally cast until about the fourteenth century.

In America the first castings were undoubtedly made by the more advanced Indian civilizations in Central and South America before the Europeans came. The first American casting made in the colonies which are now part of the United States was an iron cooking pot made near Lynn, Massachusetts, in 1642. After that, a number of small foundries were established in the colonies. Paul Revere was a foundryman; Valley Forge, where Washington spent the winter with his army, was the site of an early American foundry.

Cast iron was melted in a blast furnace, and while still in a molten state was poured into a hollowed mold. Most 18th century pots were made in this manner; the process left a raised mark where the iron entered the mold. During the first half of the 1700s this was typically a round mark (a 'sprue') on the bottom; by mid-century, a new elongated line (a 'gate') had become normal, and continued into the 1800s.

The gate or sprue left a protrusion on the bottom of the pan or kettle. This was acceptable for cookware used on a hearth, but with the introduction of the kitchen range or cookstove, it became necessary to cast pieces with smooth bottoms.

A more sophisticated casting method was developed. Rather than pouring the molten iron through the sprue directly into the mold, the sprue was connected to another channel called the 'in gate'. The iron followed the in gate and entered at the edge or side of the hollow cavity formed by the pattern. In this process, the gate was attached to the edge or side of the piece. When cooled, the gate was cut off, and then ground off. This method provided a smooth, flat bottom for the skillet or other item to sit on the flat top of a wood or coal stove. The cookware discussed and illustrated in this book will, for the most part, be from this later period.

Cast iron cookware—or as the industry referred to it, 'hollow ware'—was originally produced by stove companies. They presented hollow wares as accessories for their stoves. Some pieces were specifically designed to fit their particular lines, but for the most part hollow ware was standard.

Emerging from the industry were several foundries (other than the stove companies) which produced hollow ware. Two—the Griswold Manufacturing Company of Erie, Pennsylvania, and the Wagner Manufacturing Company of Sidney, Ohio—became world leaders in hollow ware production. Because of the large volume and diversity of their products, each became a household name. A major portion of this book is devoted to these leaders in the industry.

HOW TO USE THIS BOOK

VALUES

The values in this book are based on current selling prices. Values are not based on auction prices or asking prices but are based on current retail sales. **These values are for items in excellent condition, with no rust, chips or cracks.** These prices may vary however in different geographical locations. Values indicated in this book are to be used as a guide; they are not intended to set prices. Neither the authors nor the publisher assumes responsibility for any losses that might be incurred as a result of consulting this text.

ABBREVIATIONS & EXPLANATIONS

p/n:	pattern number
Cat. No.:	Catalog Number
Circa:	time period of manufacture based on actual records, markings, or characteristics.
EPU:	Erie, PA. U.S.A.
Logo:	Trademark
TM:	Trademark
Large block logo:	3 1/4"+ diameter
Medium logo:	2 1/4"—2 1/2" diameter
Small logo:	1 7/8" diameter
Stylized logo:	Single 'W' Wagner Ware trademark since 1915
Value:	retail market value of items in EXCELLENT CONDITION, 1995.
dia.:	diameter
h, l, w, d:	high, long, wide, deep

Where possible, the name used for the item is authentic to the period.

GRISWOLD FINISHES

Griswold made their iron hollow ware with several finishes:

1) **Extra Finish Ware**—The interior was polished, and in some cases they buffed the top of the handles.
2) **Plain iron**—Unpolished.
3) **Nickel-plated**—Available from the late 1800s until about 1930.
4) **Chromium**—There were three chromium finishes introduced around 1932:
—Chrome: a highly polished finish.
—Silverlike: an unpolished, flat chromium finish.
—Du Chro: a flat finish with polished high lights such as cover edges and handles.
5) **Porcelain**—There were three periods of enameling, or porcelainizing:
—1930s, when they enameled skillets, skillet covers, and dutch ovens. In this period the four colors were Mandarin Red, Canary Yellow, Jade Green, and Turquoise Blue;
—1940s & 1950s, when a whole line of porcelain ware was introduced which included skillets, No. 3 Oval Roaster, dutch ovens, and casserole sets. The most common colors were Flamingo Red with Cream, and Buttercup Yellow with Dove Gray interiors. They also produced plain iron with white porcelain interior. A few other color combinations have shown up from that time period.
—1960s, when multi-colored and speckled ashtrays were made. These pieces were marketed from Sidney, Ohio.

THE GRISWOLD
MANUFACTURING COMPANY
ERIE, PENNSYLVANIA

From Hardware—

(Model.)

S. SELDEN.
DOOR HANGER.

No. 246,642.   Patented Sept. 6, 1881.

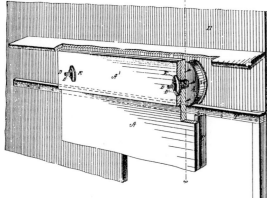

Fig.1.

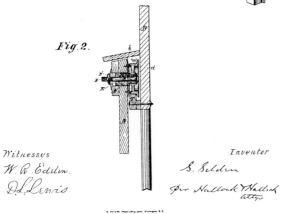

Fig.2.

Witnesses
W. R. Eddin.
D. L. Lewis

Inventor
S. Selden
Per Hullock & Hullock
Attys

—To Cookware

C. A. MASSING.
COOKING UTENSIL.
APPLICATION FILED NOV. 25, 1918.

1,330,209.   Patented Feb. 10, 1920.

FIG.1.

FIG.2.

Inventor
Charles A. Massing
By
N. C. Lord
Attorney.

Matthew Griswold (b. June 6, 1833) moved to Erie, Pennsylvania in 1865, after thirty years on the family farm in Old Lyme, Connecticut. His move was prompted not only by business considerations, but also by family relationships. His second cousin, Samuel Selden (b. July 9, 1821, in Erie) had returned there to join the paper manufacturing business after several years of managing a plantation in Cuba. Samuel's brother, John Card Selden (b. November 28, 1825, in Erie), had worked during his early adulthood as a store clerk in Troy, New York, before joining his brother George in California in 1850. He had returned to Erie in 1853, and joined his father in the mercantile business. In addition, John C. Selden was married to Matthew Griswold's sister, Lydia. After Matthew relocated to Pennsylvania, he entered into a partnership with his two cousins.

By 1868, the company formed by the partnership of Matthew Griswold and the Selden brothers was manufacturing separable butt hinges and other articles of light hardware, working in a building known as the "Butt Factory". Situated on West 10th Street, on the bank of the Erie Extension Canal west of Chestnut Street, the original factory was a picturesque old frame building partly enclosed in the rear by a long rail fence.

The closing of the Erie Extension Canal in 1871 opened up the west side streets of Erie, thus allowing for expansion of the Butt Factory. Building succeeded building until the plant extended to Walnut Street.

The name "Butt Factory" was dropped in 1873, when the company became know as the Selden & Griswold Manufacturing Company. At that time, its force of employees numbered twenty.

Samuel Selden died in 1882, and in 1884 Matthew Griswold bought out the interests held by John Card Selden and by Samuel Selden's heirs to become the sole owner. At that time, the business employed about a hundred men, who worked in facilities including a foundry (100' x 150'), a two-story finishing room (30' x 90'; the upper floor was for machinery and a mounting room), a two-story storeroom (30' x 40'), a second two-story storeroom (60' x 95'), and an engine and boiler room with a fifty-horsepower engine.

Fire swept through this old plant on August 8, 1885, but it was repaired and remodeled the same year. The firm was reorganized two years after the fire, and the Griswold Manufacturing Company was chartered. Matthew Griswold's son, Marvin Griswold, left his position as treasurer of the Shaw Piano Company to join the Griswold Manufacturing Co. as treasurer.

In 1903 the old plant was abandoned, and the firm moved into the Shaw Piano Company buildings on the corners of 12th and Raspberry Streets. Numerous other buildings were added, and by 1909 the plant occupied the entire square between Cascade, 12th, Raspberry, and the railroad tracks.

One Griswold employee, Charles A. Massing, was to become one of the driving forces of the company. Initially hired in 1899 as a clerk, Massing was given the opportunity to become a salesman. Subsequently he became a sales manager, and then vice president in charge of sales. Over the course of his career, he was responsible for several patents. Massing retired in 1955, after 56 years of service.

Matthew Griswold, Sr. stepped down from his position as president in 1905, but remained as chairman until his death on May 19, 1919. Matthew Griswold, Jr. took his father's place as president in 1905, and kept the position until he left the company in 1914. He was replaced by his brother Marvin. Marvin Griswold is credited with making the firm an acknowledged leader in the manufacture of cast iron cookware. He, together with such field representatives as Charles Massing, John Holland, and S.E. Lent, contributed the driving energy and foresight that produced Griswold's growth.

Marvin Griswold died in 1926, after which Matthew, Jr.'s son Roger Griswold served as president until 1945. Roger foresaw that electricity would be the ideal heat source for cooking operations, prompting Griswold to manufacture a commercial electric waffle baker. The line was expanded to include a complete commercial electric cooking line.

In the summer of 1937, a prolonged labor strike arose because company officials refused to recognize the CIO, a large labor union. After weeks of negotiations in which city officials and police took an active part, the strike was settled. For the first time in Erie's industrial history, laborers demands for better working conditions and higher wages had made a serious impact.

Roger Griswold, who had been the Griswold Manufacturing Company's president since 1927, died suddenly of a heart attack in December of 1944. His brother Ely Griswold, who was the controlling stock holder, assumed the presidency. Shortly thereafter, Ely announced that the company was to be sold because he wanted to retire. This prompted bitter lawsuits between the two branches of the Griswold family. Nonetheless, Ely Griswold succeeded in his goal, and the Griswold Manufacturing Company was sold in 1946 to a syndicate of New York City investors. By 1947 all members of the Griswold family had left the company, which was then headed by Isador Tachna, president, and Abe S. Weissman, general manager and treasurer.

In March of 1957, the historic Griswold Manufacturing Co. was purchased by the McGraw Edison Company of Chicago, Illinois. Within six months, McGraw Edison had sold the Housewares Division and the Griswold name and trademarks to Griswold's strongest competitor, the Wagner Manufacturing Company of Sidney, Ohio. McGraw Edison subsequently closed out the electrical cooking division, deciding to combine its entire Erie facilities with other units in Illinois.

The Wagner Manufacturing Company continued the Griswold name and trademark, but dropped the phrase "Erie, Pa." from their manufactured pieces. It was now the Griswold Manufacturing Company, Division of Wagner Manufacturing Company, Sidney, Ohio.

In January of 1959, the Wagner Manufacturing Company transferred all Griswold trademark rights to Textron Inc. of Providence, Rhode Island.

For the next ten years, cast iron cookware marketed with the Griswold trademark continued to be manufactured in the Sidney, Ohio plant under the auspices of the Randall Company, a subsidiary of the Textron Corporation.

The General Housewares Corporation acquired all rights to both the Griswold and Wagner trademarks in August of 1969. General Housewares continues to manufacture cast iron cookware in the Sidney, Ohio plant today.

the world.

Although Wagner continued to manufacture cast iron ware, they became equally noted for their

The "Butt Factory," circa 1868.

A salesmen's meeting, 1918. From left, seated, are B. Hickox, S.R. Herron, Matthew Griswold Sr., S.E. Lent, John C. Holland; from left, standing, C.T. Bowen, Roger W. Griswold, W.E. Smith, Marvin E. Griswold, Ely Griswold, C.A. Massing, J.E. Haviland, and B.M. Oxtoby.

Griswold marks 89 years of Progress

Our original cast-iron ware set, undoubtedly worthy of any museum, is a prized possession of R. W. Griswold, Jr. It consisted of 1) a pair of andirons, 2) toaster for open fire toasting, 3) tongs, 4) shovel, 5) a long handle waffle iron made with forged pans, 6) large pot for use on a crane in an open fireplace, 7) a long handle skillet for use on open fire, and 8) a broiler for the open fireplace.

We've come a long way — and our Quality Lifetime Cast Iron Ware is the finest money can buy!

GRISWOLD MANUFACTURING COMPANY
1053 W. 12TH ST.

124

An advertisement in *The Spokesman*, the Strong Vincent High School yearbook, Erie, PA., 1954.

GRISWOLD
COOKING UTENSILS

*Effectively Advertised
by Stubbs*

"ERIE" or ERIE
c. 1870s to 1900

No. 6	$150-$200
No. 7	$50-$75
No. 8	$30-$40
No. 9	$30-$40
No. 10	$75-$100
No. 11	$150-$200
No. 12	$100-$150

ERIE
(with inset heat ring)

No. 5	$175-$200
No. 6	$50-$75
No. 7	$30-$50
No. 8	$30-$50
No. 9	$40-$60
No. 10	$75-$100
No. 11	$150-$200
No. 12	$150-$200

All skillet values based on pieces in excellent condition.

GRISWOLD'S ERIE
c. 1890 to 1910

No. 5	$175-$200
No. 6	$50-$75
No. 7	$30-$50
No. 8	$30-$50
No. 9	$40-$60
No. 10	$75-$100
No. 11	$150-$200
No. 12	$150-$200

Slant/ERIE PA USA
(with heat ring)
c. 1909 to 1929

No. 2	$500-$600
No. 3	$30-$40
No. 4	$80-$100
No. 5	$30-$50
No. 6	$30-$50
No. 7	$30-$50
No. 8	$30-$50
No. 9	$30-$50
No. 10	$60-$75
No. 11	$150-$200
No. 12	$75-$100
No. 13	$1000-$1200
No. 14	$700-$800
No. 20	$700-$800

Slant/ERIE
c. 1907 to 1912

No. 1	Rare
No. 2	$400-$500
No. 3	$25-$35
No. 4	$100-$150
No. 5	$30-$40
No. 6	$30-$40
No. 7	$40-$50
No. 8	$30-$40
No. 9	$30-$50
No. 10	$50-$75
No. 11	$150-200
No. 12	$100-$150
No. 13	$600-$700
No. 14	$600-$700

Slant/ERIE PA USA (with smooth bottom)
c. 1939 to 1944

No. 2 $400-$500
No. 3 $50-$60
No. 5 $40-$50
No. 8 $40-$50
No. 9 $60-75

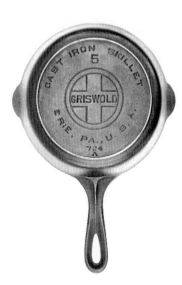

Block/ERIE PA USA
(with heat ring)
c. 1920—1930

No. 0 $75-$100
No. 2 $1000-1500
No. 3 $20-$30
No. 4 $450-$500
No. 5 $400-$500
No. 6 $75-$100
No. 7 $25-45
No. 8 $30-$40
No. 9 $30-$40
No. 10 $60-$75
No. 11 $150-$200
No. 12 $75-$100
No. 13 $1200-$1500
No. 14 $100-$150
No. 20 $500-$600

Block/ERIE PA USA
(with smooth bottom)
c. 1930 to 1939

No. 2 $350-$400
No. 3 $10-$20
No. 4 $60-$80
No. 5 $10-$20
No. 6 $20-$30
No. 7 $20-$30
No. 8 $20-$30
No. 9 $20-$30
No. 10 $60-80

Small logo
(early handle)
c. 1939 to 1944

No. 3 $5-$15
No. 5 $10-$20
No. 6 $10-$20
No. 7 $10-$20
No. 8 $10-$20
No. 9 $20-$30
No. 10 $20-$30
No. 12 $50-$75
(with heat ring)

Small logo
(late handle)
c. 1944 to 1957

No. 3	$5-$15
No. 4	$30-$50
No. 5	$15-$20
No. 6	$15-$20
No. 7	$15-$20
No. 8	$15-$20
No. 9	$20-$30
No. 10	$30-$40

Wood Handle
(various logos)
c. 1885 to 1940

No. 2	Rare
No. 3	$175-$200
No. 4	$200-$250
No. 5	$100-$125
No. 6	$100-$125
No. 7	$75-100
No. 8	$75-$100
No. 9	$50-$75
No. 10	$100-$125
No. 11	$200-$250
No. 12	$200-$250

Small logo (with hinge tab)
c. 1940s to 1957

No. 3	$30-$50
No. 5	$50-$60
No. 6	$60-$70
No. 7	$60-$70
No. 8	$40-$50
No. 9	$60-$70

Small logo
(grooved handle)
c. 1944 to 1957

No. 3	$5-$15
No. 4	$30-$40
No. 5	$15-$20
No. 6	$15-$20
No. 7	$15-$20
No. 8	$15-20
No. 9	$20-$30

VICTOR
(fully marked)
c. 1920 to 1935

No. 5	$400-$500
No. 6	$150-$200
No. 7	$35-$60
No. 8	$35-$60
No. 9	$35-$60

Deduct 30% for other
Victors

Above and Left:
SPIDER LOGO SKILLET—Size: No. 8; **p/n:** none;
Markings: spider logo, "Erie"; **Finish:** iron; **Circa:**
before 1890; **VALUE: $1500-$2000**.

REGULAR SKILLET—Size: No. 8; **p/n:** none; **Markings:** Erie, 8c;
Finish: iron; **Circa:** 1870-1880; **VALUE: $100**. This gate mark is
early and unusual.

REGULAR SKILLET—Size: No. 11; **p/n:** none; **Markings:** "ERIE";
Finish: iron; **Circa:** 1870-1900; **VALUE: $150**.

REGULAR SKILLET—Size: No. 8; **p/n:** none; **Markings:** Erie, B; **Finish:** iron; **Circa:** 1870s-1900; **VALUE: $75.**

REGULAR SKILLET-Size: No. 5; **p/n:** 3348; **Markings:** ERIE, 3348, No. 5; **Finish:** iron; **Circa:** 1907. **VALUE: $200-$300.** This is the only style of Erie skillet known in size No. 5.

Below and Left:
EXTRA DEEP SKILLET—Size: No. 8. **p/n:** 732; **Markings:** ERIE; **Finish:** iron; **Circa:** 1880-1900; **VALUE: RARE.** This skillet is rough, with very heavy casting; it weighs 7 lbs compared to 5 1/2 lbs of other Erie Deep Skillets. The waffled interior bottom is unusual.

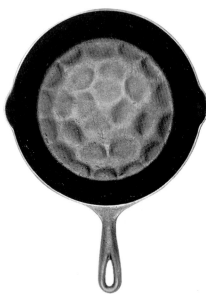

REGULAR SKILLET-Size: No. 12; **p/n:** unknown; **Markings:** ERIE; **Finish:** aluminum with iron handle; **Circa:** 1900-1910; **VALUE: $75-$100.** The cast iron handle is riveted on.

PATTERN-MAKER MARKS are found occasionally on Erie skillets. The marks may have been done as the pattern maker's signature, or may have been done as a form of quality control.

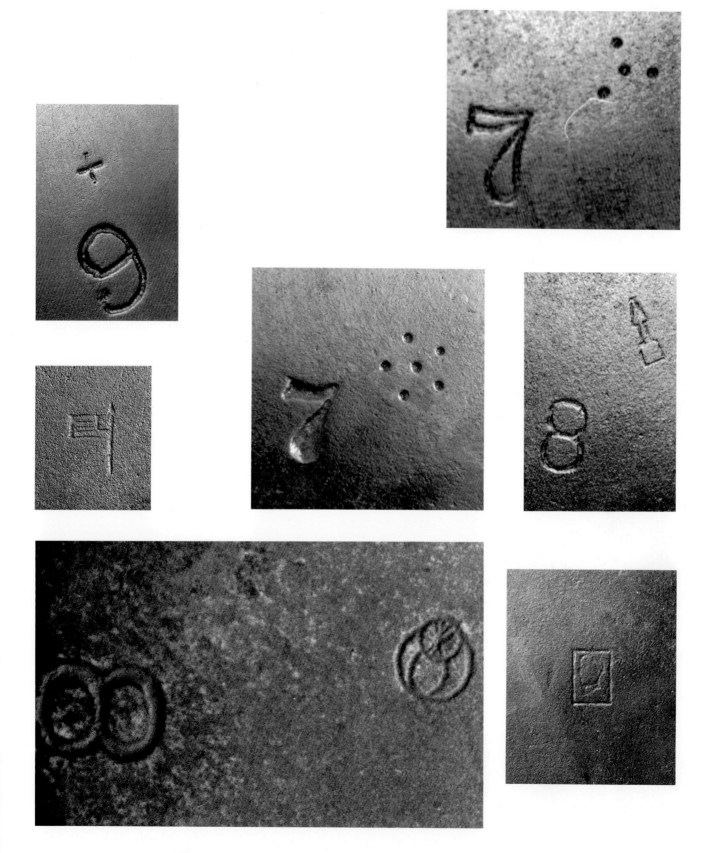

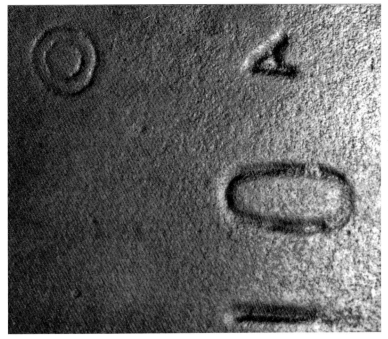

More pattern-maker marks.

VICTOR SKILLET—Size: No. 7; **p/n:** 721; **Markings:** "VICTOR"; **Finish:** iron; **Circa:** 1900. **VALUE: $50.**

VICTOR SKILLET—Size: No. 5; **p/n:** 695; **Markings:** Cast Iron Skillet, The Griswold Mfg. Co, Erie PA, USA; **Finish:** iron; **Circa:** 1935; **VALUE: $400-$500.** Victor Skillets are 1/8" to 1/2" shallower than Regular Skillets.

VICTOR SKILLET—Size: No. 8. **p/n:** 722; **Markings:** VICTOR; **Finish:** iron; **Circa:** 1910; **VALUE: No. 7, $50; No. 8, $40; No. 9, $50.**

REGULAR SKILLET—Size: No. 12; **p/n:** 719; **Markings:** slant logo, ERIE; **Finish:** iron; **Circa:** 1920s; **VALUE: $150-$200.** Griswold also made No. 14 with a loop finger handle.

REGULAR SKILLET—**Size:** No. 11. **p/n:** 717; **Markings:** slant logo, EPU; **Finish:** iron; **Circa:** 1909-1929; **VALUE: $150-$200.**

REGULAR SKILLET—**Size:** No. 13; **p/n:** 720; **Markings:** slant logo, EPU; **Finish:** iron or nickel; **Circa:** 1909; **VALUE: $1000-$1200.**

REGULAR SKILLET—**Size:** 13; **p/n:** 720; **Markings:** Block logo, REGULAR SKILLET—**Size:** No. 13; **p/n:** 720; **Markings:** block logo, EPU; **Finish:** iron, nickel, chrome, Du Chro, or Silverlike; **Circa:** 1920-1940; **VALUE: $800-$1000.**

REGULAR SKILLET—Size: No. 14; **p/n:** 718; **Markings:** slant logo, EPU; **Finish:** iron or nickel; **Circa:** 1909-1929. **VALUE: $700-$800**.

REGULAR SKILLET—Size: No. 9; **p/n:** 710B. **Markings:** slant logo ; **Finish:** iron; **Circa:** 1909-1920; **VALUE:** $40. No "ERIE" or "Erie PA USA" in the mark.

REGULAR SKILLET—Size: No. 8; **p/n:** 704B; **Markings:** slant logo, ERIE; **Finish:** iron; **Circa:** 1909-1920; **VALUE: $50-$60**. This logo is 2 1/2" diameter, compared to the usual 3 1/4" diameter.

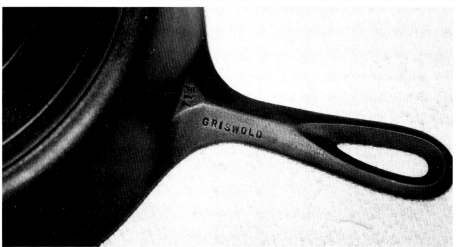

REGULAR SKILLET—Size: No. 8; **p/n:** 715; **Markings:** 8, GRISWOLD, 715; **Finish:** iron; **Circa:** 1920s-1930s; **VALUE: Rare**. Smooth flat bottom with three inset rings.

REGULAR SKILLET—Size: No. 8. **p/n:** 2808. **Marking:** small logo, EPU, 'G' around handle hole; **Finish:** iron; **Circa:** 1950s; **VALUE: $75**.

No. 12 SKILLET—Size: No. 12. **p/n;** none; **Markings:** Faint Griswold markings, EAGLE STOVE WORKS, ROME GA, in raised letters; **Finish:** iron, fair casting; **Circa:** before 1956; **VALUE: $200-$250**. This was not a Griswold-produced product. A Griswold skillet was apparently used as a pattern for this skillet.

Below and Right:
ODORLESS SKILLET—Size: No. 8. **p/n:** none; **Markings:** MADE BY W.E. BEVERIDGE, BALTIMORE MD; **Finish:** iron—Griswold quality casting; **Circa:** 1900; **VALUE: $75-$100**. An Erie "E" can be seen right of opening.

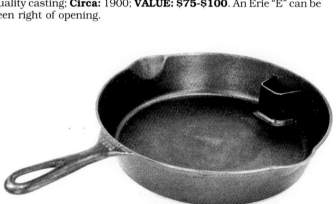

PURITAN SKILLET—Size: No. 3; **p/n:** 1501A; **Markings:** PURITAN; **Finish:** iron; **Circa:** 1920s-1930s; **VALUE:** $30. Puritan was made for Sears Roebuck & Co.

GOOD HEALTH SKILLET—Size: No. 3; **p/n:** 653; **Markings:** GOOD HEALTH SKILLET; **Finish:** iron; **Circa:** 1920s-1930s; **VALUE:** $30.

CLIFF CORNELL SKILLET—Size: No. 3; **p/n:** none; **Markings:** Compliments "Cliff" Cornell, The Cleveland Flux Co, Cleveland 13 Ohio, small logo; **Finish:** iron; **Circa:** 1930s; **VALUE:** $250-$300.

GOOD HEALTH SKILLET—Size: No. 9; **p/n:** 659; **Markings:** GOOD HEALTH SKILLET; **Finish:** iron; **Circa:** 1920s-1930s; **VALUE:** $35.

THE GRISWOLD MFG. CO
200 5th AVE. NEW YORK, N.
Room 214   GRAMERCY 1

NET PRICES ON GOOD HEALTH WARE

Packed in Standard Cartons

No.	Item	Standard Packing In Carton	Net Price
3	Skillet	4	$ .20
5	"	4	.33
6	"	4	.37
7	"	4	.40
8	"	4	.45
9	"	4	.50
10	"	4	.55
12	"	2	.75
14	"	1	1.00
	Dutch Ovens Less Trivets		
7	"	1	$1.15
8	"	1	1.25
9	"	1	1.35
10	"	1	1.80
	Handle Griddles		
8	"	4	$ .35
9	"	4	.45
	Long Griddles		
7	"		$ .55
8	"		.80
9	"		1.10

Less 10%

The GOOD HEALTH line is full sized,
full polished finish and lacquered.
It is labeled "GOOD HEALTH WARE"
with regular Iron Hollow Ware direc-
tions for seasoning.

THE GRISWOLD MFG. CO.
Erie, Pa.
5-4-31   NEW YORK OFFICE
200 Fifth Avenue   Room 214
New York, N. Y.

Griswold "Good Health Ware"—the 1931 price
list.

THE GRISWOLD MFG CO
200 5th AVE. NEW YORK, N.
Room 214   GRAMERCY 1

NET PRICES on NO NAME POLISHED WARE

No.	Item	Number In Barrel	Net Price
3	Skillet	300	$ .15
5	"	140	.25
6	"	120	.28
7	"	100	.30
8	"	90	.34
9	"	75	.39
10	"	70	.43
12	"	50	.60
14	"	35	.80
	Dutch Ovens Less Trivets		
7	"	30	$ .80
8	"	25	.88
9	"	20	1.00
10	"	18	1.38
	Chicken Pans		
8	"	30	$ .75
	Trivets (plain)		
8	"		.10
	Reg. Griddles		
8	"	100	$ .27
9	"	100	.34

NO NAME SKILLET SETS - Packed 48 sets in a barrel

Polished Skillet Set #3 - 5 - 8 $.74

THE GRISWOLD MFG. CO.
Erie, Pa.

5-5-31   Note: Sold in barrel lots only.
NEW YORK OFFICE
200 Fifth Avenue   Room 214
New York, N. Y.

Griswold "No Name Polished Ware"—1931 price list.

IRON MOUNTAIN SKILLET–Size: 5; p/n:
1030; **Markings**; 5, 1030; **Finish**: iron;
Circa: 1940; VALUE: No. 3, $10; No. 4, $60-
$80; No. 5, 6, and 7, $25; No. 8 and 9, $30;
No. 10, $40; No. 12, $50; No. 14, $75-$100.

REGULAR SKILLET—Size: No. 2; **p/n:** 703; **Markings:** block logo, EPU; **Finish:** iron, chrome, Du Chro, Silverlike; **Circa:** 1930-1939; **VALUE: iron $350-$400, chrome $200-$300.**

WOOD HANDLE SKILLET—Size: No. 2; **p/n:** 735; **Markings:** slant logo, EPU; **Finish:** iron; **Circa:** 1939-1944; **VALUE: Rare.**

REGULAR SKILLET—Size: No. 2; **p/n:** 703A; **Markings:** slant logo, EPU; **Finish:** iron; **Circa:** 1939-1944; **VALUE: $500-$600.** The slant logo with a smooth bottom is uncommon.

RAU BROTHERS SKILLET—Size: No. 2; **p/n:** 703A; **Markings:** RAU BROS, HAMBURG PA, slant logo EPU; **Finish:** iron or aluminum; **Circa:** 1920s; **VALUE: $500-$600** iron; **$300-$400** aluminum.

REPRODUCTION — NO. 2 SKILLET; very poor casting and detail.

BAILED HANDLE SKILLET—Size: No. 14 (15 1/2" top dia.); **p/n:** 694; **Markings:** block logo, EPU; **Finish:** iron; **Circa:** 1930s; **VALUE: $1000-$1200.**

Top and right:
No. 20 SKILLET—Size: 20" dia. x 2 1/2"
deep, 20 lbs 14 oz; **p/n:** 728; **Markings:**
block logo, EPU, CAST IRON SKILLET; **Finish:** iron (also porcelain); **Circa:** 1931-1957;
VALUE: $500-$600. Skillets made after 1957
were not marked "Erie PA."

No. 20 SKILLET—Size: 20" dia.; **p/n:** none;
Markings: block logo, CAST IRON SKILLET,
20 INCH; **Finish:** iron; **Circa:** 1958-1970;
VALUE: $300-$400. Made in Sidney, Ohio.

KING HARDWARE SKILLET—**Size:** No. 8; **p/n:** 667; **Markings:** 50TH ANNIVERSARY, KING HDW. CO.; **Finish:** chrome; **Circa:** 1950s; **VALUE: $50**.

WOOD HANDLE SKILLET—**Size:** No. 3; **p/n:** A2103; **Markings:** Medium logo, Erie PA; **Finish:** hammered aluminum; **Circa:** 1930s; **VALUE: $50-$75**.

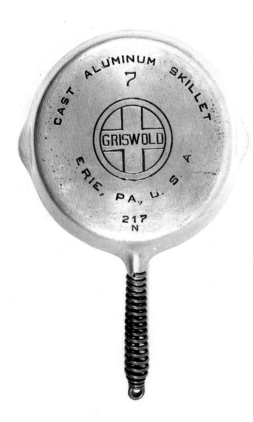

CAST ALUMINUM SKILLET—**Size:** No. 7; **p/n:** 217; **Markings:** block logo, EPU; **Finish:** aluminum with Alaskan coil handle; **Circa:** 1934; **VALUE: No. 7, $75; No. 8, $75; No. 9, $100.**

WOOD HANDLE SKILLET—**Size:** No. 3; **p/n:** A203; **Markings:** small logo, THE GRISWOLD MFG CO, ERIE PA, USA; **Finish:** aluminum with wood handle; **Circa:** 1930s; **VALUE: $75-$100**.

ALUMINUM SKILLET—Size: No. 8; **p/n:** A2108, Cover A2108C; **Markings:** Medium logo, ERIE PA; **Finish:** hammered aluminum; **Circa:** 1930s; **VALUE: $75-$100 with cover**.

WOOD HANDLE SKILLETS; Set from sizes "0", No. 2-No. 12.

SKILLET DISPLAY STAND—Size: holds seven skillets; **p/n:** plate—1066; **Markings:** THE GRISWOLD MFG CO, ERIE PENN, USA; Metal plate on front marked GRISWOLD; **Finish:** Wood base with mustard yellow paint; **Circa:** 1920s; **VALUE: $350-$450**.

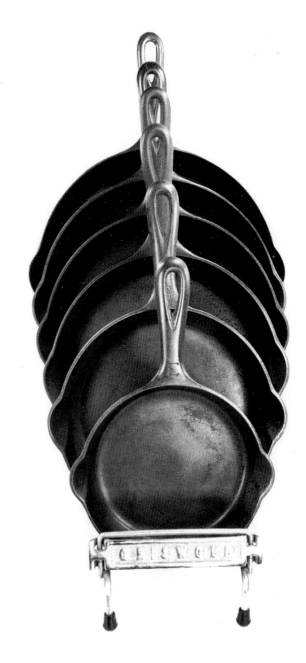

Top and right:
SKILLET DISPLAY STAND—**Size:** Holds six skillets; **p/n:** 1068 on name plate; **Markings:** GRISWOLD; **Finish:** chrome; **Circa:** 1940s; **VALUE: $150-$200.**

SKILLET DISPLAY STANDS—Size: Three section for "Home Maker Set," sizes No. 3,6,8, and a six-section counter display; **p/n:** none; **Markings:** none; **Finish:** red rubberized, for enamel-finish:skillets; **Circa:** 1950s; **VALUE: $50-$100.**

Top and right:
HAMMERED FINISH:SKILLET—**Size:** No. 3; **p/n:** 2013; **Markings:** small logo, ERIE PA; **Finish:** Du-Chro; **Circa:** 1940s-1950s; **VALUE: $40**.

Left and Below:
HINGED SKILLET—**Size:** No. 8; **p/n:** 2008, Cover 2098; **Markings:** small logo, ERIE PA, Cover—2098; **Finish:** hammered; **Circa:** 1940s; **VALUE: No. 3, $250-$300; and No. 5, $75-$150; No. 8, $60**.

Top and Right:
HINGED SKILLET with cover—Size: No. 5; **p/n:** 2505, COVER 2595; **Markings:** small logo, ERIE PA; **Finish:** iron, also available with black,"Easy Clean" cover; **Circa:** 1940s; **VALUE:** No. 3, $125-150; No. 5, $100-$125; No. 6, $75-$100; No. 7, $75-$100; No. 8, $60-75; No. 9, $125-$150.

Above and Right:
OVAL SKILLET—Size: No. 15 (15" x 9 3/4" x 2 1/2" deep); **p/n:** 1013, Cover 1013C; **Markings:** block logo, OVAL SKILLET, ERIE PA; **Finish:** iron; **Circa:** 1940-1957; **VALUE:** Skillet $300, Cover $500-$600.

EXTRA DEEP SKILLET—Size: No. 8; **p/n:** 732; **Markings:** slant logo, ERIE; **Finish:** iron or nickel; **Circa:** 1900-1909; **VALUE: No. 8, $125; No. 9, $150; No. 10, $175.**

OVAL SKILLET—Size: No. 13; **p/n:** 1012; **Markings:** block logo, EPU, Oval Skillet; **Finish:** iron; **Circa:** 1940-1957; **VALUE: $250-$300.** A cover was not made for this skillet.

EXTRA DEEP SKILLET—Size: 8 (10 7/8" top dia. x 3" deep); **p/n:** 732; **Markings:** ERIE, 732, 8; **Finish:** iron or nickel; **Circa:** 1870-1900; **VALUE: No. 8, $100, No. 9, $125; No. 10, $150.**

EXTRA DEEP SKILLET—Size: No. 8; **p/n:** 762 ; **Markings:** slant logo, EPU, CAST IRON SKILLET; **Finish:** iron or nickel; **Circa:** 1909-1929; **VALUE: No. 8, $100; No. 9, $125; No. 10, $150.**

CHICKEN PAN—Size: No. 8; **p/n:** 768; **Markings:** block logo, EPU, CAST IRON CHICKEN PAN; **Finish:** iron; **Circa:** 1925-1930; **VALUE: $100-$150 with cover**.

EXTRA DEEP SKILLET—Size: No. 9; **p/n:**733 ; **Markings:** slant logo, ERIE; **Finish:** iron; **Circa:** 1900-1909; **VALUE: $125. No. 8, $75-100; No. 10, $125-150**. This item has straight sides and a square bottom like the Erie skillets.

CHICKEN PAN—Size: No. 8; **p/n:** 777; **Markings:** block logo, EPU, CAST IRON SKILLET OR CHICKEN PAN; **Finish:** iron, chrome, Du-Chro, Silverlike; **Circa:** 1930-1939; **VALUE: $75-$100, Chrome $60**.

Left:
EXTRA DEEP SKILLET—Size: No. 9; **p/n:** 778; **Markings:** block logo, EPU, CAST IRON SKILLET; **Finish:** iron; **Circa:** 1930-1939; **VALUE: No. 8, $75; No. 9, $100; No. 10, $125.**

Below and Below Left:
"IRON MOUNTAIN" CHICKEN PAN—Size: No. 8; **p/n:** 1034, Cover 1035; **Markings:** CHICKEN PAN,1034, 8; **Finish:** iron; **Circa:** 1940; **VALUE: $60.** This was a line made to sell in hardware stores, etc. Note the shape of handle and the broken basting rings.

Left and Below:
DOUBLE SKILLET—Size: No. 80; **p/n:** 1103, 1102; **Markings:** block logo, EPU, DOUBLE SKILLET TOP, DOUBLE SKILLET BTM; **Finish:** iron or chrome; **Circa:** 1930-1940S; **VALUE:** $80-$90; **No. 90, VALUE: $100-$125, plated, $75-$85.**

Left and Below:
ALL-IN-ONE DINNER SKILLET—Size: No. 8; **p/n:** 1008; **Markings:** block logo EPU, ALL-IN-ONE, PATENT APPLIED FOR; **Finish:** iron; **Circa:** 1932-1940; **VALUE: $250-$300.**

NEW ENGLAND GRIDDLE—**Size:** No. 9 ; **p/n:** 706; **Markings:** N. E. GRIDDLE, slant logo ; **Finish:** iron or nickel; **Circa:** 1910; **VALUE: No. 8, $100; No. 9, $125; No. 10, $150; No. 12, $200.**

SHALLOW SKILLET—**Size:** No. 7 (9" dia.); **p/n:** none; **Markings:** ERIE, 7A; **Finish:** iron or nickel; **Circa:** 1890-1910; **VALUE: No. 7, $100; No. 8, $100; No. 9, $125; No. 10, $150.**

SKILLET GRIDDLE—**Size:** No. 110; **p/n:** 203; **Markings:** slant logo, THE GRISWOLD MFG CO, ERIE PA USA; **Finish:** iron or nickel; **Circa:** 1920; **VALUE: No. 107, $125; No. 108, $100; No. 109, $125; No. 110, $100-$150.**

Above and Right:
SKILLET GRIDDLE—Size: No. 108; **p/n:** 201; **Markings:** block logo, THE GRISWOLD MFG CO, ERIE PA USA, CAST IRON SKILLET GRIDDLE, Heat Ring; **Finish:** iron; **Circa:** 1930s; **VALUE:** $80-$100. **No 109,** $100-$125; **No. 110,** $150-$175.

SKILLET GRIDDLE—Size: No. 107; **p/n:** 200; **Markings:** slant logo, EPU, CAST IRON SKILLET GRIDDLE; **Finish:** iron or nickel; **Circa:** 1909-1929; **VALUE:** $125.

SKILLET GRIDDLE—Size: No. 108; **p/n:** 201; **Markings:** block logo, CAST IRON SKILLET GRIDDLE; **Finish:** iron; **Circa:** 1930s; **VALUE:** $75-85. **No. 109,** $100-$125.

Above and Right:
ROUND BREAKFAST SKILLET—Size: 12" dia.;   **p/n:** 665; **Markings:**
block logo, CAST IRON BREAKFAST SKILLET, THE GRISWOLD MFG CO,
ERIE PA, USA, PATENT APPLIED FOR; **Finish:** iron or aluminum; **Circa:**
1932; **VALUE: iron $125-$150, aluminum $100.**

ROUND BREAKFAST SKILLET—Size: 12" dia.;   **p/n:** A565; **Markings:**
same as iron; **Finish:** aluminum with wood handle; **Circa:**1932; **VALUE:**
$100.

Left and Above:
COLONIAL BREAKFAST SKILLET—Size: 9" sq. x 1"
deep; **p/n:** 666; **Markings:** block logo, EPU, COLONIAL
BREAKFAST SKILLET, PATENT APPLIED FOR; **Finish:**
iron; **Circa:** 1940s; **VALUE: $35.**

CLIFF CORNELL BREAKFAST SKILLET—Size: 9"
sq.; **p/n:** none; **Markings:** block logo, COMPLIMENTS
"CLIFF CORNELL" THE CLEVELAND FLUX CO, CLEVE-
LAND OHIO; **Finish:** iron; **Circa:** 1930s; **VALUE: $150-
$200**.

BREAKFAST SKILLET—Size: 9" sq.; **p/n:** 1257;
Markings: BEST MADE BACON AND EGG FRYER,
PATENT APPLIED FOR; **Finish:** iron; **Circa:** 1930s;
VALUE: $75.

SQUARE EGG SKILLETS—Size: 4 3/4" sq.; **p/n:**
129 or 53; **Markings:** small logo, SINCE 1865;
Finish: iron, chrome, porcelain; **Circa:** No. 53, 1960s;
No. 129, unknown; **VALUE: $35-$50**. Note that the
letter "E" is missing from the word "SQUARE" on the
chrome skillet.

CHEF SKILLET—Size: 9" dia.; **p/n:** 43; **Markings:** small logo, CHEF SKILLET; **Finish:** iron; **Circa:** 1960s; **VALUE: $30-$45**.

Above and Right:
SQUARE SKILLET—Size: No. 6; **p/n:** 2106; **Markings:** Medium logo, **SQUARE FRY SKILLET**, ERIE PA; **Finish:** iron; **Circa:** 1944-1957; **VALUE: $75-$100; No. 2103, $100-$125**.

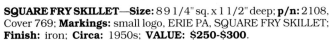

SQUARE FRY SKILLET—Size: 8 9 1/4" sq. x 1 1/2" deep; **p/n:** 2108, Cover 769; **Markings:** small logo, ERIE PA, SQUARE FRY SKILLET; **Finish:** iron; **Circa:** 1950s; **VALUE: $250-$300**.

Above and Right:
SQUARE SKILLETS—Size: No. 55 (9 1/2" sq.) and No. 57 (11 1/2 x 11 1/4"); **p/n:** 55 and 57; **Markings:** small logo; **Finish:** iron; **Circa:** 1960s; **VALUE: No. 55, $40;** and **No. 57, $50.**

DEEP SQUARE FRY SKILLET—Size: 9 1/2" sq. x 2" deep; **p/n:** 768, cover 769 ; **Markings:** small logo, ERIE PA, SQUARE FRY SKILLET; **Finish:** iron; **Circa:** 1960s; **VALUE: $300-$350.**

DEEP SQUARE FRY SKILLET (with Glass Cover)—Size: 9 1/2" sq.; **p/n:** 768; **Markings:** same as on iron, and the cover has the Griswold logo on the knob; **Finish:** nickel; **Circa:** 1960s; **VALUE: $75-150.**

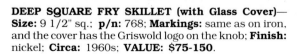

Above and Right:
TRANSPEED DEEP SKILLET—Size: No. 8;
p/n: none; **Markings:** none; **Finish:** aluminum with Bakelite handle; **Circa:** 1950s;
VALUE: $45. Transpeed utensils were used with Transpeed Electrical Hot Plates. They are commercial grade.

TRIPLICATE SAUCE PANS—Size: 8 1/2"
w x 6 3/8" x 4 1/4" deep; **p/n:** A236, cover A240C; **Markings:** block logo, Pat Feb 10, 1920; on cover, small logo, Self Basting; **Finish:** aluminum; **Circa:** 1934; **VALUE: $100-$150**.

Left and Below:
OMELETTE PAN—Size: 11" open; **p/n:** A54R, A54L; **Markings:** block logo, EPU; **Finish:** aluminum with wood handles; **Circa:** 1920-1930s; **VALUE: $100.**

Below:
"SYMBOL" WARE SAUCE PAN—Size: 2 qts.; **p/n:** 92; **Markings:** medium logo ; **Finish:** cast aluminum with pressed cover and black Bakelite handles; **Circa:** 1960s; **VALUE: $40.** Also made in 3 qt. and 1 1/2 quart sizes.

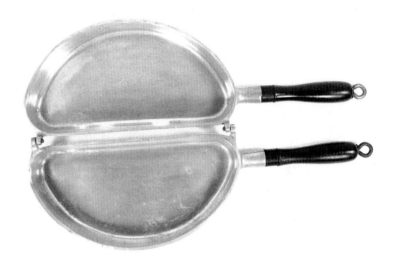

No. 3 UTILITY KETTLE—Size: 9 7/16" dia., 3 qts; **p/n:** 343; **Markings:** block logo, EPU, UTILITY KETTLE, CAST ALUMINUM; **Finish:** aluminum with wood handle; **Circa:** 1920-1940; **VALUE: $65.** Also made in 1 1/2 qt., 4 qt., and 5 qt. sizes.

SKILLET COVERS

FIVE BASIC COVER STYLES FOR REGULAR AND DEEP SKILLETS.

LOW DOME, RAISED LETTERS—(bottom left) **Size:** Nos. 3-14 (except No. 4); **Circa:** 1915-1935; **Value:** No. 3, $300-$400; No. 5, $250; No. 6, $150; No. 7, $75; No. 8, 40; No. 9, 40; No. 10, $75; No. 11, $300-$350; No. 12, $150; No. 13, Rare; No. 14, $200-$250.

LOW DOME, SMOOTH—(bottom right) **Size:** Nos. 3, 4, 10, 13, and 14; **Circa:** 1931-1957; **Value:** No. 3, $100; No. 4, $600; No. 10, $40; No. 13, $500-$700; No. 14, $200; No. 12, $100-$125.

HIGH DOME, RAISED LETTERS—(center) **Size:** Nos. 3—14 (except No. 4); **Circa:**1931-1957; **Value:** No. 3, $300-$400; No. 5, $150; No. 6, $150; No. 7, $65; No. 8, $35; No. 9, $35; No. 10, $60; No. 11, $250-$300; No. 12, $150; No. 13, Rare; No. 14, $200.

HIGH DOME, WITH LOGO —(top left) **Size:** Nos. 3—10; **Circa:** 1940s; **Value:** No. 3, $400-$450; No. 4, $600-$800; No. 5, $30; No. 6, $40; No. 7, $30; No. 8, $25; No. 9, $35; No. 10, $50.

HIGH DOME (PLAIN)—(top right) **Size:** Nos. 3—10; **Circa:** 1940s-1960s; **Value:** No. 3, $100-$125; No. 4, $400-$450; No. 5, $60; No. 6, $60; No. 7, $50; No. 8, $35; No. 9, 40; No. 10, $50.

HIGH DOME with RAISED LETTERS (left); **LOW DOME with RAISED LETTERS** (right).

HINGED SKILLET COVER—**Size:** No. 5; **p/n:** 2595; **Markings:** small logo, Erie PA (inside); **Finish:** iron, with Easy-Clean finish on inside of black cover; **Circa:** 1940s; **VALUE: No. 3, $100; No. 5, $30; No. 6, $30-$40; No. 7, $40; No. 8, $40; No. 9, $60-$80.**

HINGED SKILLET COVER—**Size:** No. 5 ; **p/n:** 2095; **Markings:** 2095; **Finish:** hammered iron; **Circa:**1940s ; **VALUE: No. 3, $75; No. 5, $60; No. 8, $40.**

STEEL SKILLET COVER—**Size:** No. 8; **p/n:** none; **Markings:** block logo; **Finish:** polished; **Circa:** 1950s; **VALUE: $20.**

Center Left and Left:
No. 20 SKILLET COVER—**Size:** 20 1/8" dia.; **p/n:** none; **Markings:** block logo, No. 20C; **Finish:** aluminum; **Circa:** 1950s; **VALUE: $500-$600.**

WASHINGTON BICENTENNIAL COVER—Size: No. 8; **p/n:** 1056; **Markings:** WASHINGTON BI-CENTENNIAL 1732—1932, 1056; **Finish:** iron or chrome; **Circa:** 1932; **VALUE: iron, $700; chrome, $600.**

SKILLET COVER DISPLAY STAND—Size: Holds six covers; **p/n:** none; **Markings:** GRISWOLD; **Finish:** chrome-plated rod with tin nameplate, red enamel with white letters; **Circa:** 1950s; **VALUE: $200.**

SQUARE SKILLET COVER—Size: 9 1/2" sq.; **p/n:** 769; **Markings:** small logo, ERIE PA, SQUARE FRY COVER; **Finish:** iron; **Circa:** 1950s; **VALUE: $200-$300.**

SQUARE FRY SKILLET COVER—Size: 9 1/2" sq.; **p/n:** 28C; **Markings:** Griswold logo on knob; **Finish:** glass; **Circa:** 1960s; **VALUE: $50-$100.**

Above and Right:
ROUND SELF BASTING GLASS COVERS—
Size: 8", 9", 10 1/2", 11 3/4"; **p/n:** none;
Markings: Griswold logo on knob; **Finish:**
glass; **Circa:** 1960s; **VALUE: $40-$60.**

SQUARE GLASS COVER—**Size:** 9 1/2" sq.;
p/n: none; **Markings:** Griswold logo on knob;
Finish: glass; **Circa:** 1960s; **VALUE: $75.**
Fits No. 55 Square Skillet.

GRIDDLES

BAILED GRIDDLE—**Size:** No. 16 (15 1/2" dia.); **p/n:** none; **Markings:** ERIE; **Finish:** iron; **Circa:** 1883; **VALUE:** $85; No. 12, $65-$75; No. 14, $75-$85.

HANDLE GRIDDLE Size: No. 6 (7 1/4" dia.); **p/n:** 736; **Markings:** ERIE; **Finish:** iron; **Circa:** 1885-1905; **VALUE:** No. 6, $40; No. 7, No. 8, and No. 9, $30.

BAILED GRIDDLE—**Size:** No. 16; **p/n:** 619; **Markings:** block logo, GRISWOLD MFG CO, ERIE PA USA; **Finish:** iron; **Circa:** 1925-1940; **VALUE:** No. 10, $125; No. 12, $75; No. 14, $75; No. 16, $125.

HANDLE GRIDDLE—**Size:** No. 8; **p/n:** 3365; **Markings:** ERIE ALUMINUM; **Finish:** aluminum; **Circa:** 1920s; **VALUE:** $50.

HANDLE GRIDDLE—**Size:** No. 6 (7 1/2" dia.); **p/n:** 376; **Markings:** diamond logo ; **Finish:** iron; **Circa:** 1884-1910; **VALUE: $150, No. 7, $75-$85; No. 8, $75-$85; No. 9, $100-125**.

HANDLE GRIDDLE—**Size:** No. 8 (9 1/4" dia.); **p/n:** 738; **Markings:** diamond logo with reinforcement heat ring; **Finish:** iron; **Circa:**1884-1910; **VALUE: $75-$100; No. 6, $125-$150; No. 7, $75-$100; No. 9, $100-$125**.

HANDLE GRIDDLE—**Size:** 8, **p/n:** 430; **Markings:** diamond logo; **Finish:** aluminum; **Circa:** 1905-1910; **VALUE: $75**.

WOOD HANDLE GRIDDLE—**Size:** No. 6; **p/n:** 341; **Markings:** **slant** logo, ERIE ; **Finish:** iron or nickel; **Circa:** 1920; **VALUE: No. 6, $150; No. 7, $100; No. 8, $125; No. 9, $125; No. 10, $150**.

HANDLE GRIDDLE—Size: No. 8; **p/n:** 738B; **Markings:** slant logo, HEAT SLOWLY, X reinforcement; **Finish:** iron or nickel; **Circa:** 1909-1920; **VALUE:** $125.

HANDLE GRIDDLE—Size: No. 8; **p/n:** 738; **Markings:** slant logo, reinforcement ring; **Finish:** iron or nickel; **Circa:** 1909-1920; **VALUE:** iron $30, nickel $25; No. 7, $30-$35; No. 9, $35-$45.

HANDLE GRIDDLE—Size: No. 9 (10 1/4" dia.); **p/n:** 739; **Markings:** slant logo, EPU, CAST IRON GRIDDLE, X reinforcement; **Finish:** iron or nickel; **Circa:** 1909-1920; **VALUE:** iron $35, nickel $25. **No. 8, $35.**

WOOD HANDLED GRIDDLE—Size: No. 8; **p/n:** 343; **Markings:** slant logo, X Reinforcement; **Finish:** iron or nickel; **Circa:** 1920; **VALUE:** iron $125, nickel $100.

REGULAR GRIDDLE—Size: No. 10; **p/n:** 610; **Markings:** block logo, GRISWOLD MFG CO, ERIE PA, USA, CAST IRON GRIDDLE; **Finish:** iron, nickel, chrome, Du-Chro, Silverlike, aluminum; **Circa:** 1925-1940; **VALUE: iron $60-$75, chrome $35;No. 6, $150; No. 7, $45-$50; No. 8, $40-$50; No. 9, $30-$40.**

REGULAR GRIDDLE—Size: No. 7 (8" dia.); **p/n:** 737; **Markings:** slant logo, THE GRISWOLD MFG CO ERIE PA, USA; **Finish:** iron or chrome; **VALUE: iron $30, chrome $25; No. 6, $75-$100; No. 8, $30; No. 9, $45-$50; No. 10, $50-$60.**

Above and Right:
REGULAR GRIDDLE—Size: No. 9; **p/n:** 639; **Markings:** small logo, ERIE PA; **Finish:** iron; **Circa:** 1950; **VALUE: $30-$40.**

HANDLE GRIDDLE—Size: No. 9; **p/n:** 2039; **Markings:** small logo, ERIE PA; **Finish:** hammered; **Circa:** 1940s; **VALUE: $75-$125**.

Below and Right:
REGULAR GRIDDLE—Size: No. 9; **p/n:** 2849; **Markings:** small logo, 'G' around hole in handle; **Finish:** iron; **Circa:** 1950s; **VALUE: $50**. This griddle has a rough, very flat bottom.

PURITAN REGULAR GRIDDLE—Size: No. 9; **p/n:** 1508; **Markings:** PURITAN; **Finish:** iron; **Circa:** 1930-1950s; **VALUE: $25**.

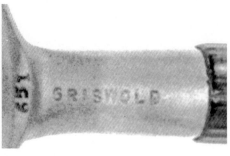

WOOD HANDLE GRIDDLE—Size: No. 9; **p/n:** 651; **Markings:** 9 (on top of handle), 651, GRISWOLD (underneath handle), bottom is milled or ground flat; **Finish:** iron; **Circa:** 1920; **VALUE: $100.**

REGULAR GRIDDLE—Size: No. 8; **p/n:** 758; **Markings: slant** logo, ERIE. X bottom; **Finish:** iron; **Circa:** 1957; **VALUE: Rare**. This is alleged to be the last item cast in the Griswold plant in Erie in 1957. The initials of the last remaining employees are cast into this griddle.

GRIDDLE DISPLAY STAND—Size: Holds five Regular Griddles; **p/n:** none; **Markings:** GRISWOLD; **Finish:** Chrome; **Circa:** 1940-1957; **VALUE:** $400-$450.

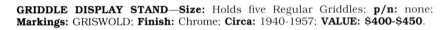

GAS OR VAPOR STOVE GRIDDLE—Size: No. 12 (11 1/2" dia.); **p/n:** 741 Griddle, 774 Base; **Markings:** ERIE GAS GRIDDLE, THE GRISWOLD MFG CO; **Finish:** iron griddle, iron hollow base "to distribute heat evenly"; **Circa:** 1905-1940; **VALUE: No. 12, $300; No. 14, $400; with aluminum griddle (fig. C), $200.**

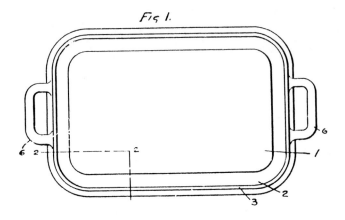

R. W. GRISWOLD.
GRIDDLE.
APPLICATION FILED NOV. 8, 1915.

1,204,429.   Patented Nov. 14, 1916.

A griddle patent from November 14, 1916.

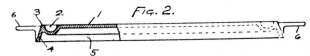

LONG GRIDDLE—Size: No. 7 (6 1/2" x 7 1/4");   **p/n:** none; **Markings:** 7, ERIE; **Finish:** iron; **Circa:** 1905; **VALUE: $60' No. 8, $60-$70; No. 9, $60-$70; No. 10, $75-$85.**

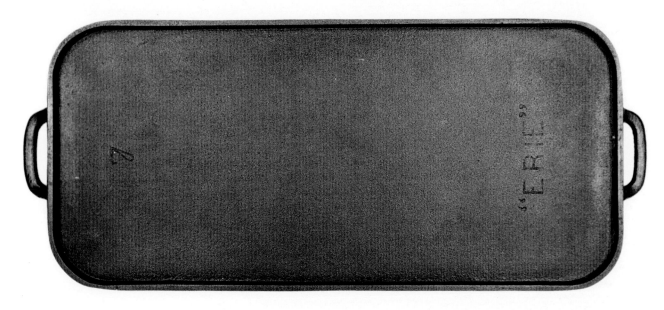

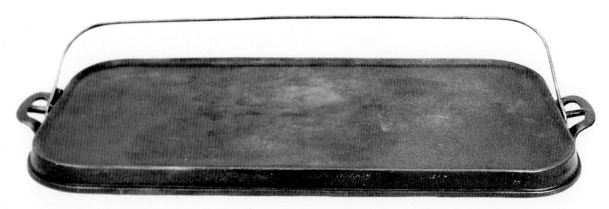

LONG GRIDDLE WITH BAIL HANDLE—Size: No. 7; **p/n:** 744; **Markings:** diamond logo ; **Finish:** iron; **Circa:** 1905-1920; **VALUE: $100.**

LONG GRIDDLE—Size: No. 11 (25" x 13 1/2"); **p/n:** 2434; **Markings:** slant logo, GRISWOLDS ERIE; **Finish:** iron; **Circa:** 1910-1920; **VALUE: $125**.

LONG GRIDDLE—Size: No. 7 (21" x 9 5/8"); **p/n:** 744; **Markings:** diamond logo; **Finish:** iron or nickel; **Circa:** 1905; **VALUE: $75**; No, 8, $60-$75; No. 9, $75-$100.

LONG GRIDDLE—Size: No. 7; **p/n:** 744; **Markings:** slant logo, ERIE; **Finish:** iron; **Circa:** 1920; **VALUE: $75**.

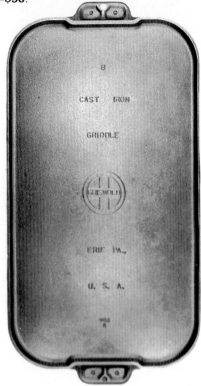

Left:
LONG GRIDDLE—**Size:** No. 7; **p/n:** 744; **Markings:** block logo, EPU, CAST IRON GRIDDLE; **Finish:** iron; **Circa:** 1925-1950; **VALUE: $60; No. 8, $45-$65; No. $9, $45-$60; No. 10, $75-$90.**

Left:
LONG GRIDDLE—**Size:** No. 8; **p/n:** 903A; **Markings:** block logo, EPU, CAST IRON GRIDDLE; **Finish:** iron; **Circa:** 1950; **VALUE: No. 8, $45; No. 9, $50; No. 10, $60-$75; No. 11, $100.**

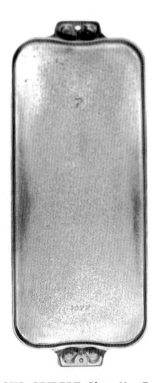

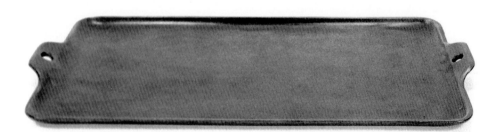

LONG GRIDDLE Size: No. 7; **p/n:** 1077; **Markings:** 7, 1077; **Finish:** iron; **Circa:** 1930s; **VALUE: $35.** Unmarked for outlets such as hardware stores and department stores.

Above and Right:
FAMILY GRILL—**Size:** No. 18, (16 3/4" x 10"); **p/n:** 1108; **Markings:** block logo, EPU, CAST IRON GRILL; **Finish:** iron or aluminum; **Circa:** 1950s; **VALUE: iron $150; aluminum $75.** Called the "Cookie Sheet."

OVAL GRIDDLE—Size: No. 10 (22 1/4" x 10 1/4"); **p/n:** 714; **Markings:** slant logo, ERIE, 714; **Finish:** iron; **Circa:** 1900-1909; **VALUE: No. 7, $150; No. 8, $150; No. 9, $200; No. 10, $250.**

SHALLOW LONG PAN—Size: No. 8; **p/n:** none; **Markings:** ERIE, 8; **Finish:** iron; **Circa:** 1880-1930s; **VALUE: $150.** This pan may have been made as early as 1870.

Above and Left:
SHALLOW LONG PAN-Size: No. 8 (17" x 7 1/2" x 3/4"); **p/n:** none; **Markings:** ERIE, 8; **Finish:** iron; **Circa:** 1883-1930s; **VALUE: No. 7, $150-$200; No. 8, $150; No. 9, $150-$200.**

(No Model.)   3 Sheets—Sheet 3.

O. R. HANCHETT.
CAKE GRIDDLE.

No. 271,942.   Patented Feb. 6, 1883.

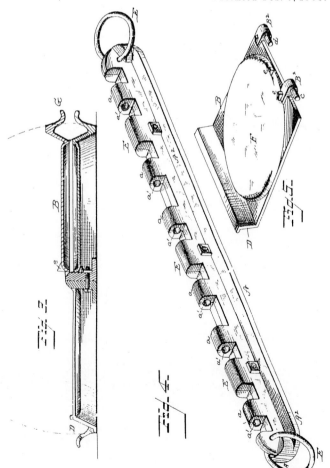

A patent drawing of a cake griddle, from February 6, 1883.

WITNESSES

INVENTOR
O. R. Hanchett
by Sell Smith
Attorney

Above and Right:
FLOP GRIDDLE—Size: No. 8; **p/n:** 2406, Rd.
Griddles 2408; **Markings:** ERIE, No 8; **Finish:**
iron; **Circa:** 1910; **VALUE:** $300; with Griswold
logo, $400.

FLOP GRIDDLE—Size: two-section; **p/n:** none; **Markings:**
PAT'D FEB 8, 1883, G. MFG. CO; **Finish:** iron; **Circa:** 1880-
1905; **VALUE:** $350-$400.

FLOP GRIDDLE—Size: three-section;
p/n: none; **Markings:** PAT'D APPLIED
FOR (at edge of hinge); **Finish:** iron;
Circa: 1880-1905; **VALUE:** $400-500.

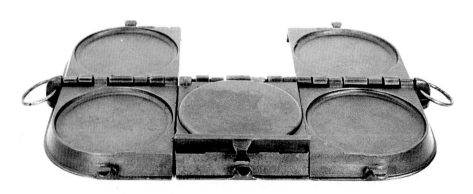

Above and Right:
FLAT TOP DUTCH OVEN—Size: No. 11; **p/n:** 836, (cover) 840; **Markings:** ERIE, 836, 11, Cover 11; **Finish:** iron; **Circa:** 1905; **VALUE: $200; No. 7, $45-$60; No. $8, $45-$60; No. 9, $60-$75; No. 10, $75-$100.**

Above and Right:
FLAT TOP DUTCH OVEN—Size: No. 8; **p/n:** none; **Markings:** ERIE, Cover 8; **Finish:** iron; **Circa:** 1890-1905; **VALUE: No. 8, $50; No. 9, $60: No. 10, $100; No. 11, $200.** Available with or without Bail Handle.

DUTCH OVEN—**Size:** No. 6; **p/n:** 2605, (cover) 2606; **Markings:** ERIE; **Finish:** iron; **Circa:** 1910; **VALUE:** $250-$300; No. 7, $75-$85; No. 8, $85-$100; No. 9, $85-$100; No. 10, $125-$150.

DUTCH OVEN—**Size:** No. 6; **p/n:** 2605, (cover) 2606; **Markings:** slant logo, ERIE; **Finish:** iron; **Circa:** 1910; **VALUE:** No. 6, $250-$300; No. 7, $75; No. 8, $75; No. 9, $85; No. 10, $150; No. 11, $175..

A patent drawing for the Self Basting Rings and the Seali of the kettle, from February 10, 1920.

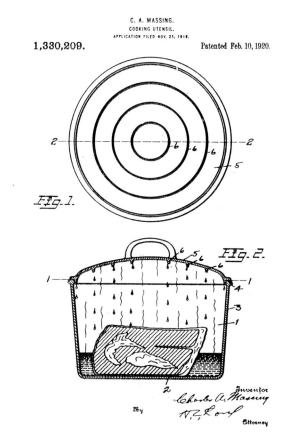

CHUCK-WAGON DUTCH OVEN–SIZE: 10; **p/n:** 180; **Markings:** Block logo, EPU, THE GRISWOLD MFG CO, CAST IRON, TITE-TOP DUTCH OVEN, PAT'D MAR 16, 20", **Cover:** slant logo, 10; **Finish:** iron; **Circa:** 1930s. From 1910-1920, sizes 8-11 were produced. Sizes 12 & 13 were added from 1920-1930s. Prior to 1950 this dutch oven was known as "Dutch Oven with legs." The title "Chuck-Wagon" was used in the 1950s. **VALUE: No. 8, $300; No. 9, $300; No. 10, $150; No. 11, $200; No. 12, $400; No. 13, $600-$700.**

TITE TOP BASTER—**Size:** No. 6; **p/n:** 2605; **Markings:** (cover) slant logo EPU, TITE-TOP BASTER, THE GRISWOLD MFG. CO.; (applied handle) TITE-TOP BASTER; **Finish:** iron; **Circa:** 1920; **VALUE: No. 6, $300-$400; No. 7, $95; No. 8, $65; No. 9, $85; No. 10, $125; No. 11, $250; No. 12, $400-$500; No. 13, $750-$850.**

J. C. HOLLANDS,
RECEPTACLE.
APPLICATION FILED MAR. 10, 1919.

1,333,917.   Patented Mar. 16, 1920.

Inventor

John C Hollands
By
Attorney

PATENT DRAWING FOR LOCKING BAIL HANDLE - March 16, 1920

TITE-TOP DUTCH OVEN—**Size:** No. 6; **p/n:** 2605, (cover) 2606; **Markings:** block logo, EPU, TITE-TOP DUTCH OVEN, PAT'D MAR 16, 20, Cover TITE-TOP DUTCH OVEN, GRISWOLD No 6; **Finish:** iron or nickel; **Circa:** 1920-1950; **VALUE: No. 6, $300-$400; No. 7, $75; No. 8, $50; No. 9, $60; No. 10, $100; No. 11, $200; No. 12, $350-$450; No. 13, $800.**

TITE-TOP DUTCH OVEN—**Size:** No. 6; **p/n:** 2605, (cover) 2606; **Finish:** chrome; **Circa:** 1920-1950; **VALUE: No. 6, $300-$400; No. 7, $50; No. 8, $50; No. 9, $60; No. 10, $100; No. 11, $175.**

No. 13 DUTCH OVEN WITH LOW DOME AND RAISED LETTER COVER (Shown next to No. 6 with High Dome Cover for comparison)—**Size:** 15 1/4" x 12 3/4" x 8", 20.5 qts.; **p/n:** 2635, (cover) 2637, (trivet) 211; **Markings:** slant logo, EPU; **Finish:** iron; **Circa:** 1920-1930; **VALUE: $700-$800.**

DUTCH OVEN OR KETTLE DISPLAY STAND—Size: Approximately 4 ft. tall; **Markings:** GRISWOLD on top plates; **Finish:** red painted legs, black top and shelves; **Circa:** unknown; **VALUE: $1800-2000.**

DUTCH OVEN—Size: No. 6; **p/n:** 462 1/2; **Markings:** block logo, EPU, CAST ALUMINUM; **Finish:** aluminum; **Circa:** 1930s; **VALUE: $75; No. 8, $50-$75; Finish: Iron, No. 6, $150-$200; No. 7, $75-$100, No. 8, $60-$75; No. 9, $60-$75.**

DUTCH OVEN—Size: No. 6; **Markings:** raised logo cover; **Finish:** aluminum; **Circa:** 1940s-1959s; **VALUE: $50; No. 8, $45-$50; No. 9, $35-$45.**

DUTCH OVEN—Size: No. 8; **p/n:** 1295; **Markings:** block logo, EPU, TITE—TOP DUTCH OVEN; **Finish:** iron; **Circa:** 1940s; **VALUE: $65.** Although this Dutch Oven did come with a glass cover, the cover shown is not the correct one. This piece did not have a bail.

DUTCH OVEN TRIVETS—No. 6, $100 to $125; No. 7, $60 to $75; No. 8, $30 to $50; No. 9, $30 to $50; No. 10, $60 to $75; No. 11, $75 to $125; No. 12, $200 to $225; No. 13, $250 to $300.

DUTCH OVEN—Size: No. 8; **p/n:** 1278; **Markings:** block logo, EPU; **Finish:** iron; **Circa:** 1950; **VALUE: $60**.

HINGED COVER DUTCH OVEN—Size: No. 8; **p/n:** 2568; **Markings:** small logo, ERIE PA; **Finish:** iron; **Circa:** 1940s-1950s; **VALUE: $95**.

DEEP DUTCH OVEN—Size: No. 8; **p/n:** 1298, Cover 1288; **Markings:** block logo, EPU, (on cover) raised logo; **Finish:** iron or chrome; **Circa:** 1950; **VALUE: iron $250, chrome $200**.

DEEP DUTCH OVEN WITH HIGH DOME AND RAISED LETTER COVER (shown with regular dutch oven for comparison)—**Size:** No. 8 (5 1/2" deep, compared to the regular 4" deep); **p/n:** 1298, Cover 2551; **Markings:** block logo, EPU; **Finish:** iron; **Circa:** 1940-1950; **VALUE: $200-$300**.

OVAL ROASTERS

There are three basic variations of Oval Roaster Cover. The fully marked examples are the most desirable.

Size: No. 9 (18" l x 12" w x 5 5/8" d, 20 qt.); **p/n:** 649, Cover 650; **Markings:** block logo, EPU, THE GRISWOLD MFG. CO., CAST IRON OVAL ROASTER; **Finish:** iron or chrome; **Circa:** 1934-1940s; **VALUE: iron $300-$400, chrome $250**

Size: No. 3 (12 3/4" l x 8" w x 3 3/8" d, 4 qt.); **p/n:** 643, Cover 644, (2627 with 2628 plain cover); **Markings:** same; **Finish:** iron, chrome, porcelain; **Circa:** 1920-1957; **VALUE: iron $600, chrome $300, porcelain $200.**

Size: No. 5 (14 1/2" x 9 3/4" x 4 1/4", 6.5 qt.); **p/n:** 645, Cover 646, (2629 with 2629 plain cover); **Finish:** iron or chrome; **Circa:** 1920-1940s; **VALUE: iron $275, chrome $200.**

Size: No. 7 (16 1/4" l x 11 1/2" w x 4 3/4" d, 10 qt.); **p/n:** 647, Cover 648 (2631 with 2632 plain cover); **Markings:** same; **Finish:** iron or chrome; **Circa:** 1920-1940s; **VALUE: iron $250, chrome $200.**

OVAL ROASTER TRIVETS—Size: Nos. 3, 5, 7, 9; **p/n:** (No. 3) 274, (No. 5) 275, (No. 7) 276, (No. 9) 277; **Markings:** THE GRISWOLD MFG. CO., OVAL ROASTER TRIVET; **VALUE: No. 3, $125; No. 5, $100; No. 7, $100; No. 9, $125.**

Above and Right:
No. 9 OVAL ROASTER (deep)—**Size:** 18 1/2" l x 12 1/2" w x 7 1/2" d; **p/n:** 2675, Cover 2626; **Markings:** block logo, EPU, THE GRISWOLD MFG. CO., CAST IRON OVAL ROASTER; **Finish:** iron; **Circa:** 1923-1930; **VALUE: $450-$600**. This was the standard depth No. 9 Oval Roaster of its time period.

Above and Right:
HAM BOILER—Size: No. 8 (24 5/8" l x 12 3/4" w x 8 3/8" d); **p/n:** 2363; **Markings:** slant logo, ERIE; **Finish:** iron; **Circa:** 1915-1925; **VALUE: $400-$500**.

KETTLES

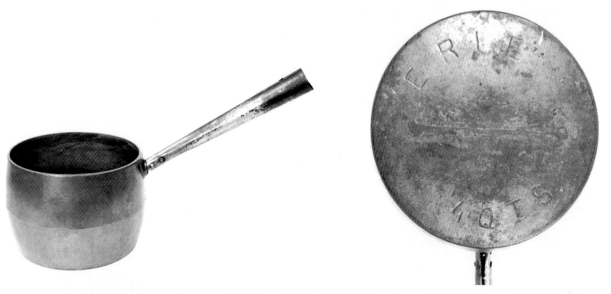

SAUCE PAN—**Size:** 4 qts.; **p/n:** none; **Markings:** 4 QTS, ERIE, (with gate mark); **Finish:** iron with tin handle riveted to pan; **Circa:** 1880-1905; **VALUE: $100**.

SAUCE PAN—**Size:** 3 qts.; **p/n:** none; **Markings:** "ERIE," 3 QTS; **Finish:** iron with wood handle; **Circa:** 1905; **VALUE: $100-$150**.

FRENCH DEEP FAT FRYER—**Size:** 7 1/8" dia. x 4 7/8" deep; **p/n:** 1003; **Markings:** small logo, Erie PA; **Finish:** iron; **Circa:** 1950s; **VALUE: with basket (not shown) $45-$60; cover $100-$125**.

FLAT BOTTOM KETTLE—Size: 5 qts.; **p/n:** none; **Markings:** 5QT, "ERIE", gate mark; **Finish:** iron; **Circa:** 1880; **VALUE: $75-$100.** Very early ears appear on this kettle.

FLAT BOTTOM BULGE KETTLE—Size: No. 7; **p/n:** none; **Markings:** ERIE; **Finish:** iron; **Circa:** 1885; **VALUE: $75.** The wire bail handle locks against the kettle ear for pouring.

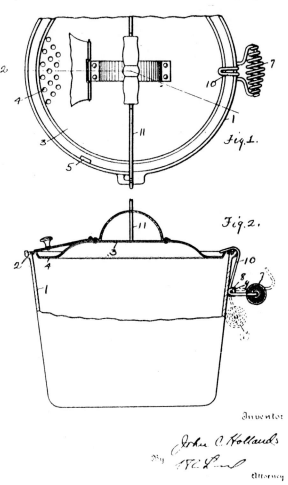

J. C. HOLLANDS.
KETTLE.
APPLICATION FILED MAR. 10, 1919.

1,377,684.   Patented May 10, 1921.

Inventor

John C. Hollands
By ...
Attorney

Safety kettle patent drawing from May 10, 1921.

SAFETY KETTLE (Round Bottom)—Size: No. 8; **p/n:** 863; **Markings:** slant logo, SAFETY; **Finish:** iron, with tin cover; **Circa:** 1920; **VALUE: $200 complete with tin trivet.**

SAFETY COOKER—Size: No. 8; **p/n:** 858A; **Markings:** slant logo, EPU, SAFETY COOKER; **Finish:** iron, with tin cover; **Circa:** 1920; **VALUE: $200 complete with tin trivet.**

M. GRISWOLD & M. GRISWOLD, Jr.
KETTLE EAR AND COVER.

No. 447,821. Patented Mar. 10, 1891.

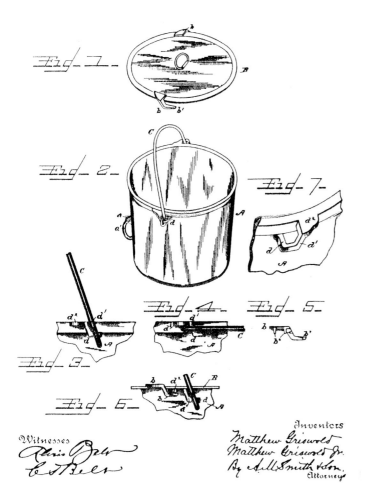

A kettle ear and cover patent drawing from March 10, 1891. This patent date on kettles and on the Bundt cake mold refers to this kettle ear design patent.

RIMMED POT—**Size:** No. 8; **p/n:** none; **Markings:** ERIE, PATD MAR 10,'91, 8 POT; **Finish:** iron or nickel; **Circa:** 1905; **VALUE: No. 7, No. 8, and No. 9, $60-$80.**

REGULAR KETTLE—**Size:** No. 7; **p/n:** 789; **Markings:** slant logo, ERIE; **Finish:** iron or nickel; **Circa:** 1905-1910; **VALUE: No. 6, $60-$75; No. 7, $60; No. 8 and No. 9, $60-$75.**

FLAT BOTTOM BUDGE KETTLE—**Size:** No. 9; **p/n:** 815; **Markings:** ERIE, PAT MAR 10,'91; **Finish:** iron; **Circa:** 1895; **VALUE: $50-$75.** Pour Ring is missing.

BULGE KETTLE—Size: No. 8; **p/n:** none; **Markings:** ERIE; **Finish:** iron; **Circa:** 1890; **VALUE:** No. 6, $100-$125; No. 7, $75; No. 8, $75; No. 9, $75.

ECCENTRIC KETTLE—Size: No. 7 (7 qts.); **p/n:** 816; **Markings:** ERIE, PAT MAR 10, 1891; **Finish:** iron or nickel; **Circa:** 1890-1905; **VALUE: No. 7, No. 8, and No. 9, $75.**

LOW KETTLE—Size: No. 8; **p/n:** 798; **Markings:** ERIE, PAT'D MAR 10, 1891; **Finish:** iron or nickel; **Circa:** 1905; **VALUE: No. 7, No. 8, and No. 9, $50-$75.**

MASLIN SHAPED KETTLE—Size: 4 qts.; **p/n:** 936; **Markings:** ERIE MASLIN KETTLE, THE GRISWOLD MFG CO., ERIE PA; **Finish:** iron or **nickel**; **Circa:** 1905; **VALUE: 4 qts., $50-$75; 6 & 8 qts., $50-$75;12 qts., $125-$150.**

YANKEE BOWL—Size: No. 4; **p/n:** 786; **Markings:** ERIE, PAT'D MAR 10, 1891; **Finish:** iron; **Circa:** 1925—1940s; **VALUE: $50-$75.**

FLAT BOTTOM KETTLE—Size: No. 8 (7 qts.); **p/n:** 811A, Cover 881; **Markings:** block logo, EPU, CAST IRON FLAT BOTTOM KETTLE **Finish:** iron; **Circa:** 1920-1940; **VALUE: No. 6, $350; No. 7, $300; No. 8, $200 (with cover); No. 9, $300; No. 10, $400 ($250 without cover).**

SCOTCH BOWL—Size: No. 2; **p/n:** 780; **Markings:** slant logo, ERIE; **Finish:** iron; **Circa:** 1900-1915; **VALUE: No. 2, $40-$60; No. 3, $40; No. 4, $40; No. 5, $60-70.**

YANKEE BOWL—Size: No. 2; **p/n:** 784; **Markings:** block logo, YANKEE BOWL; **Finish:** iron, smooth sides; **VALUE: $80-$100.** This smooth-sided style appears in catalogs dating from1890-1920, but the block logo was not used until about 1925.

FLAT BOTTOM SCOTCH BOWL—Size: No. 2; **p/n:** 837; **Markings:** slant logo EPU, SCOTCH BOWL No 2; **Finish:** iron; **Circa:** 1920; **VALUE: No. 2, $75-$100; No. 3, $65; No. 4, $65; No. 5, $75.**

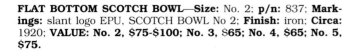

Above and Left:
SELDEN GRISWOLD TEA KETTLE—Size: 8 qts.; **p/n:** none;
Markings: SELDEN GRISWOLD MFG CO., ERIE PA; Gate mark on
bottom; **Finish:** galvanized; **Circa:** 1885; **VALUE: Rare.**

Above, Right, and Above Right:
ERIE IRON TEA KETTLES—Size: Nos. 6, 7, 8, and 9; **p/n:** none;
Markings: ERIE on cover; **Finish:** iron, galvanized or tinned,
Malaca, Nickel; **Circa:** 1880-1920; **VALUE: No. 6, $200; No. 7, No.
8, and No. 9, $40-$70.**

SPIDER LOGO TEA KETTLE—Size: No. 8 (6 qts.);   **p/n:** none; **Markings:** spider logo on cover, pit bottom; **Finish:** iron or galvanized; **Circa:** 1880-1890; **VALUE: No. 7, $500-$600; No. 8, $500; No. 9, $500**.

TEA KETTLE—Size: No. 8 (6 qts.); **p/n:** none; **Markings:** GRISWOLDS on bottom, ERIE on cover; **Finish:** iron, galvanized, Malaca; **Circa:** 1884-1904; **VALUE: No. 6, $250; No. 7, $200; No. 8, $200; No. 9, $225**.

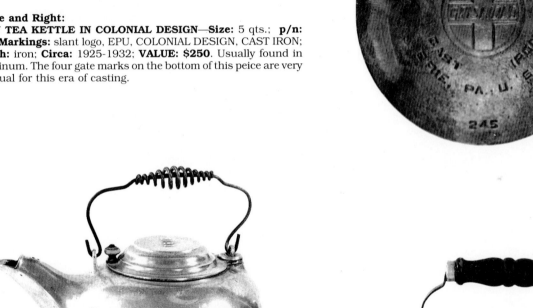

Above and Right:
IRON TEA KETTLE IN COLONIAL DESIGN—Size: 5 qts.; **p/n:** 245; **Markings:** slant logo, EPU, COLONIAL DESIGN, CAST IRON; **Finish:** iron; **Circa:** 1925-1932; **VALUE: $250**. Usually found in aluminum. The four gate marks on the bottom of this peice are very unusual for this era of casting.

ALUMINUM TEA KETTLE—Size: No. 8; **p/n:** none; **Markings:** ERIE on cover; **Finish:** aluminum; **Circa:** 1900; **VALUE: $75-$100**. This appears to be the tea kettle that was made by Alcoa for Griswold, introducing Griswold to aluminum utensils.

FLAT BOTTOM TEA KETTLE—Size: 3 qts.; **p/n:** unknown; **Markings:** Struck (stamped) logo; **Finish:** aluminum; **Circa:** 1910-1925; **VALUE: $100**. Also made sizes Nos. 4, 6, 7, 8, 9.

Right:
FLAT BOTTOM TEA KETTLE—Size: No. 8 (6 qts.); **p/n:** A508;
Markings: THE GRISWOLD MFG CO, ERIE PA, USA; **Finish:**
aluminum; **Circa:** 1925-1940; **VALUE:** $75. Also made were sizes
Nos. 4, 5, 6, 7, 9.

COLONIAL TEA KETTLE—Size: 2 qts.; **p/n:** 532; **Markings:** slant
logo, EPU, COLONIAL DESIGN, CAST ALUMINUM; **Finish:** aluminum; **Circa:** 1920-1940s; **VALUE: 2 qts., $75; No. 5, No. 6, No. 7,
No. 8, and No. 9, $60.**

"THE RAPID" TEA KETTLE—Size: 9 (8 qts.); **p/n:** unable to
determine; **Markings:** ERIE, RAPID, NO 9; **Finish:** aluminum,
corrugated bottom, with wood handle; **Circa:** 1910-1940; **VALUE:
No. 4, $100; No. 5, No. 6, No. 7, and No. 8, $75; and No. 9, $100.**

ALUMINUM TEA KETTLE—Size: 5 qts.; **p/n:** A213; **Markings:**
block logo, ERIE PA; **Finish:** hammered aluminum; **Circa:** 1950s;
VALUE: $65.

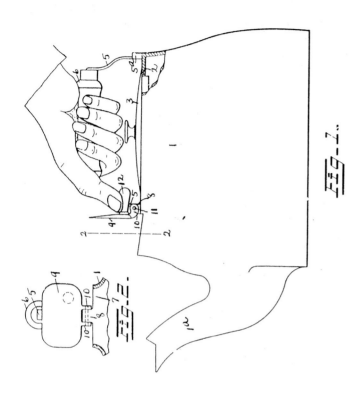

J. C. HOLLANDS.
TEA KETTLE.
APPLICATION FILED MAY 15, 1912.

1,072,461.

Patented Sept. 9, 1913.

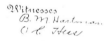

Safety Fill patent drawing from September 9, 1913.

"SAFETY FILL" TEA KETTLE—Size: 5 qts.; p/n: A545; Markings: block logo, EPU, THE COLONIAL DESIGN, CAST ALUMINUM, SAFETY FILL; Finish: aluminum; Circa: 1920-1930s; VALUE: $65. Also made were sizes No. 6 and No. 8.

ARISTOCRAFT TEA KETTLE—p/n: A1534; Markings: block logo, ARISTOCRAFT; Finish: aluminum; Circa: 1940s-1950s; VALUE: $60.

TEA POTS—Circa: 1910. (Left) The Rapid Tea Kettle; p/n: 501 1/2; Size: 3 1/2 pts.; VALUE: $100-$125. (Center) Five O' Clock Tea Kettle; p/n: none; Size: 2 pts.; Markings: (stamped) logo; VALUE: $125-$150. (Right) Tea Pot; Size: 4 pts; p/n: none; Markings: (stamped) logo only; VALUE: $100-$150.

COLONIAL TEA POT (left)—**Size:** 2 pts.; **p/n:** A142; **Markings:** slant logo, EPU; **Finish:** aluminum; **Circa:** 1920; **VALUE: $100.**
COLONIAL COFFEE POT (right)—**Size:** 4 pts.; **p/n:** A124; **Markings:** slant logo, EPU, CAST ALUMINUM, 4 PT COFFEE POT; **Finish:** aluminum; **Circa:** 1923-1940; **VALUE: $75.**

COLONIAL PERCOLATOR—**Size:** 6 pts.; **p/n:** A136; **Markings:** block logo, THE GRISWOLD MFG CO, ERIE PA, USA, CAST ALUMINUM PERCOLATOR; **Finish:** aluminum; **Circa:** 1934; **VALUE: $65.**

COFFEE POT—**Size:** 3 qts., 8" high; **p/n:** 103; **Markings:** stamped logo; **Finish:** aluminum; **Circa:** 1910-1930; **VALUE: $75.** Also made in 1 qt., 2 qt., and 4 qt. sizes.

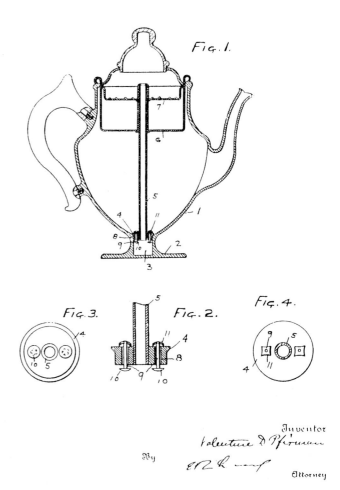

A patent drawing for a percolator, from February 19, 1918.

COFFEE PERCULATOR—Size: 6 cups; **p/n:** 176; **Markings:** stamped logo, 'Pyrex' knob; **Finish:** aluminum; **Circa:** 1920; **VALUE: 6 cups, $100; 9 cups and 13 cups, $125.**

COFFEE POT— p/n: A1602; **Markings:** block logo, ARISTOCRAFT; **Finish:** aluminum; **Circa:** 1940-1960s; **VALUE: $75.**

COFFEE POT OR PITCHER—Size: 5 pts., 16 cups; **p/n:** A116, base A116B, cover A116C; **Markings:** stamped logo; **Finish:** aluminum; **Circa:** 1930; **VALUE: $100-$150.**

BAIL WATER PITCHER—Size: 8", 2 1/2 qts.; **p/n:** none; **Markings:** stamped logo, EPU; **Finish:** aluminum; **Circa:** 1930; **VALUE: $100-$150.** For use by hotel bellboys.

DRIP COFFEE MAKER—Size: 6 cups; **p/n:** A266; **Markings:** block logo, EPU, 6 CUP COFFEE POT; **Finish:** aluminum; **Circa:** 1934; **VALUE: $75.** The coffee grounds container is not shown.

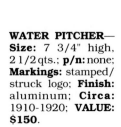

WATER PITCHER— Size: 7 3/4" high, 2 1/2 qts.; **p/n:** none; **Markings:** stamped/struck logo; **Finish:** aluminum; **Circa:** 1910-1920; **VALUE: $150.**

WAFFLE IRONS

An advertisement from a 1920 issue of *Good Housekeeping* magazine.

Above and Left: Two variations of the ball hinge.

Below: GRISWOLD WAFFLE IRON HINGES—(clockwise from top center) button hinge, finger hinge, scissor hinge, clows hinge, acorn hinge, and ball hinge.

Above and Right:
THE AMERICAN NO. 2 WAFFLE IRON—Size: No. 8&9; **p/n:** none; **Markings:** SELDEN GRISWOLD MFG CO, ERIE PA, THE AMERICAN, NO. 2, PAT APPLIED FOR; **Waffle Pattern:** standard; **Hinge:** button; **Circa:** 1870-1880; **VALUE: $150-$200**.

THE AMERICAN NO. 2 WAFFLE IRON—Size: No. 8&9; **p/n:** none; **Markings:** SELDEN GRISWOLD MFG CO, ERIE PA, THE AMERICAN NO. 2, PAT JUNE 29, 1880; **Hinge:** button; **Waffle Pattern:** standard; **Circa:** 1880; **VALUE: $150-$200**

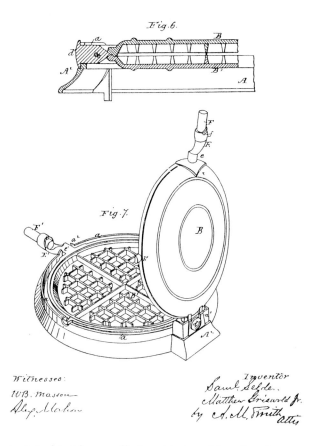

S. SELDEN & M. GRISWOLD, Jr.
Waffle Iron.

No. 229,280.   Patented June 29, 1880.

Fig. 6.

Fig. 7.

Witnesses:
W.B. Masson
Alex. Mahon

Inventor
Saml. Selden
Matthew Griswold Jr.
by A. M. Smith Atty

A patent drawing for a waffle iron hinge and handles, from June 29, 1880.

THE AMERICAN WAFFLE IRON—**Size:** No. 9; **p/n:** none; **Markings:** SELDEN GRISWOLD MFG CO, ERIE PA, 8&9; **Hinge:** button; **Waffle Pattern:** lattice; **Circa:** 1885-1895; **VALUE: $200-$250.**

Above and Right:
THE AMERICAN WAFFLE IRON—Size: No. 8, and No. 8&9; **p/n:** none; **Markings:** SELDEN GRISWOLD MFG CO, ERIE PA, THE AMERICAN; **Hinge:** button; **Waffle Pattern:** Web; **Circa:** 1883-1890; **VALUE: $200.**

THE AMERICAN WAFFLE IRON—Size: No. 7&8; **p/n:** none; **Markings:** SELDEN GRISWOLD MFG CO, ERIE PA, THE AMERICAN, PAT JUNE 29 1880; **Hinge:** button; **Waffle Pattern:** circular; **Circa:** 1890-1895; **VALUE: $175-$200**.

THE AMERICAN WAFFLE IRON—Size: No. 9&10; **p/n:** none; **Markings:** GRISWOLD MFG CO, THE AMERICAN, PAT JUNE 29, 1880; **Hinge:** button; **Waffle Pattern:** standard; **Circa:** 1880-1890; **VALUE: $100**.

Above and Right:
THE AMERICAN WAFFLE IRON—Size: No. 8&9; **p/n:** none; **Markings:** THE GRISWOLD MFG CO, ERIE PA, THE AMERICAN, PAT'D JUNE 25, 1893; **Hinge:** finger; **Waffle Pattern:** standard; **Circa:** 1890-1900; **VALUE: $75**. This waffle iron has long handles made of black, enameled wood.

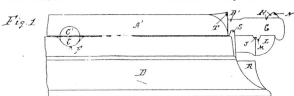

D. SHIELDS.
WAFFLE IRON.

No. 502,086.   Patented July 25, 1893.

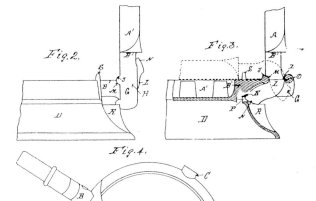

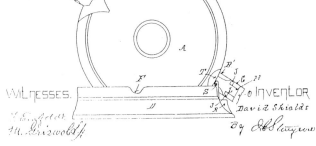

A patent drawing for a waffle iron with a finger hinge, from July 25, 1893.

THE AMERICAN WAFFLE IRON—Size: No. 8&9; **p/n:** none; **Markings:** GRISWOLD MFG CO, ERIE PA, THE AMERICAN, No 8 8&9, PAT JUNE 29, 1880, PAT'JULY 25, 1893; **Hinge:** finger; **Waffle Pattern:** standard; **Circa:** 1910; **VALUE: $125**. This short wooden handle is similar to the one on the button hinge waffle iron.

Above and Left:
THE NEW AMERICAN WAFFLE IRON—Size: No. 6; **p/n:** none; **Markings:** GRISWOLD MFG CO, ERIE PA, THE NEW AMERICAN, No 6; **Hinge:** acorn; **Waffle Pattern:** standard; **Circa:** 1910-1920; **VALUE: $250-$350.**

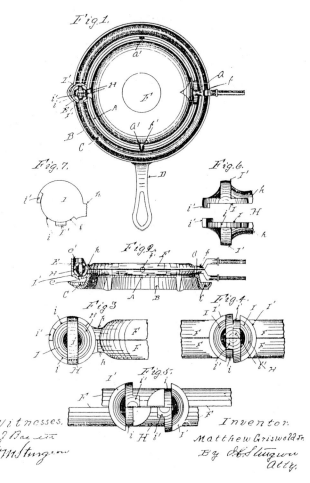

No. 674,628.   Patented May 21, 1901.

M. GRISWOLD, Jr.
WAFFLE IRON.
(Application filed Jan. 31, 1901.)

(No Model.)

A patent drawing for a waffle iron with an acorn hinge, from May 21, 1901.

VICTOR WAFFLE IRON—Size: No. 8; **p/n:** 983, 984, (base) 982; **Markings:** GRISWOLD MFG CO, ERIE PA, VICTOR; **Hinge:** scissor; **Waffle Pattern:** standard; **Circa:** 1920s; **VALUE: $200-$250.**

VICTOR WAFFLE IRON—Size: No. 8; **p/n:** (both sides) 395, (base) 396; **Markings:** No 8, VICTOR, PAT APL'D FOR; **Hinge:** ball; **Waffle Pattern:** standard; **Circa:** 1940s; **VALUE: $100.**

AMERICAN WAFFLE IRON—Size: No. 8; **p/n:** none; **Markings:** GRISWOLD MFG CO, ERIE PA, THE AMERICAN, PATD MAY 14, 1901; **Hinge:** acorn; **Waffle Pattern:** standard; **Finish:** (pan) aluminum, (base) iron, (handle) Alaskan wire riveted to the pan; **Circa:** 1916; **VALUE: $75.** The aluminum pan was probably made for Griswold by the Aluminum Cooking Utensil Co. (Wear-Ever) in New Kensington, PA.

CLOWS WAFFLE IRON—Size: No. 8; **p/n:** (both sides) 234, (base) 235; **Markings:** slant logo, EPU, PAT'D DEC 1, 1908; **Hinge:** clows, non-locking; **Waffle Pattern:** clows with standard grid; **Circa:** 1940s; **VALUE: $150-200**. This item has no leveling pins on the waffle pans, and no grooves on the base for pins.

AMERICAN WAFFLE IRON—Size: No. 8; **p/n:** 314 & 315; **Markings:** slant logo, THE GRISWOLD MFG CO, ERIE PA, USA, PAT'D DEC 1, 1908; **Hinge:** ball; **Waffle Pattern:** standard; **Circa:** 1910-1940s; **VALUE: No. 6, $350; No. 7, $75-$95; No. 8, $40-$50; No. 9, $75-$95.**

Above and Left:
HAMMERED FINISH:WAFFLE IRON—Size: No. 8; **p/n:** 171 &172, (base) 173; **Markings:** small block logo, base is octagonal; **Hinge:** ball; **Waffle Pattern:** series of octagons; **Circa:** 1950s; **VALUE: $175-$200.**

PURITAN WAFFLE IRON—Size: No. 8; **p/n:** 885, 886, (base) 9754; **Markings:** No 8, PURITAN, THE GRISWOLD MFG CO, ERIE PA; **Hinge:** ball; **Waffle Pattern:** standard; **Circa:** 1930s; **VALUE: $75**.

GOOD HEALTH WAFFLE IRON—Size: No. 8; **p/n:** (both sides) 395; **Markings:** GOOD HEALTH, PAT APL'D FOR; **Hinge:** ball; **Waffle Pattern:** standard; **Circa:** 1920s; **VALUE: $75**.

Above and Right:
WESTERN IMPORTING WAFFLE IRON—Size: No. 8; **p/n:** 886, 885, (base) 9754; **Markings:** WESTERN IMPORTING CO, MINNE-APOLIS & NEW YORK, HEART SHAPED DESIGN, PATENTED, ROSETTE TRADEMARK; **Hinge:** ball; **Waffle Pattern:** hearts; **Circa:** 1920-1930; **VALUE: $75-$100**. This design was patented December 27, 1904.

DESIGN.

C. A. MASSING.

COOKING RECEPTACLE.

APPLICATION FILED JAN. 27, 1919.

55,188.   Patented May 18, 1920.

Inventor

Charles A. Massing

By

1R. Lord

Attorney

A patent drawing for the Heart Star pattern, from May 18, 1920.

Right and Above Right:
HEART STAR WAFFLE IRON—Size: No. 18; **p/n:** 920, 919, (high base) 915; **Markings:** HEART STAR, ERIE PA, USA, PAT'D MAY 18 20; **Hinge:** ball; **Waffle Pattern:** Heart Star; **Finish:** iron and aluminum; **Circa:** 1920s; **VALUE: iron $175, aluminum $100.** This piece has the large center star.

Left and Far Left:
HEART STAR WAFFLE IRON—
Size: No. 19; **p/n:** 932, 933, (base) 318; **Markings:** HEART STAR, ERIE PA, USA, PAT'D MAY 18, 20, tabs on bottom of base ring; **Hinge:** ball; **Waffle Pattern:** Heart Star; **Finish:** ion and aluminum; **Circa:** 1923; **VALUE: iron $200-$250, aluminum $100.** This piece has the small center star.

HEART STAR WAFFLE IRON—Size: No. 19; **p/n:** (both sides) 329, (base) 157; **Markings:** HEART STAR, ERIE PA USA, PAT'D MAY 18, 20, JULY 11, 22; **Hinge:** ball, sides are interchangeable; **Waffle Pattern:** Heart Star; **Circa:** 1923; **VALUE: $200-$250.**

Above and Left:
AMERICAN WAFFLE WITH STOVE RING—Size: No. 8; **p/n:** (both sides) 151N, (base) 301; **Markings:** (pan) block logo, AMERICAN NO 8, THE GRISWOLD MFG. CO, ERIE PA, USA, PATT APPLIED FOR; (base) NO 8, PATENTED NOV. 24. 1925, THE GRISWOLD MFG. CO. ERIE, PA., U.S.A., 301; **Hinge:** ball; **Waffle Pattern:** standard; **Circa:** 1923-1930; **VALUE: $250.**

SQUARE AMERICAN WAFFLE IRON—Size: No. 11; **p/n:** 988, 989, (base) 987 ; **Markings:** (Inscribed) THE AMERICAN WAFFLE IRON No 11, PAT'D MAY 14 & 21 1901; **Hinge:** ball; **Waffle Pattern:** standard; **Circa:** 1910; **VALUE: $100, (with low base) $200.** Straight wood handles.

SQUARE AMERICAN WAFFLE IRON—Size: No. 11 (6 3/4" x 6 3/4"); **p/n:** 3269, 3270, (base) 987; **Markings:** AMERICAN No 11, slant logo ; **Hinge:** ball; **Waffle Pattern:** standard; **Circa:** 1920; **VALUE: $100, (with low base)** $200. Sculpted wood handles.

No. 12 HOTEL WAFFLE—Size: (pan) 9 1/2" x 4', (base) 15" x 12"; **p/n:** 2608, 2609, (base) 990; **Markings:** (embossed) slant logo, GRISWOLD MFG CO, ERIE PA USA, PATD MAY 14 1901, DEC 1, 1908; **Hinge:** ball; **Waffle Pattern:** three-section standard; **Circa:** 1920; **VALUE: $500-$600.**

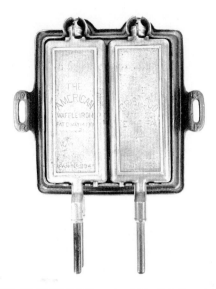

No. 12 HOTEL WAFFLE IRON—Size: (pan) 9 1/2" x 4", (base) 15" x 12"; **p/n:** 366, 367, (base) 990; **Markings:** (raised) block logo, THE GRISWOLD MFG CO, ERIE PA USA; (base) No 12; **Hinge:** ball; **Waffle Pattern:** three-section standard; **Circa:** 1920-1930; **VALUE:** $500-$600.

No. 12 HOTEL WAFFLE IRON—p/n: 993, 994, (base) 990; **Markings:** THE AMERICAN WAFFLE IRON, PAT MAY 14, 1901, MAY 21, 1901; **Hinge:** acorn; **Waffle Pattern:** three-section standard; **Circa:** 1905-1920; **VALUE:** $500.

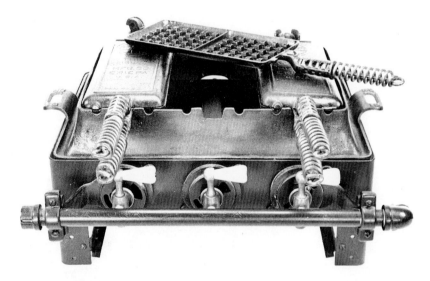

Left and Below:
No. 13 HOTEL WAFFLE IRON & STOVE—Size: 11 3/4" x 15 3/4"; **p/n:** (pans) 891 & 892, (base) 166, (stove) 130, (griddle) 214; **Markings:** slant logo, THE GRISWOLD MFG CO, ERIE PA, PAT'D MAY 14, 1901, MAY 21,1901; **Hinge:** ball; **Waffle Pattern:** two-section, standard grid; **Circa:** 1920; **VALUE:** $1000, complete with griddle $1500. Two-section waffle pans were a special order, and therefore are uncommon.

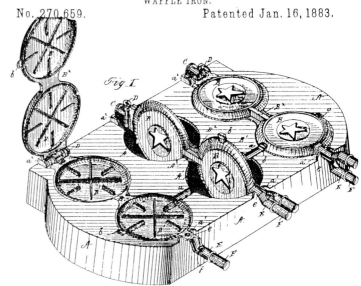

M. GRISWOLD & S. SELDEN.
S. SELDEN, Dec'd.; E. P. SELDEN, Administrator.
WAFFLE IRON.

No. 270,659.   Patented Jan. 16, 1883.

Fig. I

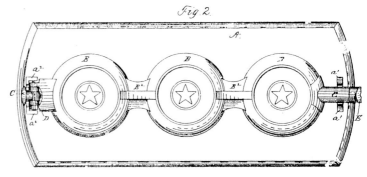

Fig. 2

Witnesses   Inventors
W. R. Edelen.   M. Griswold, Inv.
M. A. Edelen   E. P. Selden, Adr.
                                For Samuel Selden, Dec'd
                          Per Hallock & Hallock
                                    Att's

Above:
No. 14 HOTEL WAFFLE IRON—Size: 19" x 15"; **p/n:** 2608, 2609, (base) 992; **Markings:** slant logo, THE GRISWOLD MFG CO. ERIE PA USA, PAT MAY 14, 1901, DEC 1, 1908; **Hinge:** ball; **Waffle Pattern:** standard; **Circa:** 1920; **VALUE:** $800-$1000.

Right:
A patent drawing for the French waffle iron from January 16, 1883.

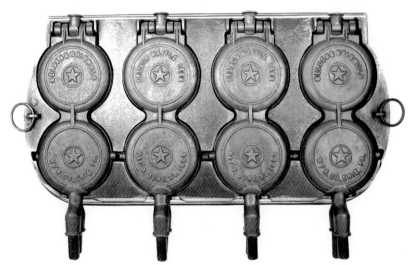

Above and Left:
No. 9 FRENCH WAFFLE IRON—Size: 22 1/2" x
11 1/2"; **p/n:** none; **Markings:** SELDEN
GRISWOLD MFG. CO. ERIE PA, FRENCH
WAFFLE IRON, PAT'D JUNE 20, 1880; **Hinge:**
button; **Waffle Pattern:** Web; **Circa:** 1883-1890;
VALUE: $1000-$1200.

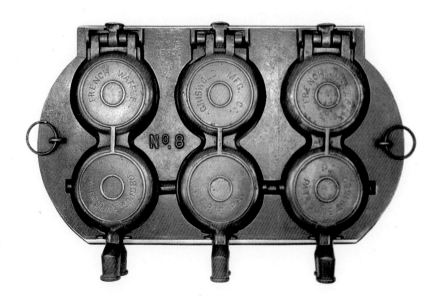

No. 8 FRENCH WAFFLE IRON—Size: 20" x 11
1/2"; **p/n:** none; **Markings:** THE GRISWOLD
MFG. CO., ERIE PA, FRENCH WAFFLE, PAT;D
JUNE 29, 1880; **Hinge:** button; **Waffle Pattern:**
standard grid; **Circa:** 1885; **VALUE: $1000-**
$1200.

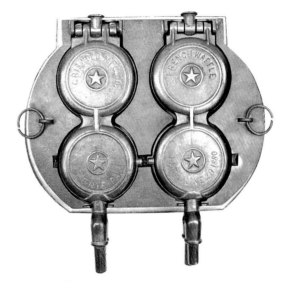

NO. 7 FRENCH WAFFLE IRON—Size: 14 1/2" x 11 1/2"; **p/n:** none; **Markings:** THE GRISWOLD MFG. CO., ERIE PA, FRENCH WAFFLE, PAT JUNE 29, 1880; **Hinge:** button; **Waffle Pattern:** Web; **Circa:** 1883-1890; **VALUE: $1000.**

NO. 7 FRENCH WAFFLE IRON—p/n: 899 (both sides, although not interchangeable); **Markings:** THE GRISWOLD MFG. CO., ERIE PA, FRENCH WAFFLE, PAT'D JUNE 29, 1880, JULY 25, 1893; **Hinge:** finger; **Waffle Pattern:** standard; **Circa:** 1900; **VALUE: $800-$1000.**

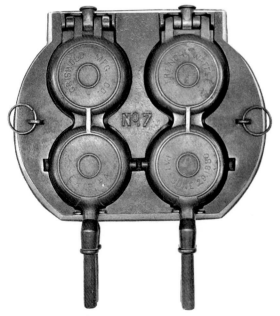

NO. 7 FRENCH WAFFLE IRON—Size: 14 1/2" x 11 1/2"; **p/n:** none; **Markings:** THE GRISWOLD MFG. CO., ERIE PA, FRNECH WAFFLE, PAT'D JUN 29, 1880; **Hinge:** button; **Waffle Pattern:** standard; **Circa:** 1885; **VALUE: $800-$900.**

Above and Right:
OVAL WAFFLE IRON—Size: No. 7 (17 3/4" x 7 1/2"), No. 8 (19 1/2" x 8 5/8"), and No. 9 (21" x 9 1/2"); **p/n:** none; **Markings:** THE GRISWOLD MFG. CO., ERIE PA; **Circa:** 1895-1910; **VALUE: $850-$1000.**

No "00" SQUARE WAFFLE IRON—Size: No. 00 (10 1/4" x 7 3/4"); six cakes, each 2 3/8" x 4 7/8"; **p/n:** 910, 911, (base) 903; **Markings:** GRISWOLD MFG CO., ERIE P2A; **Circa:** 1895-1930; **VALUE: $600-$700.**

No. "0" SQUARE WAFFLE IRON—Size: 9 3/4" x 6"; four cakes, each 2 3/4" x 4 3/4"; **p/n:** 909, 908, (base) 902; **Markings:** THE GRISWOLD MFG. CO., ERIE PA; **Circa:** 1895-1830; **VALUE: $650.**

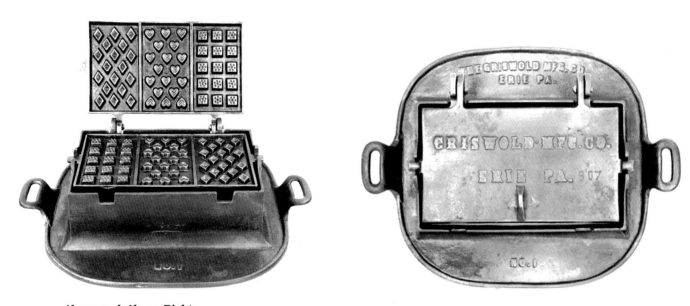

Above and Above Right:
No. 1 SQUARE WAFFLE IRON—Size: 8 3/4" x 5"; three cakes, each 2 3/4" x 4 7/8" *?*; **p/n:** 906, 907, base 901; **Markings:** THE GRISWOLD MFG.CO., ERIE PA; **Circa:** 1895-1930; **VALUE: $600-$650.**

Left and Right:
No. 2 **SQUARE WAFFLE IRON—Size:** 7 5/8" X 4 3/4"; three cakes, each 2 3/8" x 4/1/2"; **p/n:** none; **Markings:** THE GRISWOLD MFG. CO., ERIE PA; **Circa:** 1895-1930; **VALUE: $750-800.**

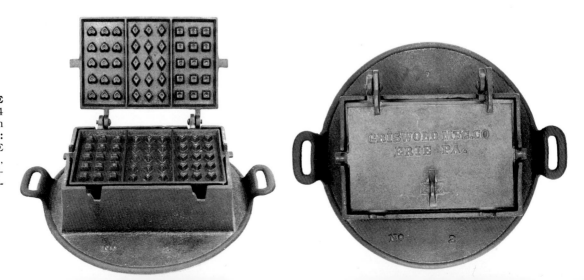

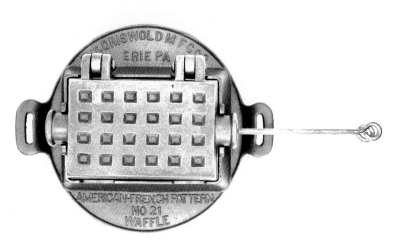

Left, Center Left:
No. 21 AMERICAN WAFFLE IRON—Size: (pan) 4" x 6 1/2"; **p/n:** 2402, 2403, (base) 2404; **Markings:** THE GRISWOLD MFG. CO., ERIE PA, AMERICAN FRENCH PATTERN, NO 21 WAFFLE; **Circa: 1910** ; **VALUE: $2000-$2500**.

Left and Above:
WAFER IRON—Size: (pan) 5 9/16" dia., (base) 8 1/2" dia.; **p/n:** 895, 995, (base) 894; **Markings:** THE GRISWOLD MFG. CO., ERIE PA, PATENTED JUNE 29, 1880; **Circa:** 1890-1910; **VALUE: $300-$400**.

No. 1 GEM PAN—Size: 11 1/2" x 11 7/8", (cups) 2 1/2 dia. x 3/4" deep; **p/n:** 940; **Markings:** No 1, 940; **Finish:** iron; **Circa:** 1890-1910; **VALUE: $100.**

No. 2 GEM PAN—Size: 12 1/2" x 8 1/2", (cups) 3" dia. x 5/8" deep; **p/n:** 941; **Markings:** No. 2, 941; **Finish:** iron; **Circa:** 1880-1900; **VALUE: $200.** The No. 2 Gem Pan is not known to be marked Erie or Griswold.

No. 3 GEM PAN—Size: 12 1/2" x 8 1/2", (cups) 2" dia. x 1" deep; **p/n:** 942; **Markings:** No. 3, 942; **Finish:** iron; **Circa:** 1890-1910; **VALUE: $200.**

No. 1 GEM PAN—Size: 11 1/2" x 11 7/8", (cups) 2 1/2" dia. x 3/4" deep; **p/n:** 940; **Markings:** slant logo, EPU, No. 1, 940; **Finish:** iron; **Circa:** 1910-1930; **VALUE: $150-$200.**

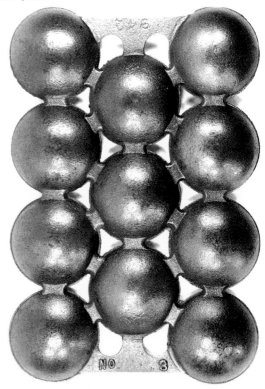

No. 3 GEM PAN—Size: 12 1/2" x 8 1/2", (cups) 2" dia. x 1" deep; **p/n:** 942; **Markings:** slant logo, No. 3, 942 **Finish:** iron; **Circa:** 1910-1925; **VALUE: $350-$400**.

No. 5 GEM PAN—Size: 12 1/4" x 7 1/2"; **p/n:** 943; **Markings:** slant logo No 5, 943; **Finish:** iron; **Circa:** 1910-1930; **VALUE: $400-$450**.

No. 5 GEM PAN—Size: 12 1/4" x 7 1/2"; **p/n:** 943; **Markings:** No 5, 943; **Finish:** iron; **Circa:** 1890-1900; **VALUE: $200**.

No. 6 GEM PAN—Size: 13" x 7 3/4", (cups) 2 7/8" dia. x 1 7/8" deep; **p/n:** 944; **Markings:** No 6, 944; **Finish:** iron; **Circa:** 1890-1910; **VALUE: $150-$200**.

No. 6 GEM PAN—Size:13" x 7 3/4"; **p/n:** 944; **Markings:** *GRISWOLD*, ERIE PA, USA, 944; **Finish:** iron; **Circa:** 1910-1930; **VALUE: $250**.

No. 8 GEM PAN—Size: 12 3/4" X 6 3/8"; **p/n:** 946; **Markings:** "ERIE," No 8 MUFFIN PAN, 946; **Finish:** iron; **Circa:** 1890-1920; **VALUE: $75-$100**.

No. 7 Gem Pan—Size:11 3/4" x 7 5/8", (cups) 3 9/16" x 2 3/8" x 5/8" deep; **p/n:** 945; **Markings:** No 7, 945 ; **Finish:** iron; **Circa:** 1890-1900; **VALUE: $150-$200**. The No. 7 Gem Pan is not known to be marked Erie or Griswold.

No. 8 GEM PAN—Size: 12 3/4" x 6 3/8"; (cups) 3" dia. x 7/8" deep; **p/n:** 946; **Markings:** slant logo; **Finish:** iron; **Circa:** 1923-1940; **VALUE: $200**.

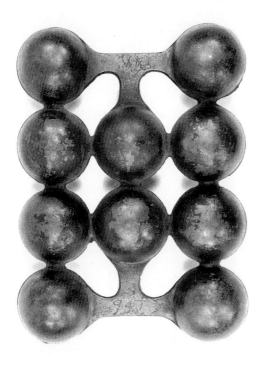

No. 947 GEM PAN—Size: 9 1/2" x 7 1/8", (cups) 2" dia. x 1" deep; **p/n:** 947; **Markings:** 947; **Finish:** iron; **Circa:** 1890; **VALUE: $150 $200**. To the authors' knowledge, this pan has never appeared in a catalog.

No. 9 BROWNIE CAKE PAN—Size: 10 3/8" x 7"; **p/n:** 947; **Markings:** 947, No 9 ; **Finish:** iron; **Circa:** 1923; **VALUE: $100**.

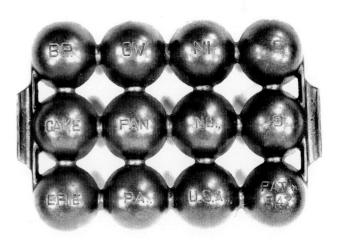

No. 9 GOLF-BALL PAN—p/n: 947; **Markings:** BR, OW, NI, E CAKE PAN, NO 9, ERIE PA USA, PAT', 947; **Finish:** iron or chrome; **Circa:** 1925-1930s; **VALUE: $150**.

No. 9 GEM PAN—Size: 10 3/8" x 7", (cups) 2" dia. x 1" deep; **p/n:** 947; **Markings:** 947; **Finish:** iron; **Circa:** 1890-1920; **VALUE: $100**.

No. 10 GEM PAN—Size: 10 1/2" x 7 1/2", (cups) **2 1/2" dia.** x 1 3/4" deep; **p/n:** 948; **Markings:** No 10, 948; **Finish:** iron; **Circa:** 1880-1900; **VALUE: $40.**

No. 10 GEM or POP-OVER PAN—p/n: 948F; **Markings:** No 10, GRISWOLD (slant), ERIE PA U.S.A., 948F; **Finish:** iron, nickel, or chrome; **Circa:** 1910-1950; **VALUE: $35.** There are twelve recorded variations of the No. 948 series.

No. 10 GEM or POP-OVER PAN—p/n: 948; **Markings:** No 10, ERIE, 948; **Finish:** iron; **Circa:** 1890-1910; **VALUE: $30-$60.**

No. 10 POP-OVER PAN—Size: 11 1/4" x 7 3/4"; **p/n:** 948 USN; **Markings:** NO 10, GRISWOLD, ERIE PA USA, 948, USN; **Finish:** iron; **Circa:** 1950; **VALUE: $100-$150.**

No. 10 POP-OVER PAN—Size: 11 1/8" x 7 3/4", (cups) 2 3/4" dia. x 1 1/2" deep; **p/n:** 949; **Markings:** No 10, GRISWOLD, ERIE PA USA, 949; **Finish:** iron; **Circa:** 1050s; **VALUE: $30**.

POP-OVER PAN—Size: 11 5/8" x 8 1/16"; **p/n:** 8010; **Markings:** slant logo, 8010; **Finish:** aluminum; **Circa:** 1930s; **VALUE: $75-$100**. This pan has a single hanging hole.

Above and Left:
No. 11 GEM PAN—Size: 12 1/2" x 7 3/4"; **p/n:** none; **Markings:** none; **Finish:** iron; **Circa:** 1890; **VALUE: $1000-$1250**. Note the design of the handle, which has steps or notches at the ends. This piece is listed in an 1890 catalog.

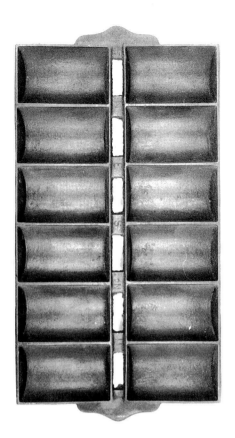

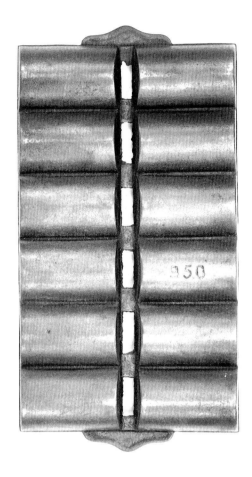

Left and Below:
No. 11 NEW ENGLAND STYLE GEM PAN—**p/n:** 950; **Markings:** 950, N.E.S. .ON 11; **Finish:** iron; **Circa:** 1890-1905; **VALUE: $75-$100.**

No. 11 MUFFIN PAN—**Size:** 12 7/8" x 6 1/4" x 7/8"; **p/n:** 850; **Markings:** No 11, GRISWOLD, ERIE PA USA, 950 A; **Finish:** iron; **Circa:** 1923-1930s; **VALUE: $35.** There are at least five marking variations of this style. It was also made with a wide center variation shown.

No. 12 GEM PAN—Size: 11" x 7 1/2", (cups) 3"dia. X 7/8"deep; **p/n:** 951; **Markings:** NO. 12, 951; **Finish:** iron; **Circa:** 1890-1920; **VALUE: $200-$300.**

No. 13 TURK HEAD PAN—Size: 9 3/8" x 5 3/4", (cups) 2 5/8" dia. x 7/8"deep; **p/n:** 640; **Markings:** GRISWOLD, ERIE PA USA, NO 13; **Finish:** iron; **Circa:** 1925-1930; **VALUE: $1200-$1500.**

No. 12 GEM PAN—p/n: 951; **Markings:** slant logo, 12, 951; **Finish:** iron; **Circa:** 1920-1940s; **VALUE: $250.**

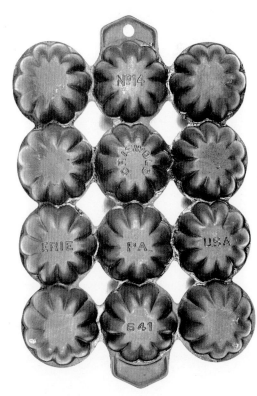

Above and Left:
No. 14 TURK HEAD PAN—Size: 13 1/8" x 8 3/8", (cups) 2 5/8" dia. x 7/8" deep; **p/n:** 641; **Markings:** No. 14, GRISWOLD, ERIE PA, USA, 641; **Finish:** iron; **Circa:** 1925-1930; **VALUE: $600-$700.**

No. 14 GEM PAN—Size: 12 1/2" x 6 5/8", (cups) 2 1/2" x 1 7/8" x 3/4" deep; **p/n:** (942); **Markings:** No. 14 (under handle), cut-outs; **Finish:** iron; **Circa:** 1890; **VALUE: (as shown) $500-$600, (without cut-outs) $800.**

Below:
No. 15 MUFFIN PAN (wide center)—Size: 14 1/4" X 8"; **p/n:** 6130; **Markings:** GRISWOLD, NO 15; **Finish:** iron; **Circa:** 1920; **VALUE: $250-$300.**

Left:
No. 15 Muffin Pan (French Roll)—Size: 14 3/8" x 7 1/2"; **p/n:** 6138; **Markings:** NO 15, GRISWOLD, ERIE PA, USA, 6138; **Finish:** iron; **Circa:** 1920-1930s; **VALUE: $250.**

No. 16 MUFFIN PAN—Size: 8 7/8" x 6 3/4"; **p/n:** 6139; **Markings:** 16, GRISWOLD, ERIE PA USA, 6139; **Finish:** iron; **Circa:** 1923-1930s; **VALUE: $150.**

No 16 MUFFIN PAN (wide center)—p/n: 6139; **Markings:** GRISWOLD NO 16 (top of center); **Finish:** iron; **Circa:** 1920; **VALUE: $1500.**

No. 17 MUFFIN PAN—
Size: 7 1/2" x 6" x 7/8"; **p/n:** 6140; **Markings:** 17, GRISWOLD, 6140, ERIE; **Finish:** iron; **Circa:** 1923-1930s; **VALUE:** $100.

No. 17 GEM PAN (wide center)—**Size:** 7 3/4" x 5 3/4" x 7/8"; **p/n:** 6140; **Markings:** GRISWOLD NO 17 (top of center); **Finish:** iron; **Circa:** 1920; **VALUE:** $150.

No. 18 POP-OVER PAN—**p/n:** 6141; **Markings:** GRISWOLD, ERIE PA, USA, 6141, NO 18; **Finish:** iron; **Circa:** 1920; **VALUE:** $100-$125.

No. 18 GEM PAN—**Size:** 9 1/8" x 5 1/2"; **p/n:** 6141; **Markings:** GRISWOLDS ERIE, NO 18; **Finish:** iron; **Circa:** 1910-1920; **VALUE:** $125-$150.

No. 18 POP-OVER PAN—**p/n:** 6141; **Markings:** NO 18, GRISWOLD, ERIE PA, USA, 6141; **Finish:** iron; **Circa:** 1930s-1940s; **VALUE:** $75-$100.

No. 19 GOLF BALL PAN—Size: 7 3/4" x 4 5/8" x 1"; **p/n:** 966;
Markings: NO 19, 966; **Finish:** iron ; **Circa:** 1923; **VALUE: $450**

No. 20 GEM PAN—Size: 10 5/8" x 7 1/2", (cups) 2" dia. x 3/4" deep;
p/n: 953; **Markings:** 953 (only); **Finish:** iron; **Circa:** 1890-1910;
VALUE: $200-$250.

Above and Right:
No. 19 GOLF BALL PAN—p/n: 966; **Markings:** NO 19,
GRISWOLD, ERIE PA, USA, 966; **Finish:** iron; **Circa:**
1925-1930s; **VALUE: $400-$500.**

No. 20 TURK HEAD PAN—Size: 10 3/8" x 7 1/8"; **p/n:** 953; **Markings:** 953, GRISWOLD, ERIE PA USA; **Finish:** iron; **Circa:** 1900-1930; **VALUE: $500-$600**.

No. 21 CORN BREAD PAN—Size: 9 1/2" x 7 1/2"; **p/n:** 961; **Markings:** NO 21, GRISWOLD CORN BREAD PAN, ERIE PENN USA; **Finish:** iron; **Circa:** 1925-1930s; **VALUE: $150-$200**.

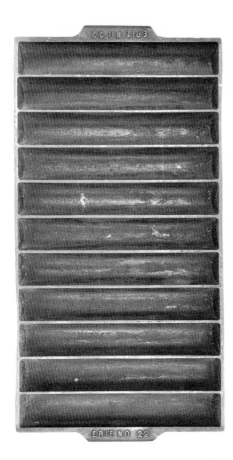

No. 22 BREAD PAN—**Size:** 13 3/8" x 7 3/8"; **p/n:** 954; **Markings:** ERIE, NO 22 on handles; **Finish:** iron; **Circa:** 1910-1920; **VALUE:** $60.

No. 22 CORN BREAD PAN—**Size:** 14 1/2" x 7 1/2"; **p/n:** 954E; **Markings:** GRISWOLD CORN BREAD PAN, ERIE PA, USA; **Finish:** iron; **Circa:** 1920s-1940s; **VALUE:** $40-$60. There are twelve recorded marking variations of this pan.

Below and Left:
No. 23 BREAD STICK PAN—**Size:** 14 1/2" x 7 1/2"; **p/n:** 955; **Markings:** NO 23 BREAD STICK PAN, GRISOLD, ERIE PA USA; **Finish:** iron; **Circa:** 1925-1940s; **VALUE:** $100-$150.

Above and Right:
No. 24 ERIE BREAD PAN—Size: 12 1/2" x 7 1/2", (cakes) 7 1/2" x 2"; **p/n:** 959; **Markings:** 959, ERIE, No. 24; **Finish:** iron; **Circa:** 1900-1915; **VALUE:** $400-$600.

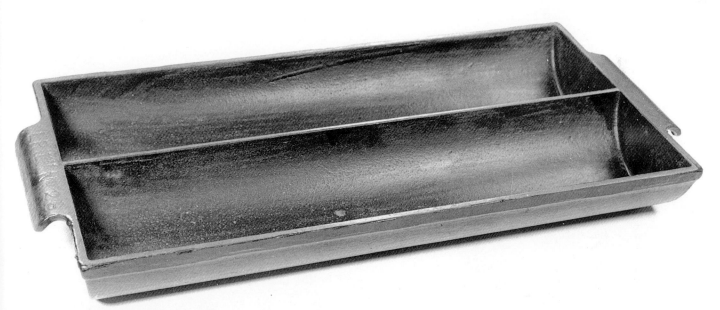

No. 26 ERIE BREAD PAN—Size: 13 7/8" x 6 1/2"; **p/n:** 960; **Markings:** ERIE No. 26; **Finish:** iron; **Circa:** 1900-1910; **VALUE:** $800-$1000; with p/n only, $700-$800.

No. 28 ERIE BREAD PAN—Size: 12" x 4"; **p/n:** unknown; **Markings:** unknown; **Finish:** iron; **Circa:** 1900-1907; **VALUE: VERY RARE.**

Below:
APPLE CAKE PAN OR EGG POACHER—Size: 9 1/2"
dia.; **Finish:** iron. Notice the raised top edge.

No. 31 DANISH CAKE PAN—Size: 9" dia., (cups)
2 1/4" x 1 1/8"; **p/n:** 963; **Markings:** GRISWOLD, NO
31, 963; **Finish:** iron; **Circa:** 1900-1930s; **VALUE:**
$150-$200.

Right:
EGG POACHER—Size: 9 1/2" dia.; **p/n:** none; **Markings:** diamond logo; **Finish:** iron, **Circa:** 1905; **VALUE:**
$100-$125.

Below:
APPLE CAKE PAN—Size: 9 1/2" dia.; **p/n:** 962;
Markings: G M Co, 962; **Finish:** iron; **Circa:** 1920s;
VALUE: $100.

Right:
No. 32 EGG POACHER OR APPLE CAKE PAN—Size:
9 1/2" dia.; **p/n:** 962; **Markings:** GRISWOLD, ERIE PA,
962, No. 32; **Finish:** iron; **Circa:** 1923-1950s; **VALUE:**
$30-$40.

Above:
No. 32 DANISH CAKE PAN OR EGG POACHER—Size: 9 1/4" dia.;
p/n: 962; **Markings:** GRISWOLD, 32 MADE IN USA; **Finish:** iron;
Circa: 1960s-1970s; **VALUE: $20.**

ANDRESEN MONK PAN—Size: 9" dia.; **p/n:** 2992; **Markings:**
ANDRESEN MONK PAN, 2992; **Finish:** iron; **Circa:** 1900-1915;
VALUE: $150. Alfred Andresen founded a buisiness called "Alfred
Andresen & Company, the Western Importers" in 1896 in Minne-
apolis, Minnesota. He left the firm in 1913, and the name was
changed to "The Western Importing Company." This company was
not a manufacturing company, but an importer and distributor.
The pattern number 2992 identifies this pan as one made by
Griswold for the Alfred Andresen company.

Left and Below:
No. 33 MUNK PAN—Size: 9" dia.; **p/n:** 2992; **Markings:** MUNK
PAN, 2992; **Finish:** iron; **Circa:** 1923-1930s; **VALUE: $250-$350.**

Above and Right:
PLETT PAN—Size: 9 1/2" dia., (cups) 3" x 1/4"; **p/n:** 2980A; **Markings:** slant logo, 2980A; **Finish:** iron; **Circa:** 1919; **VALUE:** $40-$50.

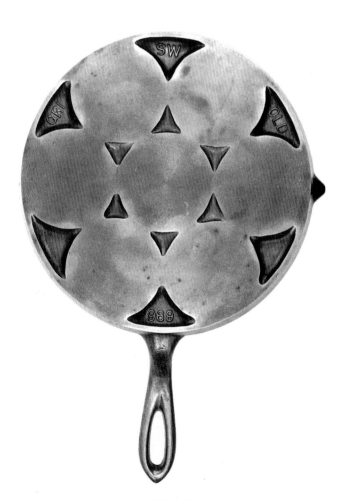

WESTERN IMPORTING CO. MUNK PAN—Size: 9" dia.; **p/n:** 2992, (cups) 2 1/4" x 1 1/8"; **Markings:** WESTERN IMPORTING CO, MUNK PAN, 2992; **Finish:** iron; **Circa:** 1920-1930s; **VALUE:** **$100**. The pattern number 2992 identifies this pan as one made by Griswold.

PLETT PAN—Size: 9 1/2" dia., (cups) 3" x 1/4"; **p/n:** 969; **Markings:** GRI-SW-OLD, 969; **Finish:** iron; **Circa:** 1940; **VALUE:** **$100-$125**.

No. 34 PLETT PAN—Size: 9 1/2" dia.; **p/n:** 2980; **Markings:** large block logo, No 34, 2980; **Finish:** iron; **Circa:** 1923-1940s; **VALUE:** $30-$40.

No. 34 PLETT PAN—p/n: 2980A; **Markings:** small logo, No 34, 2980A; **Finish:** iron; **Circa:** 1950s-1960s; **VALUE:** $20.

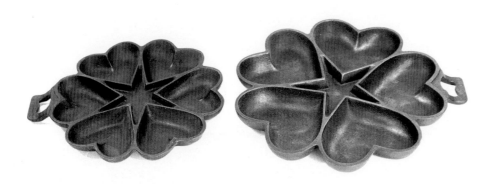

Left:
No. 50 (left) and No. 100 (right) HEART STAR GEM PANS

Below:
No. 100 HEART-STAR GEM PAN—Size: 7 3/4" x 7 3/4"; **p/n:** 960; **Markings:** No. 100, same as No. 50; **Finish:** iron or aluminum; **Circa:** 1920-1930; **VALUE:** $800-$1000.

No. 50 HEART-STAR GEM PAN—Size: 6 1/2" x 6 1/2"; **p/n:** 959; **Markings:** NO 50, HEARTS STAR, GRISWOLD, ERIE PA, USA, 959, PATD MAY 18, 1920; **Finish:** iron & aluminum; **Circa:** 1920-1930; **VALUE:** $1500-$2000.

No. 140 TURK HEAD—Size: 12 5/8"
x 8 1/4"; **p/n:** 635; **Markings:**
GRISWOLD, ERIE PA, USA, NO 140,
635; **Finish:** iron; **Circa:** 1932-1940;
VALUE: $150-$200.

No. 130 TURK HEAD—Size: 10" x
5 9/16", (cups) 2 5/8" x 7/8"; **p/n:** 634;
Markings: GRISWOLD, ERIE PA USA, NO.
130; **Finish:** iron; **Circa:** 1932-1940;
VALUE: $500-$700.

No. 240 TURK HEAD—Size: 14 5/8" x 10", (cups)
2 3/4" x 7/8"; **p/n:**631 ; **Markings:** GRISWOLD, ERIE
PA, USA, NO 240, 631; **Finish:** iron; **Circa:** 1932-1940s;
VALUE: $250-$300.

Above and Right:
No. 1 VIENNA ROLL PAN—Size: 13 1/2" x
4 1/2"; **p/n:** unknown; **Markings:** VIENNA
ROLL PAN № 1; **Finish:** iron; **Circa:** 1890;
VALUE: $1750-$2000. Markings are raised
letters inside the pan.

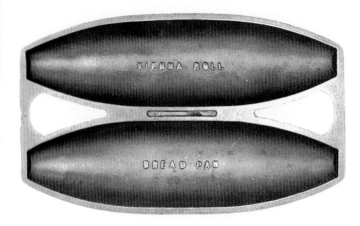

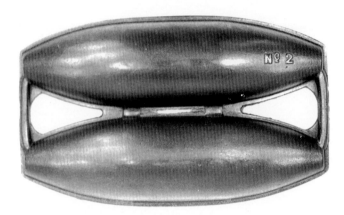

No. 2 VIENNA BREAD PAN—Size: 12" x 7 1/2", (cups) 12" x 3";
p/n: 956; **Markings:** VIENNA ROLL BREAD PAN (inside), No 2
(bottom); **Finish:** iron; **Circa:** 1890-1915; **VALUE: $800-$1000**.

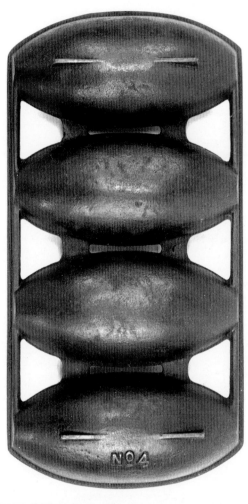

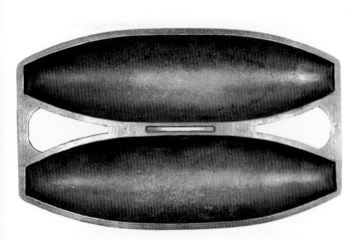

No. 4 ERIE BREAD PAN—Size: 12 1/2" x 6 1/2" x 6 1/2"; **p/n:**
957; **Markings:** Nº 4; **Finish:** iron; **Circa:** 1890-1910; **VALUE:
$400-$600**. To find this piece marked with the pattern number is
rare. This piece is known by some makers as a Corn Pone Pan.

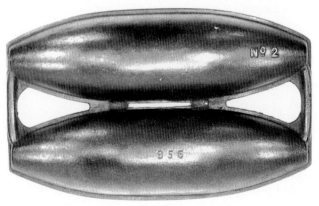

Above and Right:
No. 2 VIENNA BREAD PAN—Size: 12" x 7 1/2"; **p/n:** 956;
Markings: 956, No 2 ; **Finish:** iron; **Circa:** 1890-1915; **VALUE:
$1000-$1200**. Examples that are plain inside are more uncommon. Examples marked with pattern number are rare.

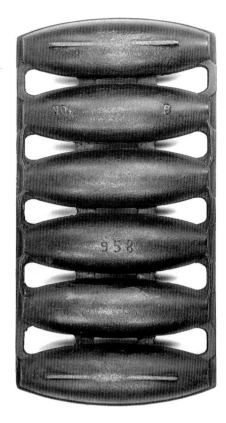

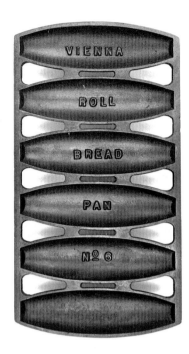

No. 6 VIENNA BREAD PAN—**Size:** 12 1/2" x 6 1/2", (cups) 6" x 1 3/4"; **p/n:** 958; **Markings:** No. 6, 958; **Finish:** iron; **Circa:** 1880-1890; **VALUE: $150**.

No. 6 VIENNA BREAD PAN—**Size:** 12 1/2" x 6 1/2'; **p/n:** 958; **Markings:** VIENNA, ROLL, BREAD, PAN, No 6; **Finish:** iron; **Circa:** 1890-1900; **VALUE: $200-$250**. Markings are raised letters inside the (cups).

No. 26 VIENNA BREAD PAN—**Size:** 12 1/2" X 6 1/2"; **p/n:** 958; **Markings:** No 26, GRISWOLD, ERIE, 958; **Finish:** iron; **Circa:** 1915-1935; **VALUE: $150**.

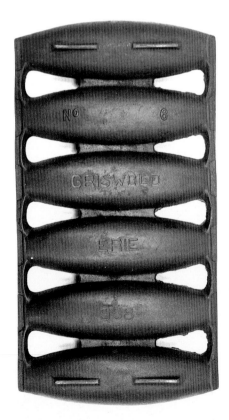

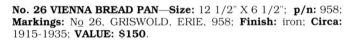

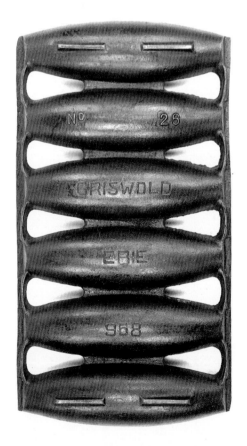

No. 6 VIENNA BREAD PAN—**Size:** 12 1/2" x 6 1/2"; **p/n:** 958; **Markings:** No 6, GRISWOLD, ERIE, 958; **Finish:** iron; **Circa:** 1900-1915; **VALUE: $200**.

FIG. 1.

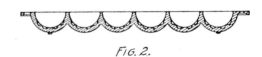

FIG. 2.

INVENTOR.

Charles A. Massing

BY

ATTORNEYS.

No. 27 WHEAT STICK PAN—Size: 10 7/8" x 5 7/8"; **p/n:** 638;
Markings: No 27, WHEAT & CORN, STICK PAN, GRISWOLD, ERIE
PA USA, PAT NO 73,326,638; **Finish:** iron; **Circa:** 1925-1930;
VALUE: $250-$300.

A patent drawing for the Wheat Pattern baking pan, from December 21, 1923.

Left and Below:
No. 27 WHEAT STICK PAN—Size: 10 7/8/" x 5 7/8"; **p/n:** 638;
Markings: No 27. WHOLE WHEAT, STICK PAN, GRISWOLD, ERIE
PA USA, 638; **Finish:** iron; **Circa:** 1925; **VALUE: $200-$250.**

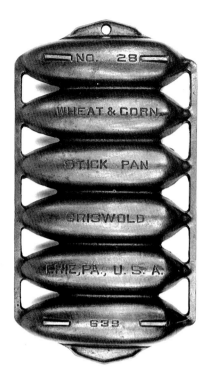

No. 28 WHEAT STICK PAN—Size: 12 5/8" x 7"; **p/n:** 639; **Markings:** No 28, WHEAT & CORN, STICK PAN, GRISWOLD, ERIE PA USA, 639; **Finish:** iron; **Circa:** 1925-1930; **VALUE: $200-$250.** A variation of this piece marked "WHOLE WHEAT" can be found.

No. 262 CORN STICK PAN—Size: 8 1/2" x 4 1/8" (tea size); **p/n:** 625; **Markings:** GRISWOLD, CRISPY CORN OR WHEAT ERIE PA. USA, 625 ; **Finish:** iron, chrome, porcelain; **Circa:** 1932-1950s; **VALUE: $75-$125.**

No. 262 CORN OR WHEAT STICK PAN—Size: 8 1/2" x 4 1/8" (tea size); **p/n:** none; **Markings:** NO 262, GRISWOLD, CRISPY, CORN OR WHEAT STICK PAN; **Finish:** iron; **Circa:** 1960s; **VALUE: $65.** Because "ERIE PA" is not marked on the pan, it can be deduced that it was probably made in Sidney, OH. The hole in each end is typical of Wagner.

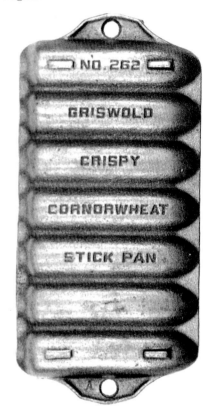

Above and Right:
REPRODUCTIONS OR FAKES of the tea-size Corn Stick Pan. These imitations have very poor casting quality and very poor kernel detail.

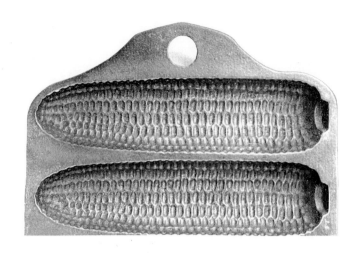

Below and Right:
Note the crude casting and lack of detail in the reproduction (left), compared to the original (right).

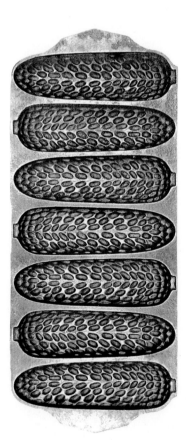

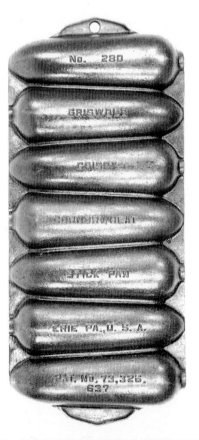

No. 280 CORN OR WHEAT STICK PAN—
Size: 15" x 6 3/4"; **p/n:** 637; **Markings:**
same as No. 270; **Finish:** iron; **Circa:** 1925;
VALUE: $800-$1000.

No. 270 CORN OR WHEAT STICK PAN—Size: 13 1/4" x 5 3/4"; **p/n:** 636; **Markings:** NO 270, GRISWOLD, CRISPY, CORN OR WHEAT, STICK PAN, ERIE PA USA, PAT NO 73,326,637; **Finish:** iron; **Circa:** 1925; **VALUE: $250-$300.** The 270 and 280 are the only Griswold corn pans with alternating cobs.

Left and Below:
No. 272 CORN OR WHEAT STICK PAN—
Size: 13 1/4" X 5 3/4"; **p/n:** 629; **Markings:** NO 272, GRISWOLD, CRISPY, CORN OR WHEAT, STICK PAN, ERIE PA USA, 629; **Finish:** iron; **Circa:** 1930; **VALUE:** $150-$200.

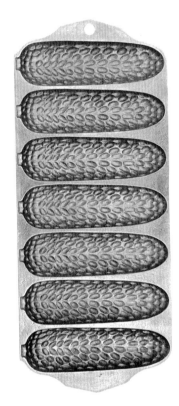

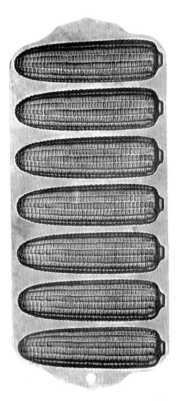

No. 282 CORN OR WHEAT STICK PAN—
Size: 15" X6 3/4"; **p/n:** 630; **Markings:** same as No. 272; **Finish:** iron; **Circa:** 1930; **VALUE:** $200-250.

No. 273 CORN STICK PAN—Size: 13 1/4" x 5 3/4"; **p/n:** 930; **Markings:** GRISWOLD, CRISPY, CORN, STICK PAN; **Finish:** iron, chrome, hammered, porcelain, aluminum; **Circa:** 1932-1960s; **VALUE:** $35.

No. 283 CORN STICK PAN—Size: 15" x 6 3/4": **p/n:** 931; **Markings:** same as No. 273; **Finish:** iron, chrome, hammered, porcelain, aluminum; **Circa:** 1932-1940s; **VALUE: $150-200**.

CORN STICK PANS No. 283, No. 273, and No. 262—for size comparison

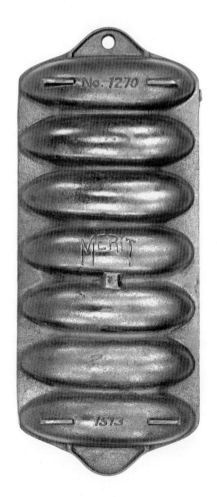

Left and Above:
No. 1270 MERIT WHEAT STICK PAN—Size: 13" x 5 1/2; **p/n:** 1513; **Markings:** NO 1270, MERIT, 1513; **Finish:** iron; **Circa:** 1920s; **VALUE: $100**.

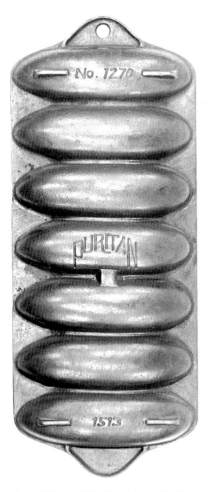

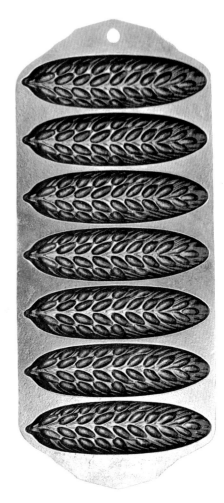

No. 1270 PURITAN WHEAT STICK PAN—
Size: 13" x 5 1/2"; **p/n:** 1513; **Markings:**
NO 1270, PURITAN, 1513; **Finish:** iron;
Circa: 1920s; **VALUE: $100.**

No. 2700 WHEAT & CORN STICK PAN—Size: 13 1/2" x 5 3/4"; **p/n:** 632; **Markings:** NO
2700, GRISWOLD, WHEAT & CORN, STICK PAN, ERIE PA USA, PAT 73,326,632; **Finish:**
iron; **Circa:** 1925; **VALUE: $300-$350.**

Left:
**BEST MADE WHEAT STICK
PAN—Size:** 13 1/4" x 5 3/4";
p/n: 1270; **Markings:** NO
1270, S.R. AND CO., BEST
MADE, WHEAT & CORN,
STICK PAN, PAT NO 73,326,
1270; **Finish:** iron; **Circa:**
1920s; **VALUE: $150.**

Right:
**2800 WHEAT & CORN
STICK PAN—Size:** 15" x 6 3/
4"; **p/n:** 633; **Markings:** NO
2800, GRISWOLD, WHEAT
& CORN, STICK PAN, ERIE
PA USA, PAT NO 73,326,633;
Finish: iron; **Circa:** 1925;
VALUE: $2000-$2500.

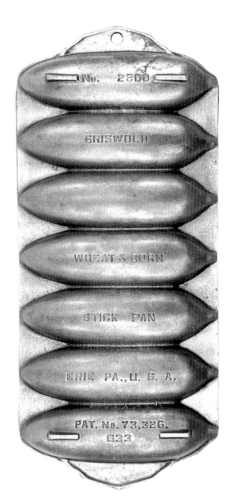

Below and Right:
(BUNDT) CAKE MOLD—**Size:** 9 1/2" dia. x 4 1/2" deep; **p/n:** 965;
Markings: THE GRISWOLD MFG CO, ERIE PA, CAKE MOLD;
Finish: iron; **Circa:** 1910-1940; **VALUE: $1000-$1200.**

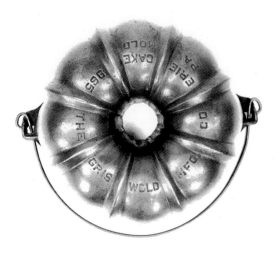

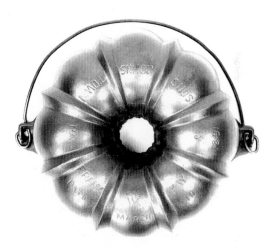

FRANK HAY CAKE MOLD—**Size:** 9 1/2" dia. x 4 1/2" deep;
p/n: none; **Markings:** FRANK W. HAY & SONS, JOHNSTOWN
PA, PATD MARCH 10, 1891; **Finish:** iron; **Circa:** 1918;
VALUE: $300-$400.

Above two photos and Right:
LOAF PAN—**Size:** 9 5/8" x 5 3/16" x 2 1/2" deep; **p/n:** 877, cover
859; **Markings:** block logo, LOAF PAN, THE GRISWOLD MFG CO,
ERIE PA USA; **Finish:** iron, chrome, Du-Chro; **Circa:** 1930s;
**VALUE: Iron $600-$800 with cover, $350-$400 without; chrome
$500-600 with cover, $250-$300 without.**

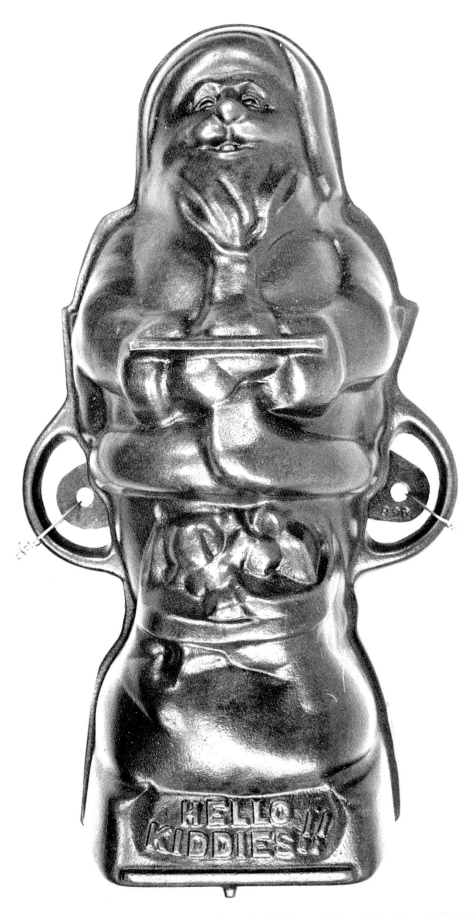

SANTA CAKE MOLD—Size: 12 1/8" x 6 7/8" x 4 5/8"; **p/n:** 897 front, 898 back; **Markings:** HELLO KIDDIES, GRISWOLD MFG. CO., ERIE PA.; **Finish:** iron or chrome; **Circa:** 1940s-1950s; **VALUE: $550-$600**.

SANTA CAKE MOLDS REPRODUCTIONS are fairly easy to recognize if you know what to look for: 1) the repro casting is grainy and lacks detail especially around the eyes; 2) the repro Santa does not have a tongue, while the original does (figs. 1 & 2); 3) the markings on the repro are crudely done. (figs. 3 & 4); the original Santa has what appears to be a casting flaw down the side of the bag, while the repro does not (fig. 5).

Fig 2. **ORIGINAL**; smooth, good detail, tongue.

Fig 1. **REPRODUCTION**; rough casting, lacks detail, no tongue.

ORIGINAL; lettering is evenly spaced, maintains margin.

REPRODUCTION; lettering is crude, uneven, runs off edge.

ORIGINAL; has casting flaw, reproduction does not.

RABBIT CAKE MOLD—Size: 10" x 11" x 4" deep; **p/n:** 862, 863; **Markings:** GRISWOLD MFG. CO., ERIE PA (on loop) 862, 863; **Finish:** iron or chrome; **Circa:** 1940s-1950s; **VALUE: iron $275-$300, chrome $250.** Collectors should be aware that these are being reproduced.

ORIGINAL   **REPRODUCTION**

The Rabbit mold is being reproduced. Distinguishing points of the original (left) is the style of the "I" in the words "GRISWOLD" and "ERIE" and the style of the number "3". Compare these to the letter "I" and number "3" of the reproduction (right).

LAMB CAKE MOLD—Size: 14 1/2" long; **p/n:** 947 front, 948 back; **Markings:** pattern numbers only; **Finish:** iron; **Circa:** 1920; **VALUE: $150-$200.** This is the largest of the three Griswold Lambs.

LAMB CAKE MOLD—Size: 13" long; **p/n:** 865 front, 866 back; **Markings:** pattern numbers only; **Finish:** iron; **Circa:** 1930; **VALUE: $125.** Back overlaps front.

LAMB CAKE MOLD—**Size:** 10 1/8" l (plus handles) x 4 1/8" w x 7" h; **p/n:** 921, 922; **Markings:** 866, 921, 922; **Finish:** iron; **Circa:** 1930s-1960s; **VALUE: $125**. Front over back. The Lamb is now being reproduced.

LAMB CAKE MOLD—The 1960s (left) and 1925 (right) for size comparison.

MINIATURES & TOYS

IRON TOY SET—**Size:** No. 2; **Markings:** ERIE; **Circa:** 1890-1910; **VALUE: $2000-$3000**.

Right:
TOY REGULAR KETTLE—**Size:** No. 2; **p/n:** none; **Markings:** ERIE, 2; **Finish:** iron; **Circa:** 1890-1910; **VALUE:** $250-$300.

TOY BAIL GRIDDLE—**Size:** No. 2 (3 1/4" dia.); **p/n:** none; **Markings:** USE ERIE WARE THE BEST ; **Finish:** iron; **Circa:** 1900; **VALUE:** $500-$600.

TOY FLAT BOTTOM KETTLE—**Size:** No. 2; **p/n:** none; **Markings:** "ERIE", 2; **Finish:** iron; **Circa:** 1890-1910; **VALUE:** $250-300.

WORLD'S FAIR GRIDDLE—**Size:** No. 2; **p/n:** none; **Markings:** THE WORLDS FAIR AWARDED TO "ERIE" WARE AM. DAMPERS, WAFFLE IRONS FIVE HIGHEST HONORS, GRISWOLD MFG. CO.; **Finish:** iron; **Circa:** 1893; **VALUE:** $400-$600.

Right:
TOY SCOTCH BOWL—**Size:** No. 2; **p/n:** none; **Markings:** "ERIE"; **Finish:** iron; **Circa:** 1890-1910; **VALUE:** $250-$300.

Left:
TOY SKILLET—**Size:** No. 2; **p/n:** none; **Markings:** ERIE; **Finish:** iron; **Circa:** 1890-1910; **VALUE:** $200-$250.

TOY TEA KETTLE—**Size:** No. 2 (2" high x 2 1/2" dia.); **p/n:** none; **Markings:** USE ERIE WARE THE BEST; **Finish:** nickel or iron; **Circa:** 1890-1910; **VALUE:** $250-300.

SIZE "0" TEA KETTLE (left) and **SIZE 2 TEA KETTLE** (right)

TOY SKILLET—**Size:** No. "0"; **p/n:** none; **Markings:** ERIE, 4; **Finish:** nickel; **Circa:** 1900; **VALUE: Rare**.

TOY SKILLETS—**Size:** No. "0"; **p/n:** none; **Markings:** GRISWOLDS, diamond logo; **Finish:** (left) iron, (right) aluminum with plated brass applied handle; **Circa:** 1910; **VALUE: iron $300-$400, aluminum $200-$300**.

Right and Above Right:
FACSIMILE WAFFLE IRON—**Size:** 1 7/8" dia.; **p/n:** none; **Markings:** FACSIMILE AMERICAN WAFFLE, GRISWOLD MFG. ERIE PA ; **Finish:** iron w. japanned base; **Circa:** 1880s; **VALUE: $500-$700**. Salesman's Sample.

Above:
MINIATURE SKILLET—**p/n:** none; **Markings:** "ERIE"; **Finish:** polished brass; **Circa:** unknown; **VALUE: Rare.**

TOY SKILLET—**Size:** No. "0"; **p/n:** none; **Markings:** ERIE, 4; **Finish:** nickel; **Circa:** 1900; **VALUE: Rare.**

TOY TEA KETTLE—**Size:** No. 2 (2" x 2 1/2" dia.); **p/n:** none; **Markings:** ERIE on cover, "2" on spout; **Finish:** iron or nickel; **Circa:** 1890-1910; **VALUE: $250-$300.**

TOY SKILLET—**Size:** No. 2 (2 3/4" dia.); **p/n:** none; **Markings:** USE ERIE WARE THE BEST; **Finish:** iron or nickel; **Circa:** 1890s; **VALUE: $250-$300.**

Above:
ALUMINUM TOY SET—Size: No. 2; **Circa:** 1930; **VALUE:** $700-$900. This set also came with a Waffle Iron, Value: $1200-$1500.

TOY TEAKETTLE—Size: No. 2 (2 5/8" dia.); **p/n:** A-51; **Markings:** block logo, EPU; **Finish:** aluminum with wood handle; **Circa:** 1930; **VALUE:** $150-$200.

TOY SKILLET—Size: No. 2; **p/n:** A-20; **Markings:** block logo, EPU; **Finish:** aluminum; **Circa:** 1930; **VALUE:** $100-$200.

Right:
TOY HANDLE GRIDDLE—Size: No. 2 (2 1/2" dia.); **p/n:** A 303; **Markings:** block logo, EPU; **Finish:** aluminum; **Circa:** 1930; **VALUE:** $100-$200.

TOY KETTLE with BAIL—Size: No. 2 (2 1/2" dia.); **p/n:** A-470; **Markings:** block logo; **Finish:** aluminum; **Circa:** 1930; **VALUE:** $100-$200.

Left:
TOY SAUCE PAN—Size: No. 2; **p/n:** A-4-0; **Markings:** block logo, EPU; **Finish:** aluminum; **Circa:** 1930; **VALUE:** $100-$200.

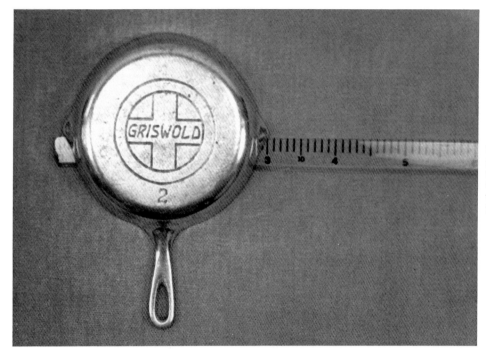

TOY SKILLET—Size: No. 2 (2 1/2" dia.); **p/n:** none; **Markings:** slant logo, 2; **Finish:** aluminum; **Circa:** 1925; **VALUE: $75-$100**. The No. 2 Toy Set without "Erie PA" was sold as a six-piece set including a waffle iron.

TOY SKILLET—Size: No. 2 (2 1/2" dia.); **p/n:** none; **Markings:** diamond logo; **Finish:** aluminum; **Circa:** 1930; **VALUE: $200-$250**.

TOY SKILLET—Size: No. 2; **p/n:** 409; **Markings:** slant logo, "0", 409; **Finish:** aluminum; **Circa:** 1930s; **VALUE: $100**.

"0" SIZE TOY SET

TOY WAFFLE IRON—Size: No. "0" (3 1/2" dia., 5 1/8" base dia.); **p/n:** 406,407, (base) 408; **Markings:** block logo, THE GRISWOLD MFG. CO., ERIE PA, USA, PAT'D DEC 1, 1908, AMERICAN No "0"; **Finish:** iron with japanned base; **Circa:** 1930s; **VALUE: $2500-$3000**.

TOY HANDLE GRIDDLE—Size: No. "0" (4 5/8" dia.); **p/n:** 565; **Markings:** block logo, CAST IRON GRIDDLE, GRISWOLD MFG CO, ERIE PA, USA; **Finish:** iron; **Circa:** 1930s; **VALUE: $500-$650**.

TOY COLONIAL TEA KETTLE—Size: No. "0" (4 1/2" dia.); **p/n:** 576; **Markings:** block logo, EPU, No 0, COLONIAL DESIGN,; **Finish:** iron; **Circa:** 1930s; **VALUE: iron $300-$400; chrome $300-$400.**

TOY SKILLET—Size: No. "0" (4 3/8" top dia. x 7/8" deep); **p/n:** 562; **Markings:** block logo, EPU, CAST IRON SKILLET, 562; **Finish:** iron, nickel; **Circa:** 1930s; **VALUE: $100.**

TOY DUTCH OVEN—Size: No. "0" (4 3/8" top dia. x 1 3/4" deep); **p/n:** 568, cover 569, trivet 573; **Markings:** block logo, THE GRISWOLD MFG CO, ERIE PA, USA, CAST IRON TITE TIP DUTCH OVEN, PATD MAR 15, 1920. (Cover) GRISWOLD No. TITE TOP DUTCH OVEN. (Trivet) THE GRISWOLD MFG CO, ERIE PA, O TRIVET; **Finish:** iron; **Circa:** 1930s; **VALUE: $400-$600, trivet $200.** The loop cover handle is the earlier one. The knob handle shown here for comparison.

TOY WAFFLE IRON—Size: No. "0" (3 1/2" waffle dia., 4 1/2" base dia.); **p/n:** none; **Markings:** GRISWOLD MFG CO, ERIE PA, AMERICAN, PAT'D JUNE 29,1880; **Finish:** iron with japanned base; **Circa:** unknown; **VALUE: Rare.** While all toy waffle irons are rare, this one is the only known example with a finger hinge.

TOY WAFFLE IRON—Size: 3 1/2" waffle dia., 5 1/4" base dia.; **p/n:** 407; **Markings:** THE GRISWOLD MFG CO, ERIE PA, THE AMERICAN, PAT'D MAY 21, 1901; **Finish:** iron with japanned base, black enameled wood handles; **Circa:** unknown; **VALUE: Rare**.

TOY SKILLETS—(left) Size: No. 1; **p/n:** 411; **Markings:** slant logo, ERIE, 1; **Finish:** iron; **Circa:** 1900; **VALUE: Rare**. **(right) Size:** 0; **p/n:** 562; **Markings:** block logo, EPU, CAST IRON SKILLET, 0, 562; **Finish:** iron or chrome; **Circa:** 1930s; **VALUE: $60-$100**.

TOY SKILLETS—Size: No. "0"; **p/n:** 562; **Markings:** block logo, EPU, CAST IRON SKILLET; **Finish:** iron; **Circa:** (left) 1930s, (right) 1950s; **VALUE: (left) $60-$100, (right) $125**.

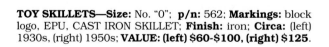

SQUARE TOY SKILLET—Size: 3 7/8" sq.; **p/n:** 775; **Markings:** block logo, TOY SKILLET, 775; **Finish:** iron; **Circa:** 1950; **VALUE: $150-$200.** This piece was sold with the Mother & Daughter Set.

PATTY MOLDS & PATTY BOWLS

PATTY BOWLS—(left to right) No. 72, No. 71, and No. 870.

DEEP PATTY BOWL—**Size:** 5" dia. x 2 5/8" deep; **p/n:** 72; **Markings:** small block logo, EPU, DEEP PATTY BOWL, 72; **Finish:** iron; **Circa:** 1940s-1950s; **VALUE: $35-$50**.

TABLE PLANTER—**Size:** 5" dia. x 2 5/8" deep; **p/n:** 72; **Markings:** small block logo, EPU, DEEP PATTY BOWL, 72; **Finish:** iron with brass base; the wire bail on the bowl is not notched; **Circa:** 1950s; **VALUE: $75**.

DEEP PATTY BOWL WITH TRIVET & COVER—**Size:** 4 1/2" dia. x 2 3/8" deep; **p/n:** 71, cover 71C; **Markings:** block logo, EPU, DEEP PATTY BOWL, 71; **Finish:** iron; **Circa:** 1950s; **VALUE: $75-$100 without cover or trivet. Rare with cover and trivet.**

JUNIOR PATTY BOWL—**Size:** 3 7/8" dia. x 2 1/2" deep; **p/n:** 870; **Markings:** block logo, EPU, JUNIOR PATTY BOWL, 870; **Finish:** iron; **Circa:** 1930s; **VALUE: $200-$300**. The center of the bail is notched to rest the handle of the patty mold.

PATTY BOWL—**Size:** 7 1/2" dia. x 3 1/8" deep; **p/n:** 871; **Markings:** block logo, EPU, PATTY BOWL, 871; **Finish:** iron; **Circa:** 1930s; **VALUE: $100**.

Griswold Patty Irons or Timbale Irons are made in two patterns and four designs of desirable sizes. Two wire handles furnished with each set. Packed one set in attractive board display box with beautifully colored label illustrating patties with vegetables, fruits, etc., or, when preferred, packed one set in bulk.

PATTY OR TIMBALE MOLDS
Shallow Pattern

No.	Pattern	Dimensions Diameter	Depth	Packed Weight in Box	Packed Weight in Bulk
1	Round	2⅛"	⅞"	1 lb. 2 oz.	1 lb.
	Fluted	3"	⅞"		

No. 1 Patty Set in Display Box

PATTY OR TIMBALE MOLDS
Deep Pattern

No.	Pattern	Dimensions Diameter	Depth	Packed Weight in Box	Packed Weight in Bulk
2	Fluted Round	2¼"	1½"	1 lb. 11 oz.	1 lb. 7 oz.
	Fluted Heart	2⅝" x 2½" x 1½"			
3	Fluted Round	3"	1½"	1 lb. 13 oz.	1 lb. 9 oz.
	Fluted Heart	3¾" x 3" x 1½"			

Nos. 2 or 3 Patty Sets in Display Boxes

MULTIPLE PATTY MOLD SET
For use when a quantity of patties are needed

This set consists of four round design and three fluted design low patty molds attached to heavy wire handle with arms, making one piece, so that seven patties are made at one time.

Packed knocked down, in carton, weight 3½ pounds.

A PAGE FROM 1934 GRISWOLD CATALOG—(top) **VALUE:** $30, (center) **VALUE:** $35, (bottom) **VALUE:** $100-$150.

PATTY MOLDS—VALUE: No. 1 (top), $30; No. 2 (center), $30-$40, No. 3 (bottom), $60.

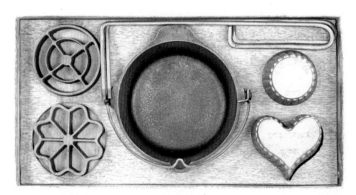

No. 3 PATTY MOLD SET -Contains No. 1 and No. 2 Patty Molds and No. 72 Deep Patty Bowl, but not the No. 3 Patty Molds. **Circa:** 1950s-1960s; **VALUE:** $150.

No. 3 PATTY MOLDS—Size: (round) 3" dia., (heart) 3 5/8" across; **p/n:** none; **Markings:** GRISWOLD; **Finish:** iron; **Circa:** 1930s-1940s; **VALUE:** $60. The No. 3 molds are significantly larger that the No. 2 molds.

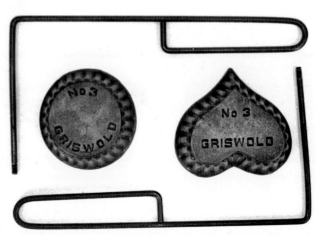

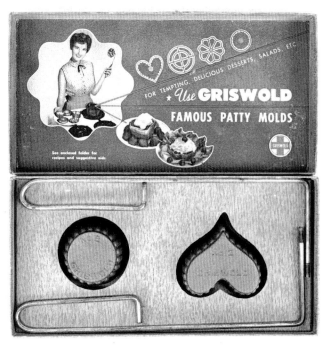 

No. 2 PATTY MOLD SET (deep)—Size: (round) 2 1/4" dia., (heart) 2 7/8" across x 2 1/8" deep; **p/n:** none; **Markings:** GRISWOLD; **Finish:** iron; **Circa:** 1930-1950s; **VALUE: $30-$40.**

No. 1 PATTY MOLD SET (SHALLOW)—Size: (round) 2 5/15" dia., (fluted) 3" dia. x 9/16" deep; **p/n:** none; **Markings:** GRISWOLD; **Finish:** iron; **Circa:** 1930-1960s; **VALUE: $30.**

SERVERS, PLATTERS & SPOONS

AL CARDER'S SERVING KETTLE—Size: 4 1/4" dia. x 1 7/8" deep; **p/n:** 580, cover 581; **Markings:** 580, cover: AL CARDER'S SERVING KETTLE, 581; **Finish:** chrome; **Circa:** 1940s; **VALUE: $100.**

OVAL CASSEROLE—Size: No. 91 (6 1/2" x 3 3/4" x 2 1/2"); **p/n:** 91, cover 91C; **Markings:** block logo, EPU; **Finish:** iron; **Circa:** 1940s; **VALUE: $300.** The loop handle is unusual, this casserole usually has a Tee handle. Also made in chrome Finish:with no holes in handles of the casserole; **Circa:** 1950, **VALUE: $200-$300.**

OVAL CASSEROLE—Size: (left) 3 3/8" x 5 1/4" x 8 1/4", (right) 2" x 3 1/2" x 6"; **p/n:** (left) 93, cover 93C (right) 90, cover 90C; **Markings:** block logo, EPU, OVAL CASSEROLE; **Finish:** (left) iron with chrome cover, (right) satin finish chrome with polished cover; **Circa:** 1950s; **VALUE: $100.**

Left:
STEAK PLATTERS—(left to right) No. 848, (7" x 10 1/4"); No. 851, (8 1/4" x 12"); No. 856, (9 1/8" x 13 3/4").

STEAK PLATTER—**Size:** 7" x 10 1/4"; **p/n:** 848; **Markings:** block logo, EPU, STEAK PLATTER, 848; **Finish:** chrome, Du-Chro, Silverlike; **Circa:** 1930s-1950s; **VALUE:** (size shown) $60, (sizes No. 849, No. 851, and No. 856, $65).

STEAK PLATTER—**Size:** 7"; **p/n:** A1055; **Markings:** block logo, EPU, THE GRISWOLD MFG. CO; **Finish:** aluminum; **Circa:** 1930s; **VALUE:** $30. Also made: A1056.

STEAK PLATTER—**Size:** 7" x 10 1/4"; **p/n:** 848; **Markings:** block logo, EPU, STEAK PLATTER, 848; **Finish:** chrome, Du-Chro, Silverlike; **Circa:** 1930s; **VALUE:** $60. The stepped edge is unusual.

HOT SERVICE PLATES—**Size:** (left) 9", (right) 7 1/2"; **p/n:** (left) 850, (right) 855; **Markings:** block logo, EPU, HOT SERVICE PLATE; **Finish:** Du-Chro, Silverlike, Chrome; **Circa:** 1930s-1950s; **VALUE:** No. 850, $100, No. 855, $75.

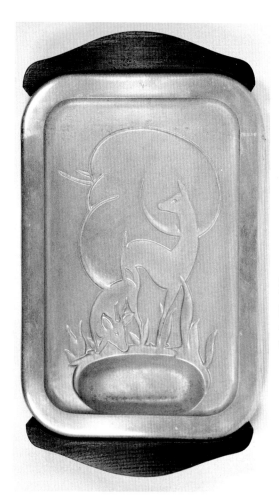

Left:
DEER PLATTER—Size: 18" x 12 1/2"; **p/n:** A2083; **Markings:** ARISTO CRAFT WARE, GRISWOLD MFG CO, ERIE PA; **Finish:** aluminum; **Circa:** 1940s; **VALUE: $100-$125.** Also made: A2082.

Right:
TREE PLATTER—Size: 14 1/2" x 8 1/2"; **p/n:** 861; **Markings:** GRISWOLD TREE PLATTER; **Finish:** Du-Chro; **Circa:** 1930s; **VALUE: Du-Chro $100-$125, A1082—aluminum $75.**

HOSTESS PLATTER—Size: 18 1/2" x 13"; **p/n:** A 209; **Markings:** ARISTOCRAFT WARE, block logo; **Finish:** aluminum on wood frame; **Circa:** 1950s; **VALUE: $150-$250.**

Below:
FAMILY TREE PLATTER—Size: 14 1/4" x 9 1/2"; **p/n:** A2191; **Markings:** FAMILY TREE PLATTER, GRISWOLD, No A2191; **Finish:** aluminum; **Circa:** 1930s; **VALUE: $75-$100.** Also made: A2190 and A2192.

Right:
ALUMINUM SPOONS
(left to right)
Basting spoon with a stamped logo—**Circa:** 1910; **VALUE:** $40.
Ladle—**p/n:** A709; **Circa:** 1930s; **VALUE:** $60.
Flat spoon—**p/n:** A715; **Circa:** 1930s; **VALUE:** $40.
Mixing spoon—**p/n:** A710; **Circa:** 1930s; **VALUE:** $50.
Ladle with a wood handle—**Circa:** 1910; **VALUE:** $75.

LEMON SQUEEZERS

CLASSIC LEMON SQUEEZER—Size: 9 3/8"; **p/n:** none; **Markings:** ERIE PA, USA; **Finish:** japanned, aluminum cups; **Circa:** 1900s; **VALUE: $75-$100.**

GRISWOLD LEMON SQUEEZER—Size: 9 1/4"; **p/n:** 250, 251, insert 180C; **Markings:** GRISWOLD MFG CO, ERIE PA; **Finish:** japanned, aluminum insert; **Circa:** 1900s; **VALUE: $100.**

LEMON SQUEEZER No. 1—Size: 8 3/8"; **p/n:** none; **Markings:** THE GRISWOLD MFG CO, ERIE PA; **Finish:** japanned, aluminum cups; **Circa:** 1910; **VALUE: $100.**

**CLASSIC LEMON SQUEEZER
No. 2—Size:** 9 3/8"; **p/n:**
none; **Markings:** GRISWOLD
MFG CO; **Finish:** japanned,
aluminum cups; **Circa:** 1910;
VALUE: $100-$150.

**LEMON SQUEEZER No. 6—
Size:** 10 1/2"; **p/n:** 367;
Markings: 367; **Finish:**
tinned iron; **Circa:** 1910;
VALUE: $75-$100.

**CLASSIC No. 7 LEMON
SQUEEZER—Size:** 10 5/8";
p/n: 363; **Markings:** CLASSIC
7; **Finish:** japanned, aluminum cups; **Circa:** 1900s;
VALUE: $100.

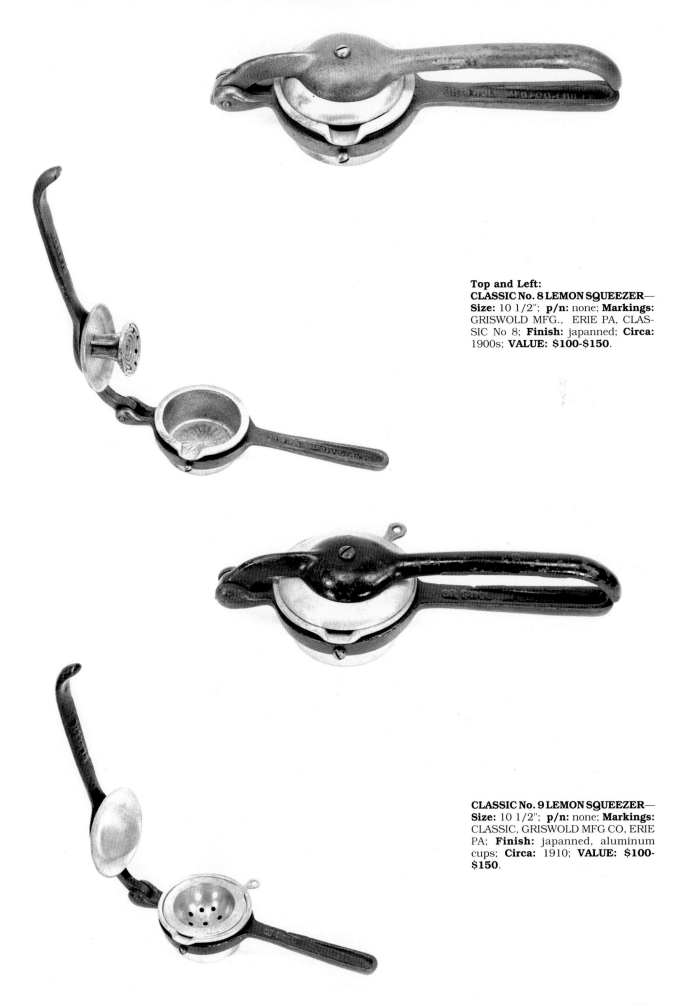

Top and Left:
CLASSIC No. 8 LEMON SQUEEZER—
Size: 10 1/2"; **p/n:** none; **Markings:** GRISWOLD MFG., ERIE PA, CLASSIC No 8; **Finish:** japanned; **Circa:** 1900s; **VALUE: $100-$150.**

CLASSIC No. 9 LEMON SQUEEZER—
Size: 10 1/2"; **p/n:** none; **Markings:** CLASSIC, GRISWOLD MFG CO, ERIE PA; **Finish:** japanned, aluminum cups; **Circa:** 1910; **VALUE: $100-$150.**

LARD PRESSES, FRUIT PRESSES & FOOD CHOPPERS

No. 2 FRUIT & LARD PRESS—Size: 4 qts.; **p/n:** 2610, (yoke) 2611; **Markings:** GRISWOLD MFG CO., ERIE PA, 2, 4 QUARTS; **Finish:** galvanized ; **Circa:** 1905; **VALUE: $200.**

No. 110 FRUIT & LARD PRESS—Size: 10 qts., 8" dia. x 12" deep; **p/n:** (base) 100, (yoke) 110; **Markings:** PAT APPLIED FOR; **Finish:** tin, battleship gray with wood slats; **Circa:** 1923-1930s; **VALUE: $150-$200.**

No. 1 & No. 2 FRUIT & LARD PRESS—Size: 2 qts.; **p/n:** (bottom) 40, (yoke) 43, (press) 42; **Markings:** (No. 1) CLASSIC, 2 QUARTS, (No. 2) block logo on cylinder, GRISWOLD MFG CO, FRUIT & LARD PRESS; **Finish:** (No. 1) bright tin, (No. 2) tin or gray; **Circa:** (No. 1) 1910-1920, (No. 2) 1925-1940; **VALUE: No. 1, $75; No. 2, $100.**

No. 10 FRUIT & LARD PRESS (shown with No. 2)—**Size:** 31 lbs.; **p/n:** 54; **Markings:** block logo on cylinder, GRISWOLD MFG CO, ERIE PA; **Finish:** tin or gray; **Circa:** 1910-1940; **VALUE:** $150-$200.

GRISWOLD FOOD CHOPPERS—VALUE: No. "0" (not shown), $45; No. 1, $15; No. 2, $20; No. 3, $20; No. 4, $30; **Stuffing Attachment,** $25.

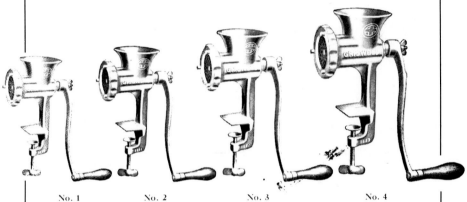

Griswold Combination Meat and Food Chopper

		No. 1	No. 2	No. 3	No. 4

No.	Size	Capacity Meat cut per minute	Diameter Hopper Inches	Height from Table Inches	Length Barrel Inches	Length Crank Inches	Net Weight Each	Packed Weight 6 in Case	Packed Weight 12 in Case
1	Small family	2 1/2 lbs.	2 1/2x3 1/4	5 1/4	3 13/32	6 3/8	3 lbs. 13 oz.	30 lbs.	61 lbs.
2	Regular family	3 lbs.	2 3/4x3 3/4	6	3 27/32	7 1/2	4 lbs. 14 oz.	40 lbs.	77 lbs.
3	Large family	3 1/2 lbs.	3 1/8x4 1/4	6 1/2	3 27/64	7 1/2	5 lbs. 3 oz.	43 lbs.	80 lbs.
4	Hotel and Restaurant	4 lbs.	3 7/8x4 7/8	7 1/4	4 15/32	9 3/8	7 lbs. 6 oz.	60 lbs.	......

Packed one in a heavy cardboard box, six and twelve in a case.

Stuffing Attachments
For Choppers Nos. 1, 2, 3, 4

No. 1 Attachment will fit Chopper No. 1.

No. 2 Attachment will fit Choppers Nos. 2 and 3.

No. 3 Attachment will fit Chopper No. 4.

STUFFING ATTACHMENTS are made for all sizes of Combination Meat and Food Choppers. They are seamless, in one piece of drawn aluminum. *Furnished only when specified.*

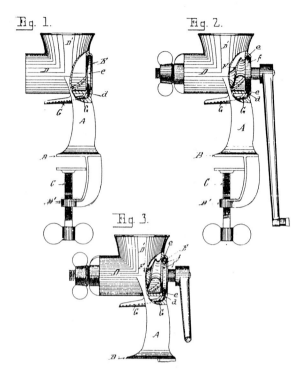

No. 727,130.   PATENTED MAY 5, 1903.

M. GRISWOLD, Jr.
FOOD CHOPPER.
APPLICATION FILED JUNE 26, 1902.

NO MODEL.

Fig. 1.   Fig. 2.

Fig. 3.

Witnesses.   Inventor.
                              Matthew Griswold Jr.
                              By Jno. Sturgeon
                                  Atty.

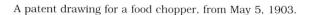

A patent drawing for a food chopper, from May 5, 1903.

FOOD GRINDER STORE DISPLAY STAND—Size:
9 5/8" across top x 12" dia. base x 7 3/4" high; **p/n:**
none; **Markings:** THE GRISWOLD MFG. CO., ERIE PA;
Finish: japanned swivels, wood base and top; **Circa:**
1930s; **VALUE: $600-$700.** Grinders were clamped to
the top, which rotates. Holes on the top accommodated
an advertising sign bracket.

FOOD CHOPPER STAND—Size: 8 1/4" x 4" x 5 3/4"
high; **p/n:** 1335; **Markings:** block logo, FOOD CHOP-
PER STAND; **Finish:** iron with matte green finish; **Circa:**
1930-1940; **VALUE: iron $300-$500, aluminum $200-
$300.**

COFFEE GRINDERS & COFFEE ROASTER

COFFEE MILL—p/n: 145; **Markings:** GRISWOLD MFG. CO. (on the back); **Finish:** japanned with gold trim; **Circa:** 1900; **VALUE: $1500.**

COFFEE MILL—p/n: 115; **Markings:** GRISWOLD MFG. CO. (on the back); **Finish:** japanned with gold trim; **Circa:** 1900; **VALUE: Rare.** The receptacle underneath is not original. The original was tin.

No. 616,614.

M. GRISWOLD, Jr.
COFFEE MILL.
(Application filed Jan. 20, 1897.)

Patented Dec. 27, 1898.

(No Model.)

2 Sheets—Sheet 1.

Fig. 1.

Fig. 2.   Fig. 3.   Fig 5.

Fig. 4.

WITNESSES:
Fred Einfeldt
F. J. Barritt

INVENTOR
Matthew Griswold Jr.
BY G. B. Stirgwer
ATTORNEY

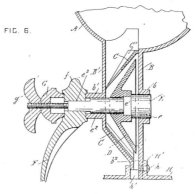

No. 616,614.

M. GRISWOLD, Jr.
COFFEE MILL.
(Application filed Jan. 20, 1897.)

Patented Dec. 27, 1898.

(No Model.)

2 Sheets—Sheet 2.

FIG. 6.

WITNESSES
J. Grigg Poole
R. R. Johnson

INVENTOR
Matthew Griswold, Jun
by Herbert W. Jenner
Attorney

Left:
Coffee mill patent drawings, from December 27, 1898.

COFFEE MILL—Size: 10 3/4"
x 5 1/4" sq.; **p/n:** 35 (drawer
front); **Markings:** THE GRIS-
WOLD MFG. CO., ERIE PA;
Finish: red, black, or burnt
orange enamel with gold trim;
Circa: 1920s; **VALUE: $1200-
$1500.**

No. 2 COFFEE ROASTER—Size: (cylinder) 8" x 5 1/2"; **p/n:** none;
Markings: GRISWOLD MFG. CO., ERIE PA, NO. 2; **Finish:** iron base,
tin cannister; **Circa:** 1910; **VALUE: $1000-$1500 complete with
handle (not shown).** Also made were sizes No. 1 and No. 3.

GRAND UNION COFFEE MILL—Size: 10 3/4" high;
p/n: none; **Markings:** GRAND UNION TEA CO.; **Finish:**
burnt orange enamel with gold trim; **Circa:** 1920; **VALUE:
$400-$600.** The front door swings open for access to the
ground coffee drawer, which was tin.

BROILERS

Above and Right:
LONG BROILER—Size: No. 7 (17 1/2" x 8" x 1 1/2"); **p/n:** none;
Markings: ERIE, No. 7; **Finish:** iron; **Circa:** 1890-1910; **VALUE:**
No. 7, with cover $350; No. 8 and No. 9, $250-$300.

(No Model.)

M. GRISWOLD & M. GRISWOLD, Jr.
GRIDIRON.

No. 472,537.   Patented Apr. 12, 1892.

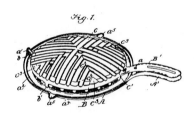

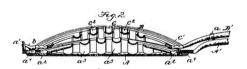

DOUBLE BROILER—Size: 10 1/2" dia., two sections; **p/n:** none;
Markings: ERIE, PATENTED APRIL 12, 1892; **Finish:** iron; **Circa:**
1890-1910; **VALUE: $300-$400.**

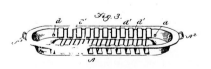

A patent drawing for a gridiron, from April 12, 1892.

Witnesses
Edwin L Bradford
Anni Belt

Inventors:
Matthew Griswold,
By *Matthew Griswold Jr.*
A.H. Smith & Son
Attorneys

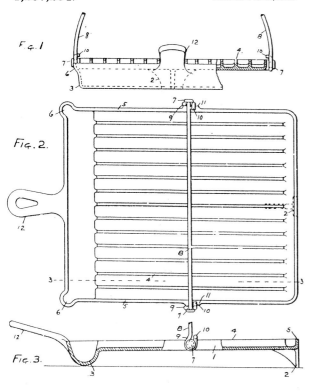

1,257,234.

Patented Feb. 19, 1918.

F₁ɢ. 1.

Fɪɢ. 2.

Fɪɢ. 3.

Inventor
John C. Hollands

By
J. Z. Earl.

Attorney

A patent drawing for
a broiler, from February 19, 1918.

DOUBLE BROILER—**Size:** (base)12" dia., (top grid) 9 1/4"; **p/n:** (base) 875, (top grid) 876; **Markings:** DOUBLE BROILER, GRISWOLD MFG. CO.; **Finish:** iron; **Circa:** 1930s-1940s; **VALUE: $250-$300.**

STOVE DAMPERS, LID LIFTERS & SKELETON GRATES

An assortment of damper handles

4 1/2 INCH NEW AMERICAN DAMPER—p/n: 1437; **Markings:** GRISWOLD NEW AMERICAN, ERIE PA, USA; **Finish:** iron with wood handle; **Circa:** 1910; **VALUE: $15**. Also made were sizes ranging from 3" to 7".

6 INCH AMERICAN DAMPER—p/n: 52; **Markings:** AMERICAN, ERIE PA, PAT'D MAR 26, 1875, MAR 13, 1877, APR 20, 1880, JUNE 18, 1889; **Finish:** iron; **Circa:** 1880-1900; **VALUE: 6", $25;** other **sizes through 9", $25; 10", $40.** Note wood handle with cast iron holder.

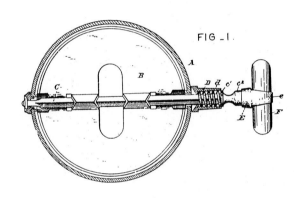

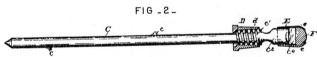

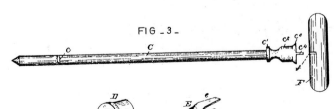

A patent drawing for a damper, from June 18, 1889.

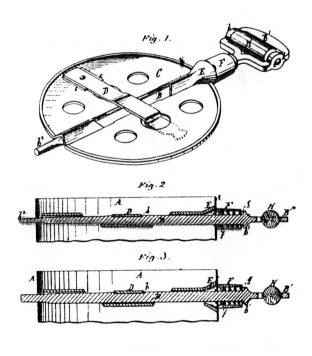

A patent drawing for a damper, from March 23, 1875.

9 INCH DAMPER—**p/n:** 545; **Markings:** 545, GRISWOLD MFG. CO.; **Circa:** 1900; **VALUE: $15-$30.**

6 INCH AMERICAN DAMPER—**p/n:** 517C; **Markings:** AMERICAN 6 INCH, THE GRISWOLD MFG. CO., ERIE PA, USA, PATENTED JUNE 18, 89; **Finish:** iron with Eagle handle; **Circa:** 1900; **VALUE: $40.**

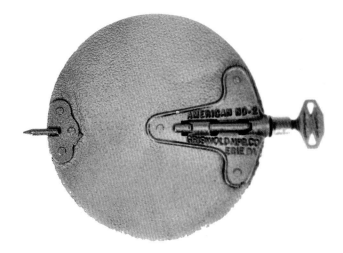

AMERICAN No. 2 DAMPER CLIP—**Size:** 9"; **p/n:** none; **Markings:** AMERICAN NO. 2, GRISWOLD MFG. CO., ERIE PA; **Finish:** Iron hardware riveted on tin; **Circa:** 1910; **VALUE: $40.**

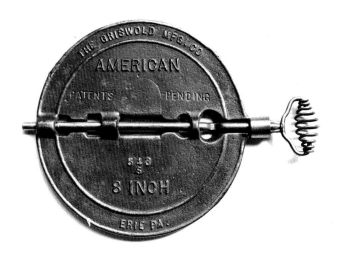

8 INCH AMERICAN DAMPER—**p/n:** 453S; **Markings:** AMERICAN 8 INCH, THE GRISWOLD MFG. CO, ERIE PA, PATENTS PENDING; **Finish:** iron; **Circa:** 1930s; **VALUE: $20.** The spindle is not pointed.

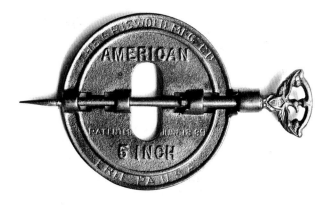

5 INCH AMERICAN DAMPER—**p/n:** none; **Markings:** AMERICAN 5 INCH, THE GRISWOLD MFG. CO., ERIE PA, PATENTED JUNE 18, 89; **Finish:** iron with Eagle handle; **Circa:** 1900; **VALUE: $40.**

1,146,807.

Patented July 20, 1915.

A patent drawing for a stove pipe damper, from July 20, 1915.

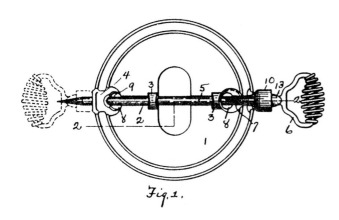

Fig. 1.

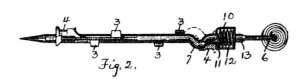

Fig. 2.

Witnesses
B. M. Hartman
J. E. Free

Inventor
Charles A. Messing
By R. Lord

16 INCH AMERICAN DAMPER (shown with 3")—**p/n:** 52; **Markings:** Griswold logo, AMERICAN, 16 INCH; **Finish:** iron; **Circa:** 1920s-1930s; **VALUE: $125**. Also made 14", 15", and 16" versions for commercial use.

REVERSIBLE SOLID DAMPER FOR OIL BURNER—Size: No. 5 and No. 5 1/2; **p/n:** 514X, 515X; **Markings:** GRISWOLD, ERIE PA, USA, AMERICAN, REVERSIBLE SOLID STEEL SPINDLE, FOR OIL BURNERS, PAT'D JULY 20, 1915; **Finish:** iron with coil handle; **Circa:** 1934; **VALUE: $25**.

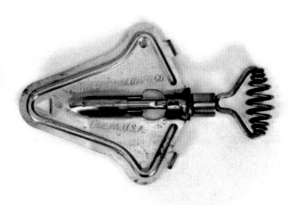

STEEL DAMPER CLIP—Size: 5" x 2"; **p/n:** none; **Markings:** GRISWOLD MFG. CO. ERIE PA, USA; **Finish:** steel; **Circa:** 1923-1940s; **VALUE: $15**.

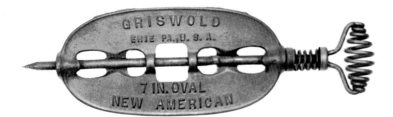

7 INCH OVAL NEW AMERICAN DAMPER—p/n: 1487; **Markings:** GRISWOLD, ERIE PA, USA, 7 IN OVAL NEW AMERICAN; **Finish:** iron with coil handle; **Circa:** 1915-1930s; **VALUE: $20.** Also made were 4" and 8" dampers.

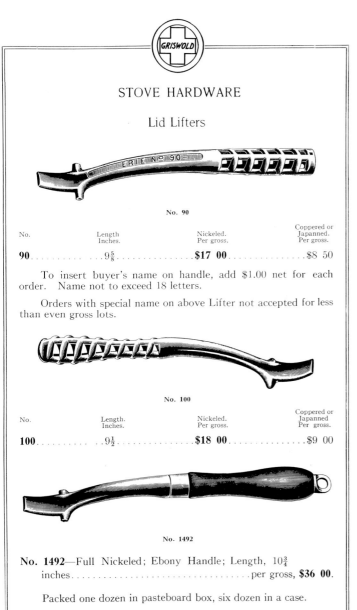

STOVE HARDWARE

Lid Lifters

No. 90

No.	Length. Inches.	Nickeled. Per gross.	Coppered or Japanned. Per gross.
90	9⅝	$17 00	$8 50

To insert buyer's name on handle, add $1.00 net for each order. Name not to exceed 18 letters.

Orders with special name on above Lifter not accepted for less than even gross lots.

No. 100

No.	Length. Inches.	Nickeled. Per gross.	Coppered or Japanned Per gross.
100	9½	$18 00	$9 00

No. 1492

No. 1492—Full Nickeled; Ebony Handle; Length, 10¾ inches.............................per gross, **$36 00.**

Packed one dozen in pasteboard box, six dozen in a case.

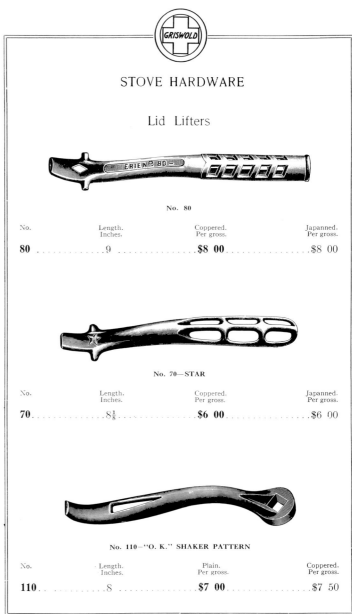

STOVE HARDWARE

Lid Lifters

No. 80

No.	Length. Inches.	Coppered. Per gross.	Japanned. Per gross.
80	9	$8 00	$8 00

No. 70—STAR

No.	Length. Inches.	Coppered. Per gross.	Japanned. Per gross.
70	8⅛	$6 00	$6 00

No. 110—"O. K." SHAKER PATTERN

No.	Length. Inches.	Plain. Per gross.	Coppered. Per gross.
110	8	$7 00	$7 50

Left and Above:
STOVE LID LIFTERS—Size: 8" to 10 1/2"; **Circa:** 1890-1920; **VALUE: marked "ERIE" or "GRISWOLD" $150-$200, others $25.**

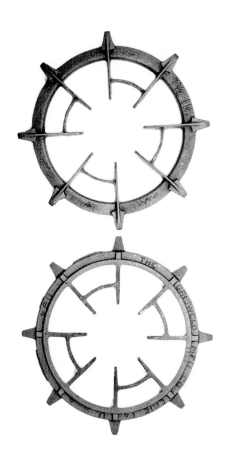

SKELETON GRATES—Size: made for all sizes of lid openings; **Markings:** THE GRISWOLD MFG Co., ERIE PA U.S.A.; **Finish:** iron; **Circa:** 1910-1920s; **VALUE:** **$10**. When gas kitchen ranges were introduced, the tops remained solid over the gas burners. Skeleton Grates were manufactured to be substituted for the solid stove lids to save fuel. An advertisement called it "a neat, substantial grate which will soon pay for itself in fuel saved."

GRISWOLD'S GAS RANGES

Four Burner Top. Low Broiler

No. 100 GAS HEATER—Size: 19 1/2" high, 7" dia.; **p/n:** 100; **Markings:** Griswold logo, 100 on base; **Finish:** black with nickel trim; **Circa:** 1910-1920; **VALUE: $200.**

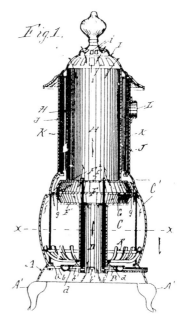

No. 710,053.

M. GRISWOLD, JR.
GAS STOVE.
(Application filed July 23, 1901.)

(No Model.)

Patented Sept. 30, 1902.

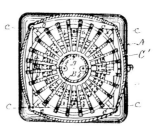

A patent drawing for a gas heater, from September 30, 1902.

No. 100 GAS HEATER—Size: 19 1/2" high x 7" dia.; **p/n:** 100; **Markings:** Griswold logo, 100 on base; **Finish:** black with nickel trim; **Circa:** 1910-1929; **VALUE: $200.** Note variation of top.

ERIE 200 GAS HEATER—Size: 21 1/2"
high; **p/n:** (base) 100, (pot) 114; **Markings:**
GRISWOLD MFG. CO. ERIE PA; **Finish:**
black with nickel trim; **Circa:** 1900; **VALUE:**
$300.

ERIE No. 40 KEROSENE HEATER—Size: 15" base dia. x 24" high;
p/n: (base) 200, (top) 205; **Markings:** ERIE, No. 40; **Finish:** black
with nickel trim, brass burner; **Circa:** 1900; **VALUE: $500-$600**.

Above and Right:
CLASSIC No. 15 GAS HEATER—p/n: unknown; **Markings:**
CLASSIC, THE GRISWOLD MFG. CO., ERIE PA, No. 15; **Finish:**
black iron with nickel trim; **Circa:** 1920s; **VALUE: $1500-$2000**.

CLASSIC No. 3 QUADRUPLE GAS HEATER—p/n: unknown; **Markings:** CLASSIC No 3 QUADRUPLE, THE GRISWOLD MFG. CO, ERIE PA, PATENTED MAY 29, 1900; **Finish:** black with nickel trim; **Circa:** 1920s; **VALUE: $2500-$2750.** The stacks are steel sheeting.

CLASSIC No. 3 QUADRUPLE HEATER—Markings: CLASSIC QUADRUPLE, THE GRISWOLD MFG. CO., EIRE PA, PATENTED MAY 29, 1900; **Finish:** black with nickel trim; **Circa:** 1920s; **VALUE: $2500-$2750.**

Left:
CLASSIC No. 4 QUADRUPLE CENTER DRAFT—Markings: CLASSIC QUADRUPLE; **Finish:** black iron, (heat tubes) japanned, (trim) nickel; **Circa:** 1900-1920; **VALUE: $2500-$3000.**

Right:
CLASSIC No. 826 GAS HEATER—Markings: CLASSIC; **Finish:** black with nickel trim; **Circa:** 1900-1920; **VALUE: $1500-$1750.**

CLASSIC No. 816—Markings: GRISWOLD MFG. CO, ERIE PA; **Finish:** black with nickel trim; **Circa:** 1900-1920; **VALUE: $1800-$2000.** Lion's head ornaments on both sides.

No. 2511 REFLECTOR HEATER—Size: 23" h x 17" w x 11" d; **p/n:** base 2585, 1140; **Markings:** Griswold logo, No. 2511; **Finish:** black with nickel trim, copper reflector; **Circa:** 1910; **VALUE: $250-$350.**

No. 513 (left) **& No. 510** (right) **REFLECTOR HEATERS—Size:** No. 513 (22 3/4" h x 14 1/2" w x 9 3/4" d) and No. 510 (20" h x 11 1/2" w x 8 1/2" d); **Markings:** GRISWOLD; **Finish:** (case) steel, (trim) nickel, (reflectors) copper; **Circa:** 1920; **VALUE: No. 513 $250, No. 510 $200.**

Left:
CLASSIC No. 712 GAS HEATER—Size: No. 712; **p/n:** none; **Markings:** CLASSIC, No. 712; **Finish:** (back) asbestos, (trim) nickel; **Circa:** 1900-1910; **VALUE: $500-$750.**

M. GRISWOLD, Jr. & D. SHIELDS.
GAS STOVE.

No. 601,039.   Patented Mar. 22, 1898.

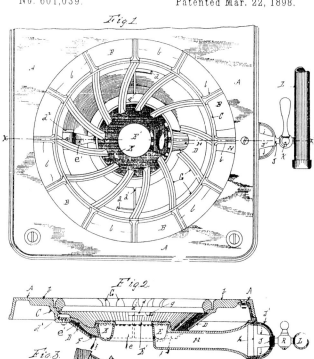

WITNESSES: INVENTORS.
F. J. Barrett   Matthew Griswold Jr.
Fred Enfeldt   David Shields
                         BY J. H. Sturgeon
                                      ATTORNEY

CHARCOAL STOVE—ELDORADO—Size: No. 2; **p/n:** 1556; **Markings:** ELDORADO, 2; **Finish:** iron; **Circa:** 1895-1910; **VALUE: $500-$700.**

Right:
A patent drawing for a gas stove, from March 22, 1898.

GAS HOT PLATE—Size: No. 2 (burner, 22" x 11"); **p/n:** 302; **Markings:** GRISWOLD, 302, scrolled design; **Finish:** japanned; **Circa:** 1910-1920; **VALUE: $100-$125.**

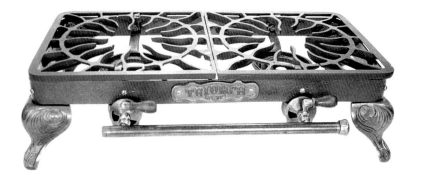

"TRIUMPH" BRAND HOT PLATE—Size: 22" x 11"; **p/n:** 302; **Markings:** TRIUMPH, 302, scrolled design the same as Griswold; **Finish:** japanned; **Circa:** 1910-1020; **VALUE: $100.**

No. 502 GAS HOT PLATE—p/n: 1181; **Markings:** GRISWOLD on plate, open filigree legs; **Finish:** japanned; **Circa:** 1920; **VALUE:** $150.

No. 501 CLASSIC SINGLE HOT PLATE—p/n: none; **Markings:** CLASSIC, open filigree legs; **Finish:** iron; **Circa:** 1910; **VALUE:** $125.

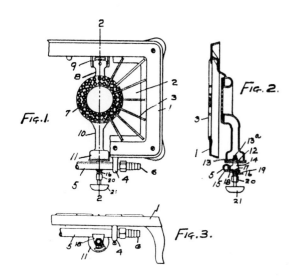

R. W. GRISWOLD.
HOT PLATE.
APPLICATION FILED OCT. 30, 1915.

1,179,716.   Patented Apr. 18, 1916.

Fig. 2.

Fig. 1.

Fig. 3.

Inventor
Roger W. Griswold
By
Attorney

THE COLUMBIA PLANOGRAPH CO. WASHINGTON. D. C.

A patent drawing for a hot plate, from April 18, 1916.

No. 1002 GAS HOT PLATE—Size: 17 1/4" x 8 1/4"; **p/n:** 1002; **Markings:** G M CO. underside; **Finish:** gray iron, or nickel; **Circa:** 1920-1925; **VALUE:** $125-$150.

No. 1001 SINGLE GAS HOT PLATE —p/n: 1329, grate 1336; **Markings:** G M Co. (under side); **Finish:** nickel or iron; **Circa:** 1920-1925; **VALUE:** $100.

No. 101 ELECTRIC HOT PLATE—**p/n:** 1226; **Markings:** THE GRISWOLD MFG. CO., ERIE PA; **Finish:** nickel; **Circa:** 1920-1930; **VALUE: $125**. The unit has no switch; it had to be unplugged when not in use.

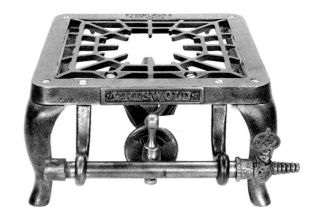

No. 601 GAS HOT PLATE—**p/n:** 6667; **Markings:** GRISWOLD; **Finish:** black enamel; **Circa:** 1925-1935; **VALUE: $100**.

No. 101 ELECTRIC HOT PLATE—**p/n:** 1224; **Markings:** GRISWOLD MFG. CO., ERIE PA; **Finish:** iron or nickel; **Circa:** 192; **VALUE: $100**.

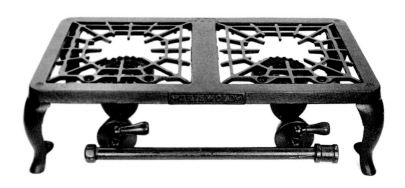

No. 602 GAS HOT PLATE— **Markings:** GRISWOLD; **Finish:** japanned; **Circa:** 1920; **VALUE: $75**.

No. 702 GAS HOT PLATE—**p/n:** 1605; **Markings:** GRISWOLD; **Finish:** japanned; **Circa:** 1930s-1940s; **VALUE: $125**.

No. 711 GAS HOT PLATE WITH SIMMER BURNER—**p/n:** 182, (twin burner) 1691; **Markings:** GRISWOLD; **Finish:** japanned; **Circa:** 1920s-1930s; **VALUE: $200**.

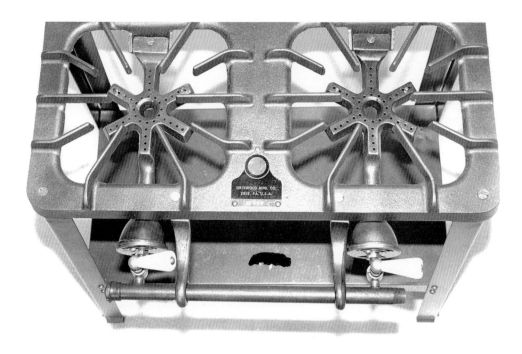

ELEVATED HOT PLATE—p/n: 2020; **Markings:** (steel plate) block logo, THE GRISWOLD MFG. CO.; **Finish:** gray enamel; **Circa:** 1930s; **VALUE: $175-$200.**

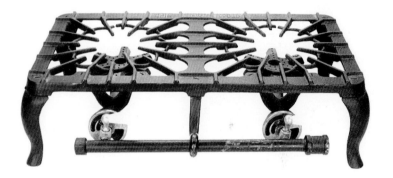

No. 32 GAS HOT PLATE—Size: 19 1/2" x 9 1/2"; **p/n:** 32; **Markings:** GRIS 32 WOLD; **Finish:** japanned; **Circa:** 1930s-1940s; **VALUE: $45-$65.**

ELEVATED HOT PLATE—p/n: 7032; **Markings:** GRISWOLD MFG. CO., ERIE PA, USA; **Finish:** black enamel; **Circa:** 1940s; **VALUE: $175.**

No. 703 ELEVATED HOT PLATE—Size: 29" x 9 1/2"; **Markings:** GRISWOLD; **Finish:** black enamel; **Circa:** 1940s; **VALUE: $150-$200.**

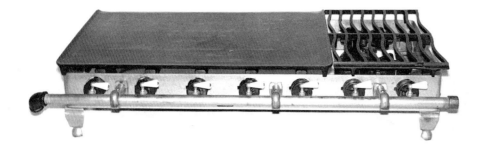

Above and Right:
HOTEL/RESTAURANT GAS STOVE—Size: 35" x 17",
seven burners; **p/n:** 260, (griddle) 1305, (grate) 1689;
Markings: block logo; **Circa:** 1920-1930; **VALUE:**
$750-$1000.

Above and Right:
No. 100-E ELECTRIC NURSERY BURNER—Size: 5"
dia. x 3" high; **p/n:** none; **Markings:** (metal plate)
Griswold logo, THE GRISWOLD MFG. CO., ERIE PA,
USA; **Finish:** gray iron or nickel; **Circa:** 1930s; **VALUE:**
$100.

PIE OVEN—Size: 11 1/8" h x 12 1/8" w
x 10 3/16" d; **p/n:** 355; **Markings:** block
logo, No 355; **Finish:** black enamel; **Circa:**
1930s; **VALUE: $150-$200 with box,
$75-$100 without box.**

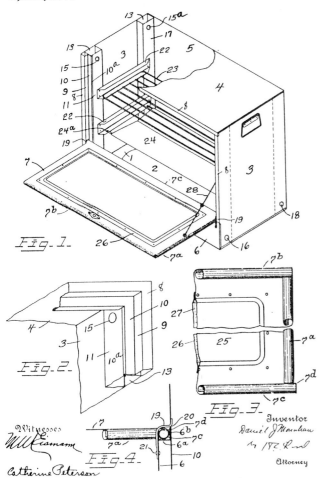

D. J. MONAHAN.
OVEN.
APPLICATION FILED AUG. 14, 1912.

1,100,087.   Patented June 16, 1914.

Fig. 1.

Fig. 2.

Fig. 3.

Fig. 4.

Witnesses

Inventor
Daniel J Monahan

Attorney

A patent drawing for a pipe oven, from June 16, 1914.

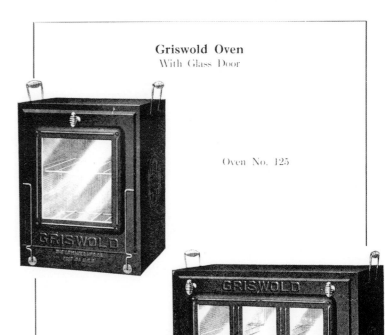

Griswold Oven
With Glass Door

Oven No. 125

Oven No. 140

BOLO OVENS—Size: No. 125 and No. 140; **VALUE: No. 125, $75; No. 140, $150.**

Polished steel body. Electric welded case. Perfect fitting glass drop door. Corrugated tin lining. Asbestos lined. Two electric welded wire racks. Nickel Alaska handles and door catches. Strong door supports. Packed one in strong corrugated carton.

No.		Height Inches	Width Inches	Depth Inches	Wt. Carton Pounds
125	Inside	$12\frac{1}{4}$	$11\frac{1}{4}$	$12\frac{3}{8}$	
	Outside	$16\frac{5}{8}$	$13\frac{1}{4}$	$12\frac{7}{16}$	$16\frac{1}{2}$
140	Inside	$12\frac{1}{4}$	$18\frac{3}{8}$	$12\frac{3}{8}$	
	Outside	$16\frac{5}{8}$	21	$12\frac{7}{16}$	$21\frac{1}{2}$

Griswold Pie Oven

With Glass and Steel Doors.

Oven No. 155

BOLO OVENS—Size: No. 155 and No. 150; **VALUE: $75 each.**

Oven No. 150

Polished steel body. Electric welded case. Swing door. Double side walls. Two electric welded wire racks. Packed four in strong corrugated carton.

No.			Height Inches	Width Inches	Depth Inches	Packed In Carton	Wt. Carton Pounds
155	Glass Door	Inside	$8\frac{3}{8}$	$12\frac{1}{16}$	$9\frac{7}{8}$		
		Outside	$11\frac{1}{8}$	$12\frac{1}{8}$	$10\frac{3}{16}$	4	28
150	Steel Door	Inside	$8\frac{3}{8}$	$12\frac{1}{16}$	$9\frac{7}{8}$		
		Outside	$11\frac{1}{8}$	$12\frac{1}{8}$	$10\frac{3}{16}$	4	28

Griswold Bolo Oven

With Glass Door

Oven No. 160

BOLO OVENS—Size: No. 160 and No. 180; **VALUE: No. 160, $100; No. 180, $150.**

Oven No. 180

Polished steel body. Electric welded case. Rabbeted door joint. Patented removable flue plate. Full tin lined. Nickel Alaska handles and door catch. Nickel plated steel hinges and corner pieces. Electric welded racks. Glass in two pieces. Perfect circulation. Packed one in strong corrugated carton.

No.		Height Inches	Width Inches	Depth Inches	Wt. Carton Pounds
160	Inside	$13\frac{3}{4}$	12	$12\frac{1}{4}$	
	Outside	$18\frac{1}{2}$	$14\frac{1}{8}$	$13\frac{9}{16}$	$21\frac{1}{2}$
180	Inside	$13\frac{3}{4}$	18	$12\frac{1}{4}$	
	Outside	$18\frac{1}{2}$	20	$13\frac{9}{16}$	$26\frac{1}{2}$

SAD IRONS, FLUTERS, HEATERS, & HEAT REGULATORS

SAD IRONS WITH HANDLE—**p/n:** none; **Markings:** GRISWOLDS ERIE, (bottom left) THE GRISWOLD MFG. CO., ERIE PA; **Circa:** 1900; **VALUE:** (with handle) $75-$100 each.

Right:
DOME SAD IRON HEATER—**Size:** 5 5/8" x 8 1/2" across; **p/n:** 1314; **Markings:** 1314; **Finish:** iron; **Circa:** 1900; **VALUE:** (with p/n only) $300-$400, (marked "Erie, Griswold Mfg. Co.") $500-$600.

SAD IRON SET IN BOX—**Size:** 4 lbs. and 5 1/2 lbs. with box; **p/n:** none; **Markings:** ONE SET, No. 150, GRISWOLDS ERIE COLD SAFETY HANDLE, ASBESTOS INSULATED SAD IRONS; **Circa:** 1920s; **VALUE:** $300-400.

Right:
ERIE FLUTER WITH FIXED HANDLE—**p/n:** none; **Markings:** THE FLUTER; **Finish:** nickel or iron; **Circa:** 1890s; **VALUE:** $400-$500 with base (not shown).

Left and Below:
ERIE FLUTER–p/n: 297, base-298; **Markings:**
THE ERIE FLUTER; **Finish;** nickel, iron, polished,
or bronzed; **Circa:** 1890-1910; **VALUE; $250-
$300.**

ROUND SAD IRON HEATER—Size: 12" dia.; **p/n:** 1313; **Markings:** CLASSIC SAD IRON HEATER, THE GRISWOLD MFG. CO. ERIE PA; **Finish:** iron; **Circa:** 1910; **VALUE: $150-$200.** Also made with block logo .

SQUARE SAD IRON HEATER—Size: 10 1/8" sq.; **p/n:** 2485A; **Markings:** block logo THE GRISWOLD MFG. CO. ERIE PA, SQUARE SAD IRON HEATER; **Finish:** iron; **Circa:** 1920s-1930s **VALUE: $225.**

Left:
SQUARE SAD IRON HEATER—Size: 10 1/8" sq.; **p/n:** 2485; **Markings:** SQUARE SAD IRON HEATER, GRISWOLD MFG, CO. ERIE PA (hand inscribed); **Finish:** iron; **Circa:** 1910; **VALUE: $150-$200.**

HEAT REGULATOR—Size: 7 3/8" dia.; **p/n:** 300; **Markings:** HEAT REGULATOR, THE GRISWOLD MFG. CO., ERIE PA, USA; **Finish:** iron; **Circa:** 1930s; **VALUE: $200-$250**. The design is the same on both sides.

No. 2 CLASSIC SAD IRON STAND—Size: 5 7/8" x 4 1/4"; **p/n:** 1602; **Markings:** CLASSIC, THE GRISWOLD MFG. CO., ERIE PA; **Finish:** japanned; **Circa:** 1910; **VALUE: $75-$100**.

Right:
COOKER PLATE (heat regulator)—**Size:** 7 1/2" dia.; **p/n:** none; **Markings:** COOKER PLATE, GMO CO, ERIE PA; **Finish:** steel; **Circa:** 1940s; **VALUE: $20**.

Above and Right:
HEAT REGULATOR—Size: 7 3/8" dia.; **p/n:** 300; **Markings:** HEAT REGULATOR, GRISWOLD, ERIE PA, USA. The opposite side is smooth, marked SMOOTH SIDE UP; **Finish:** iron; **Circa:** 1930s; **VALUE: $200-$250**. Using the regulator with the smooth side up allows a stove lifter to be inserted in the slot.

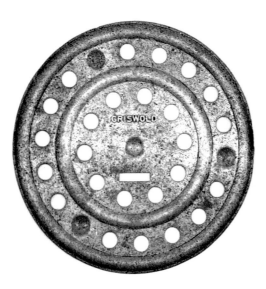

DUTCH OVEN TRIVET—Size: 8" dia.; **p/n:** none; **Markings:** GRISWOLD; **Finish:** aluminum; **Circa:** 1960s; **VALUE: $10**.

SKILLET GRILL—Size: 8 1/2" dia.; **p/n:** 299; **Markings:** (top) GRISWOLD, (bottom) ERIE PA, USA, SKILLET GRILL, PATENT APPLIED FOR, 299; **Finish:** iron or aluminum; **Circa:** 1930s-1940s; **VALUE: iron $150, aluminum $100**.

TRIVETS

FLAT IRON DESIGN TRIVET—p/n: 1725 or 1900, (Mini) 1733 or 1906; **Markings:** GRISWOLD TRIVET; **Finish:** Colonial black; **Circa:** 1950s; **VALUE: $25, Mini $30**.

FAMILY TREE DESIGN TRIVET—p/n: 1725 or 1901, (Mini) 1735 or 1907; **Markings:** GRISWOLD TRIVET; **Finish:** Colonial black; **Circa:** 1950s; **VALUE: $25, Mini $30**.

Left:
ROUND DESIGN TRIVET—
p/n: 1727 or 1902; **Markings:**
GRISWOLD TRIVET; **Finish:**
Colonial black; **Circa:** 1950s;
VALUE: $35.

Right:
EAGLE DESIGN TRIVET—
p/n: 1730 or 1905, (Mini) 1736
or 1908; **Markings:** GRISWOLD
TRIVET; **Finish:** Colonial black;
Circa: 1950s; **VALUE: $30,
Mini $35**.

TASSEL AND GRAIN DESIGN TRIVET—
p/n: 1728 or 1903; **Markings:** GRISWOLD
TRIVET; **Finish:** Colonial black; **Circa:** 1950s;
VALUE: $30.

OLD LACE DESIGN TRIVET—p/n: (large) 1739, (small) 1738; **Markings:** GRISWOLD
TRIVET; **Finish:** Colonial black; **Circa:** 1950s; **VALUE: large $125, small $150-$200**.

Left:
GRAPE DESIGN TRIVET—p/n:
1729 0r 1904, (Mini) 1737 or
1909; **Markings:** GRISWOLD
TRIVET; **Finish:** Colonial black;
Circa: 1950s; **VALUE: $25, Mini
$30**.

Right:
STAR DESIGN TRIVET—p/n:
1740, **Markings:** GRISWOLD
TRIVET; **Finish:** Colonial black;
Circa: 1950s; **VALUE: $35**.

MAIL BOXES

Left and Far Left:
No. 1 MAIL BOX—Size: 5 1/2" w x 10 1/2" 1 x 2 1/2" d; **p/n:** (door) 381, (lid) 382; **Markings:** No. 1 GRISWOLD; **Finish:** black, or black with green lid; **Circa:** 1930s; **VALUE: $150-$200.**

Below:
No. 3 MAIL BOX (FIGURAL)—Size: 6" w x 12" h x 3" d; **p/n:** 352, (door) 358, (lid) 361; **Markings:** pattern numbers only; **Finish:** japanned or antique bronze; **Circa:** (no wire holder, with peephole cover) 1910, (wire holder and peephole cover) 1920, (wire holder, no peephole cover)1923-1930; **VALUE: $100.**

Below and Right:
No. 2 POST BOX—p/n: 347, (cover) 348; **Markings:** THE GRISWOLD MFG. CO., ERIE PA USA, 347, 348; **Finish:** black enamel; **Circa:** 1920-1940s; **VALUE: $75-$100.**

Below:
No. 3 MAIL BOX—Size: 6 1/2" w x 12" l x 3" d; **p/n:** (lid) 105, (door) 106; **Markings:** GRISWOLD, ERIE PA; **Finish:** black, green, or gray enamel; **Circa:** 1950s-1960s; **VALUE: $75**.

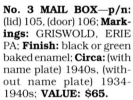

No. 3 MAIL BOX—p/n: (lid) 105, (door) 106; **Markings:** GRISWOLD, ERIE PA; **Finish:** black or green baked enamel; **Circa:** (with name plate) 1940s, (without name plate) 1934-1940s; **VALUE: $65**.

No. 4 POST BOX—Size: 6" w x 2"h x 2 3/4" d; **p/n:** door 356, door 355; **Markings:** GRISWOLD MFG. CO., ERIE PA, USA; **Finish:** japanned or black enamel; **Circa:** 1910-1940s; **VALUE: $75**.

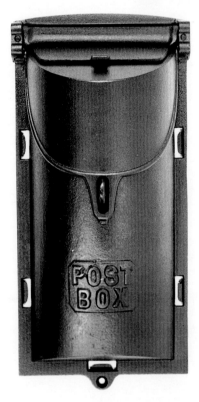

Above and Left:
SELDEN GRISWOLD No. 4 POST BOX—Size: 6" w x 12" h x 2 3/4" d; **p/n:** none; **Markings:** SELDEN GRISWOLD, MFG CO., ERIE PA, No. 4; **Finish:** japanned or gold; **Circa:** 1890-1920; **VALUE: $250-$300**. A "Selden Griswold" marking indicates earlier manufacture (1875-1880), but no records have been found.

181

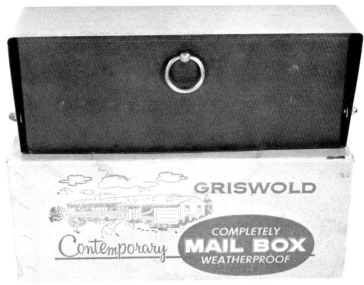

No. 5 POST BOX—Size: 6 1/4" w x 12" h; **p/n:** 358; **Markings:** 358, POST BOX; **Finish:** japanned and gold, bronze; **Circa:** 1890-1910; **VALUE:** $150.

Above:
CONTEMPORARY MAIL BOX—Size: 11" h x 4" d x 6 1/4" w; **p/n:** 705; **Markings:** none; **Finish:** black enamel, brass trim; **Circa:** 1950s-1960s; **VALUE:** $30-$40 with box.

Above and Right:
SELDEN GRISWOLD No. 6 POST BOX—Size: 7" w x 15" h x 1 34" d; **p/n:** none; **Markings:** SELDEN GRISWOLD MFG. CO., ERIE PA, NO. 6; **Finish:** japanned; **Circa:** prior to 1915; **VALUE:** $250-$300.

TOBACCO CUTTERS

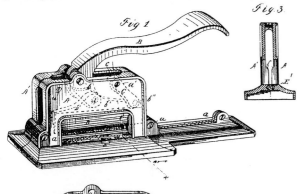

(No Model.)

O. R. HANCHETT.
TOBACCO CUTTER.

No. 286,607.   Patented Oct. 16, 1883.

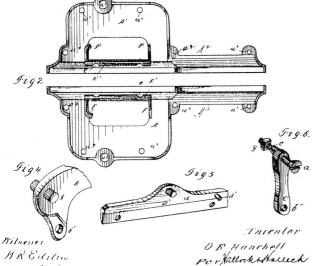

A patent drawing for a tobacco cutter, from October 16, 1883.

Above and Left:
No. 1 ERIE TOBACCO CUTTER—Size: (opening) 4 1/2" x 1 1/2"; **p/n:** none; **Markings:** GRISWOLD MFG. CO., ERIE PENN; **Finish:** japanned, gold stripe; **Circa:** 1910; **VALUE:** **$150.**

No. 2 ERIE TOBACCO CUTTER—Size: (opening) 4 1/2" x 1 3/8"; **p/n:** none; **Markings:** GRISWOLD MFG. CO. ERIE PENN; **Finish:** japanned, japanned with nickel, or full nickel; **Circa:** 1910; **VALUE: $150-$200.**

No. 3 TRIUMPH TOBACCO CUTTER—Size: (opening) 4 1/2" x   1 5/8"; **p/n:** (base) 391, (arm) 397, (cutter) 394 (side plate) 392, 393; **Markings:** S.C.W.W. Co., TRIUMPH; **Finish:** japanned, gold stripe; **Circa:** 1910; **VALUE: $100.**

No. 4 STANDARD TOBACCO CUTTER—Size: (opening) 3 5/8" x 1 1/2"; **p/n:** none; **Markings:** STANDARD No. 4; **Finish:** japanned, gold stripe; **Circa:** 1910-1920; **VALUE: $150-$200.**

No. 3 STAR TOBACCO CUTTER—Size: (opening) 4 1/2" x 1 5/8"; **p/n:** (base) 2494S, (handle) 2500; **Markings:** STAR MFG BY GRISWOLD MFG. CO. ERIE PA; **Finish:** japanned; **Circa:** 1920s; **VALUE: $125.**

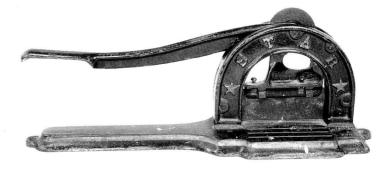

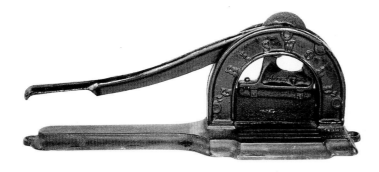

GRISWOLD TOBACCO CUTTER—p/n: (base) 2494, (handle) 2500; **Markings:** GRISWOLD; **Finish:** japanned, gold lettering; **Circa:** 1915-1940; **VALUE: $150.**

ASHTRAYS WITH MATCH HOLDERS—Size: (left) No. "0", (right) No. "00"; **p/n:** (No. "0") 560, (No. "00") 570A; **Markings:** (No. "0") block logo, EPU, CAST IRON SKILLET, 0, (No. "00") block logo, ERIE PA, QUALITY WARE, 00, 570A; **Finish:** iron; **Circa:** 1936; **VALUE: No. "0"** Rare, **No. "00"** $20-$30.

SQUARE ASHTRAY—Size: 4" sq.; **p/n:** 770; **Markings:** block logo, SQUARE ASH TRAY; **Finish:** iron, porcelain; **Circa:** 1950s; **VALUE:** $45-$50.

ADVERTISING ASHTRAYS—p/n: 570A; **Markings:** (on bottom) block logo, QUALITY WARE, OO; (marking inside center ashtray) block logo, GRIDDLES, OVENS, FRYERS, RANGES, SINCE 1865; **Finish:** iron; **Circa:** 1930s; **VALUE:** $75-$100.

Above and Right:
COWBOY HAT ASHTRAY—Size: 5 7/8" x 5 1/8" x 2 1/4"; **p/n:** 31; **Markings:** HATS OFF TO GRISWOLD, 31, ERIE PA; **Finish:** iron, chrome, or aluminum; **Circa:** 1930s; **VALUE: black iron $700-$800, chrome $600-$700, aluminum $500-$600.**

COLONIAL SMOKING SET—Size: No. "00"; **p/n:** (Skillet ashtray, left) 771, (bailed kettle, center) 773, (handled kettle, right) 772; **Markings:** Griswold logo ; **Finish:** black enamel; **Circa:** 1950s; **VALUE: No. 771, $100; No. 772 or No. 773, $50-$75.**

CUSPIDORS

No. 1 AMERICAN CUSPIDOR—Size: 5 1/2" x 7"; **p/n:** none; **Markings:** GRISWOLD MFG. CO., No. 1, PATENTED JULY 15, 1884; **Finish:** iron; **Circa:** 1883-1900; **VALUE: Rare.** Also sizes No. "0" and No. 2.

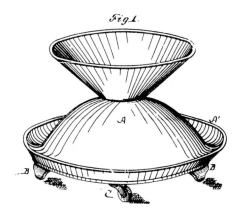

M. GRISWOLD.
CUSPIDOR.

No. 301,882. Patented July 15, 1884.

Fig.1

Fig.2

Witnesses.
Robert H. Porter.
W. R. Eddem.

Inventor
Matthew Griswold
Per Hullock & Halleck
Att'y

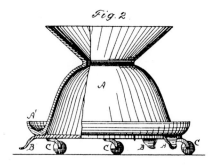

A patent drawing for a cuspidor.

STANDARD CUSPIDOR (shown with salesman's sample)—**Size:** 5" x 10"; **p/n:** none; **Markings:** GRISWOLD MFG. CO. ERIE PA, PAT'D JULY 15, 1884; **Finish:** japanned and painted, painted and enameled, or enameled with nickel edges; **Circa:** 1890-1900; **VALUE:** $1500-$2000.

Above and Right:
SALESMAN'S SAMPLE CUSPIDOR—**Size:** 2 7/8" top dia. x 2" high; **p/n:** none; **Markings:** same as standard cuspidor; **Finish:** red enamel with nickel trim, gold stripe; **Circa:** 1890-1900; **VALUE:** Rare.

MISCELLANEOUS...

MORTAR AND PESTLE—Size: 1 qt.; **p/n:** none; **Markings:** (mortar) GRISWOLD MFG. CO. ERIE PA, 1 Q., (pestle) 1; **Finish:** iron; **Circa:** 1895-1900; **VALUE: $250-$300.** Note the shape of the pestle.

ERIE WAX LADLE—Size: 7 3/4" long; **p/n:** 964; **Markings:** ERIE, 964; **Finish:** iron; **Circa:** 1890-1910; **VALUE: $75-$100.**

MORTAR AND PESTLE—Size: 1 pt.; **p/n:** none; **Markings:** (mortar) GRISWOLD MFG. CO, ERIE PA, 1 PINT, (pestle) 1-P; **Finish:** iron; **Circa:** 1895; **VALUE: $250-$300.** Note the shape of the pestle.

MILK BOX—Size: 13" w x 10 7/8" h x 8 1/2" d; **p/n:** none; **Markings:** GRISWOLD MILK BOX; **Finish:** black enameled steel; **Circa:** 1940s; **VALUE: $250-$300.**

Keep Milk clean and wholesome
with GRISWOLD SANITARY MILK BOXES

NO wonder she is contented—the milk was delivered long before daylight but she knows her Griswold Milk Box will keep it clean and wholesome, free from contamination, just as it was delivered.

You can imagine a dozen things which could happen to milk left on porch or doorstep. Don't take a chance—keep it under cover.

The Griswold Milk Boxes are made in three sizes of sheet steel in black Japan finish. (Description given with each illustration.) Easily fastened to house.

NUMBER SIX
Capacity 6 one-quart bottles. 12¾" long, 8½" wide, 9¾" deep. Net weight 3 lbs. 7½ oz.
Packed 2 in carton.
Weight 11 lbs.

NUMBER FOUR
Capacity 4 one-quart bottles. 8½" long, 8½" wide, 9¾" deep. Net weight 2 lbs. 11 oz.
Packed 4 in carton.
Weight 14¾ lbs.

NUMBER TWO
Capacity 2 one-quart bottles. 8½" long, 4½" wide, 9¾" deep. Net weight 1 lb. 15 oz.
Packed 6 in carton.
Weight 15¾ lbs.

Do you Receive your milk as clean as it is Delivered?

A magazine advertisement for milk boxes

No. 1 ICE SHAVE—p/n: 258; **Markings:** THE GRISWOLD MFG. CO., ERIE PA, USA; **Finish:** tinned; **Circa:** 1900-1920; **VALUE:** $100-$200.

No. 2 CLASSIC ICE SHREDDER—Size: 6" long; **p/n:** none; **Markings:** THE GRISWOLD MFG. CO., ERIE PA USA, CLASSIC ICE SHREDDER NO. 2; **Finish:** tinned; **Circa:** 1910; **VALUE:** $200-$250.

Above and Right:
ICE PICK—Size: 8 1/2"; **p/n:** none; **Markings:** GRISWOLDS, PAT'D 03-24-14; **Finish:** nickel; **Circa:** 1913-1920; **VALUE:** $75-$100, May not be Griswold Mfg. Co., Erie, Pa.

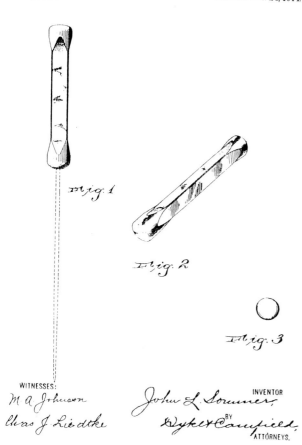

A patent drawing for an ice pick, from March 24, 1914.

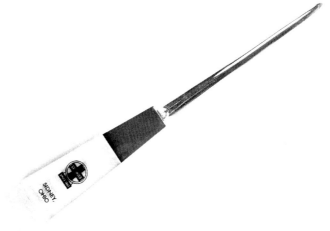

LETTER OPENER—**Size:** 9"; **p/n:** none; **Markings:** Griswold logo, Since 1865, SIDNEY OHIO; **Finish:** (blade) chrome steel, (handle) clear plastic with red trim; **Circa:** 1960s; **VALUE: $50-$100.**

FIRE SHOVEL—**Size:** 14 3/4" x 4 38"; **p/n:** none; **Markings:** ERIE; **Finish:** iron; **Circa:** 1870; **VALUE: $200-$300.**

CAN OPENER—**Size:** 6 1/2"; **p/n:** none; **Markings:** ERIE, 227,761; **Finish:** steel, (collar) brass, (handle) wood; **Circa:** 1930s; **VALUE: $150-$200.**

NUT CRACKER—**p/n:** (Jaw) 373, (handle) 374, (base) 371 & 372; **Markings:** p/n's only; **Finish:** iron with maple or walnut base; **Circa:** 1890; **VALUE: $250-$300.**

BLACKSMITH TONGS—**p/n:** none; **Markings:** ERIE; **Finish:** iron; **Circa:** 1868-1890; **VALUE:** $100-$150.

Below:
UMBRELLA STAND—**p/n:** unknown; **Finish:** iron; **Circa:** 1890; **VALUE:** Rare.

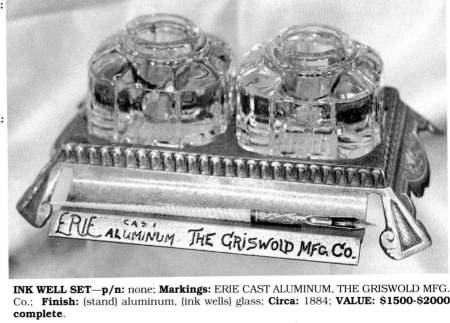

INK WELL SET—**p/n:** none; **Markings:** ERIE CAST ALUMINUM, THE GRISWOLD MFG. Co.; **Finish:** (stand) aluminum, (ink wells) glass; **Circa:** 1884; **VALUE:** $1500-$2000 complete.

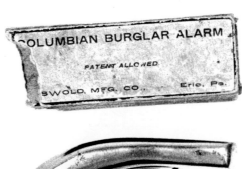

COLUMBIAN BURGLAR ALARM—**Size:** 3 1/2"; **p/n:** none; **Markings:** none; **Finish:** nickel; **Circa:** 1900; **VALUE:** $400-$500 with box, $300-$400 without box.

(No Model.)

J. F. HARVEY & D. SHIELDS.

BURGLAR ALARM.

No. 515,677.   Patented Feb. 27, 1894.

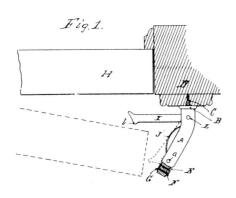

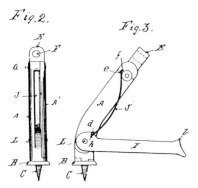

WITNESSES.   INVENTORS
E. Walker   John F. Harvey
F. Einfeldt   David Shields
                                     By H. Sturgeon
                                            atty.

A patent drawing for a burglar alarm, from February 27, 1894.

Above and Right:
**PUP   PAPER
WEIGHT—Size:** 1
5/8" high; **p/n:** 30;
Markings: 30,
GRISWOLD, PUP;
Finish: iron or alu-
minum; **Circa:** 1937
and 1951; **VALUE:
iron $250-$300,
aluminum $150-
$200.**

LAMP BRACKETS.

No. 1.

No. 2.

Above and Right:
No. 1 and No. 2 LAMP BRACKET—p/n: unknown; **Mark-
ings:** unknown; **Finish:** iron with bronze finish; **Circa:** 1900;
VALUE: $300.

Values given here for porcelain pieces are based on pieces in pristine condition. Any damage or chips greatly reduce the value.

PORCELAIN COLORS OF THE 1920S-1930S were Mandarin Red, Jade Green, Canary Yellow, and Turquoise Blue. Skillets came in sizes No. 3, $75-$100; No. 6, $50-$60; No. 7, $60-$75; No. 8, $60-$75; No. 9, $60-$75. Dutch ovens were available in green or blue only.

DUTCH OVEN-Size: No. 8; **p/n**: 833; **Markings**: block logo; **Finish**: blue porcelain; **Circa**: 1920s-1930s; **VALUE: $100-$150.**

ELECTRIC SANDWICH GRILL-**Finish**: blue porcelain, nickel trim; **Circa**: 1930s; **VALUE: $200-$400.**

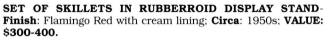

SET OF SKILLETS IN RUBBERROID DISPLAY STAND-
Finish: Flamingo Red with cream lining; **Circa**: 1950s; **VALUE**: $300-400.

REGULAR SKILLET-**Size**: No. 8: **p/n**: 704L; **Markings**: ERIE (rounded bottom edges); **Finish**: blue green, porcelain; **Circa**: 1930s; **Value**: $50.

REGULAR SKILLET-**Size**: No. 8: **p/n**: 704; **Markings**: block logo; **Finish**: black porcelain exterior with white porcelain interior; **Circa**: 1950s; **VALUE**: $60-$100.

HEARTS STAR GEM PAN-**Size**: No. 100; **p/n**: 960; **Markings**: barely visible due to porcelain; **Finish**: light blue porcelain; **Circa**: 1950s; **VALUE: $600-$800.**

DUCH OVENS-Size: No. 8; **p/n**: left: 1278, right: 1295;
Markings; block logo. EPU. TITE TOP DUTCH OVEN; **Finish**:
porcelain, Flamingo Red with cream lining; Circa: 1950s; **VALUE:
$125. OBLONG BAKING PAN-Size**: 10 3/4" x 6 1/8" x 1 3/4";
Markings: block logo; **VALUE: $75-100.**

NO. 18 CAST IRON GRILL (in background)-**VALUE: $100-125.**
NO. 87 AU GRATIN DISH (left)-**VALUE: $75-100.**
NO. 67 CASSEROLE (center)-**VALUE: $75.**
NO. 95 OVAL CASSEROLE (right)-**VALUE: $60.**
All the above are marked with medium logo, and are circa 1950s.

NO. 273 CORN STICK PAN AND "0" SKILLET-**Finish**: Flamingo
Red with cream lining porcelain; **Circa**: 1950s; **VALUE: No. 273,
$75-100; No. "0", $75.** Also available in Buttercup Yellow.

NO. 107 SKILLET GRIDDLE (background)- **p/n**: 200; **Markings**: slant logo; **VALUE: $75-100.**
NO. 3 OVAL ROASTER (center)-**p/n**: 643; **Markings**: block logo; **VALUE: $150-200.**
OVAL CASSEROLE (front)- **p/n**: 96; **Markings**: block logo; **VALUE: $60; Finish:** Flamingo Red
porcelain with cream lining; **Circa**: 1950s. Also available in Buttercup Yellow.

SAUCE PAN- Size: 7 1/2" dia. x 3 3/8" deep; p/n: 84; **Markings**: block logo, 84; **Finish**: Flamingo Red porcelain with cream lining; Circa: 1950s; **VALUE: $75-100.**

CASSEROLE SET-Size: No. 58 Casserole, with four No. 67 "0" size Table Service Dutch Ovens; **Finish**: Flamingo Red with cream lining porcelain; Circa: 1950s; **VALUE: $250-300.** Also available in Buttercup Yellow.

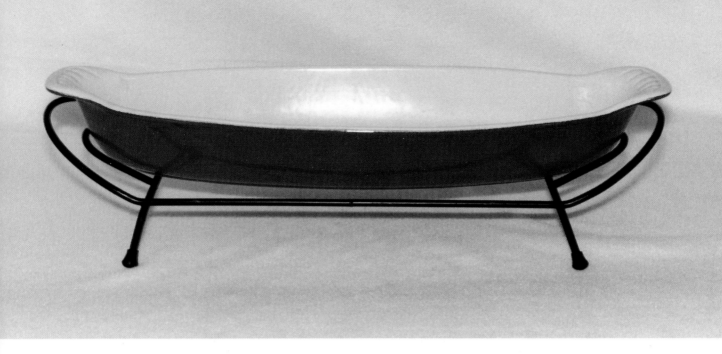

OVAL FISH BAKING PAN-**Size**: 17" x 6 1/4" x 2"; **p/n**: 67; **Markings**: block logo 67; **Finish**: Flamingo Red with cream lining porcelain; **Circa**: 1950s; **VALUE: $100-125 with stand.** Also available in Buttercup Yellow.

NO. 58 ROUND CASSEROLE and **NO. 67 "O" size. TABLE SERVICE DUTCH OVEN**. Note color variation of No. 67 Table Service Dutch Oven.

ROUND CASSEROLE SET-**Size**: No. 68 Round Casserole with four No. 67 Service Casseroles; **Finish**: Buttercup Yellow with Dove Gray lining; Circa: 1950s; **VALUE: $200-250**. Also available in Flamingo Red.

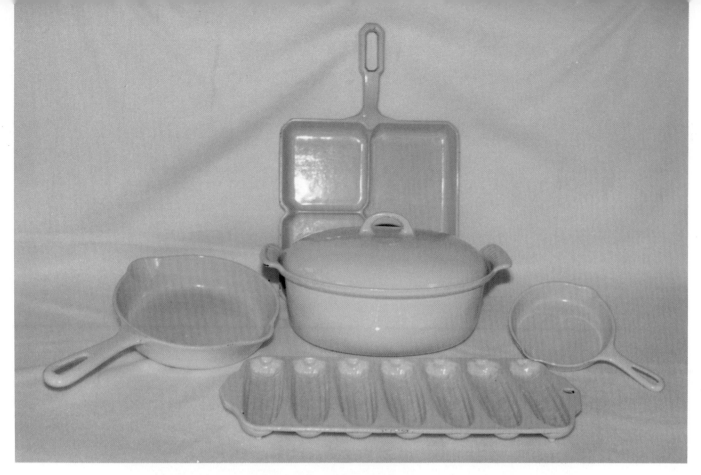

No. 3 SKILLET-VALUE: $30. COLONIAL BREAKFAST SKILLET-VALUE: $125. OVAL CASSEROLE-VALUE: $100. "0" SKILLET-VALUE: $75. NO. 273 CORN STICK PAN-VALUE: $100. Shown in Buttercup Yellow.

NO. 68 ROUND CASSEROLE WITH COVER, and **NO. 83 SHIRRED EGG DISH**-Finish: Buttercup Yellow with Dove Gray lining porcelain. **Circa**: 1950s; **VALUE: Casserole $100, Egg Dish $40.** Also available in Flamingo Red.

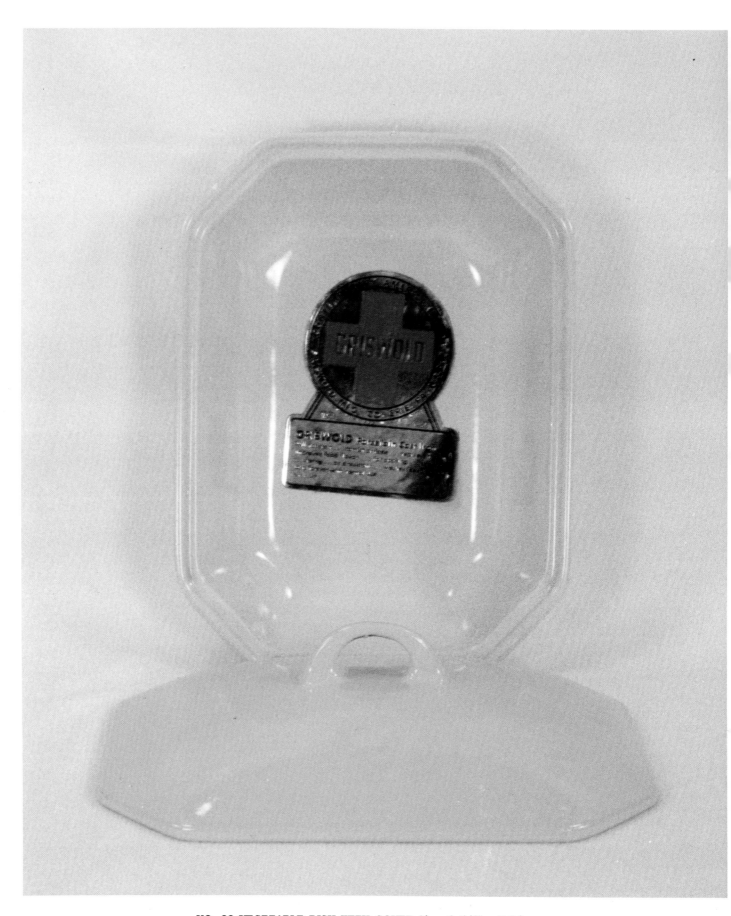

NO. 89 VEGETABLE DISH WITH COVER-**Size**: 9 5/8" x 7 3/8" x 2 3/8"; **p/n**: 89; **Markings**: block logo; **Finish**: Buttercup Yellow with Dove Gray lining; **Circa**: 1950s; **VALUE: $75**. Also available in Flamingo Red.

NO. 2705 SKILLET, NO. 68 COVERED CASSEROLE (with its cover), **and NO. 83 SHIRRED EGG DISH**-**Finish**: black iron exterior with white porcelain lining; **Circa**: 1950s; **Value**: No. 2705, $50; No. 68, $100; No. 83, $50.

AU GRATIN BAKING DISH-**Finish**; black iron exterior with white porcelain lining; **Circa**: 1950s; **VALUE**: $100-$150.

No. 82 OVAL FISH BAKING DISH-**Size**: 17" x 6 1/4"; **p/n**: 82; **Markings**: block logo; **Finish**: white porcelain; **Circa**: 1950s; **VALUE: $150-200.** White both inside and outside is unusual. Value is based on near perfect condition.

REGULAR SKILLET-**Size**: No. 3; **Markings**: small logo; ERIE PA; **Finish**: robin's egg blue with white interior; **Circa**: 1960s; **VALUE: $150.**

REGULAR SKILLET-Size: No. 3; **Markings:** slant logo, ERIE;
Finish: porcelain dark blue with white lining; **Circa:** 1950s;
VALUE: $75.

CHEF SKILLET-p/n: 43; **Markings**: small logo; **Finish**: brown porcelain; **Circa**: 1960s; **VALUE: $30.**

WOOD HANDLE SKILLET-Size: No. 3; **p/n**: 757A; **Markings**: block logo, EPU; **Finish**: chrome with red enameled handle; **Circa**: 1950s; **VALUE: $100-150.** Red handles are unusual.

OVAL CASSEROLE-Size: 8 1/4" x 5 1/4"; **p/n**: 93; **Finish**: robin's egg blue porcelain; **Circa**: 1960s; **VALUE: $100-125.**

'SYMBOL' WARE SAUCE PAN-Size: 2 qt.; **p/n**: none, **Markings**: small logo; **Finish**: aluminum with enameled cover, plastic knob; **Circa**: 1960s; **VALUE: $40.**

WOOD HANDLE ALUMINUM KETTLES
Candy Kettle- left: **Size**: No. 1 1/2; **p/n**: 141 1/2; VALUE: $100.
Utility Kettle- center: **Size**: No. 3; **p/n**: 343; **VALUE: $75.**
Oyster Bowl- right: **Size**: No. 1 1/2; **p/n**: 241 1/2; **VALUE: $75**; **Circa**: 1920-1940.

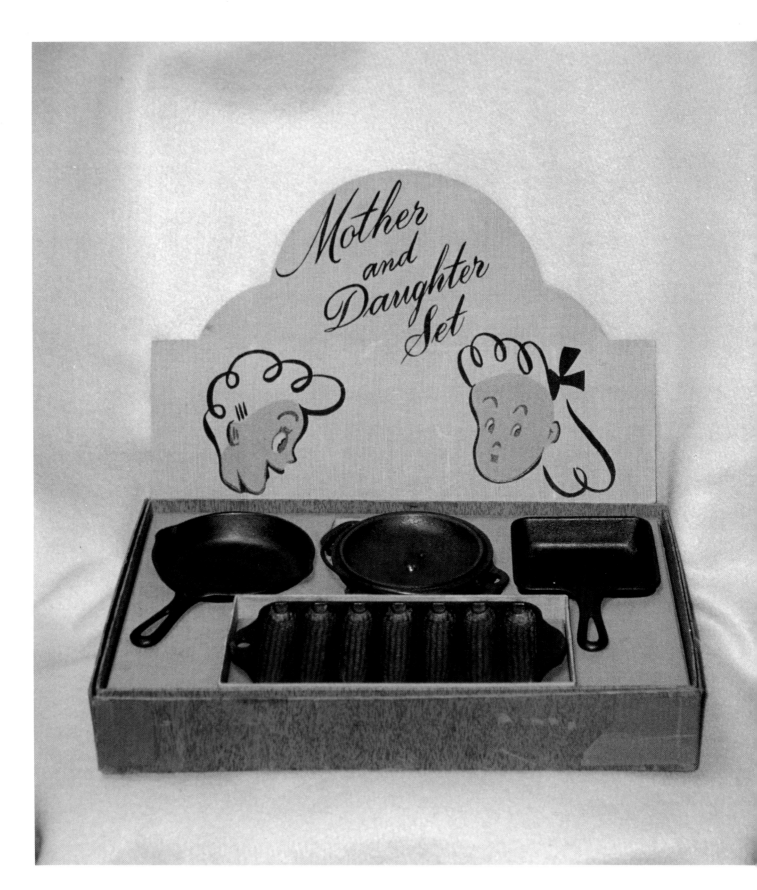

GRISWOLD MOTHER AND DAUGHTER SET-Set consists of an "0" Skillet, "0" Table Service Dutch Oven; Square Toy Skillet and No. 262 Corn Stick Pan; **Circa**: 1950s; **VALUE: $400-500.**

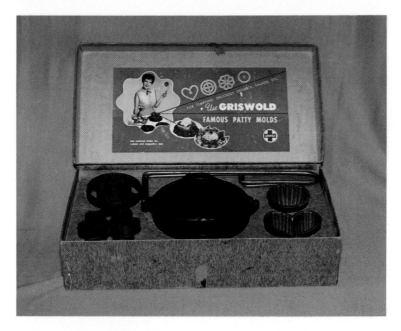

No. 3 PATTY MOLD SET-Contains No. 1 and No. 2 Patty Molds and No. 72 Patty Bowl. Circa: 1950s; **VALUE: $135.**

SUN DIAL-**Size**: 10 1/2" dia.; **p/n**: 357; **Markings**: THE GRISWOLD MFG. CO., ERIE PA U.S.A.; **Finish**: blue/white porcelain; **Circa**: 1930s; **VALUE: porcelain $500-600, iron $400-500, chrome $400.**

BREAD SLICER-Size: 10"l x 6 3/4"h x 6"w; **p/n**: A980R & L; **Markings**: block logo; **Finish**: aluminum on wood base; **Circa**: 1920s-1930s; **VALUE: $250-350.**

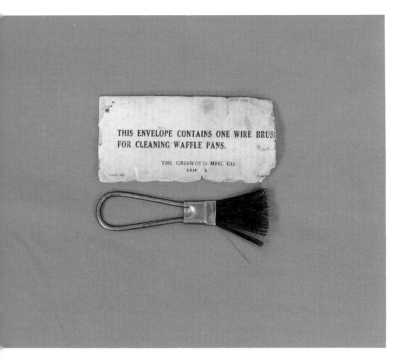

BRUSH FOR CLEANING WAFFLE IRONS-VALUE: $75.

DUTCH OVEN STAND-5 TIER-Circa: 1930s; **VALUE: $1750-2000.** Holds sizes No. 10 through No. 6 for store display.

DUTCH OVEN RACK-3 TIER-**Circa**: 1930s; **VALUE: $750-1250**. Furnished free with order of twelve or more dutch ovens.

ASSORTMENT OF PORCELAIIN ASHTRAYS, and a **BRONZE ASHTRAY**-**Marking**: block logo; **Circa**: 1950s-1960s; **VALUE**: porcelain **$10-20**, bronze **$45**.

STEP STOOLS-**Circa**: 1960s; **Markings**: Step pads are marked with Griswold logo; **VALUE**: two step **$200**, three step **$200-300**. Marketed by Griswold, Sidney, Ohio, but not made by them.

ASHTRAYS-Markings: stylized Wagner Ware in oval; **Finish**: porcelain; **Circa**: 1950s-1960s; **VALUE: $10.**

ASHTRAYS-Markings: stylized Wagner Ware in oval; **Finish**: porcelain; **Circa**: 1950s-1960s; **VALUE: $10.**

FAVORITE PIQUA WARE

SALESMANS SAMPLE SKILLET-Size: No. 4; **Markings**: FAVORITE PIQUA WARE; **Finish**: half blue and half gray porcelain; **Circa**: 1916-1935; **VALUE**: **$150-200.**

REGULAR SKILLETS-Size: Nos. 1-12; **Markings**: FAVORITE PIQUA WARE; **Finish**: blue porcelain; **Circa**: 1916-1935. Sizes No. 13 & No. 14 were not done in porcelain finish.

WOOD HANDLE SKILLET-**Size**: No. 5: **Markings**: FAVORITE PIQUA WARE; **Finsih**: blue porcelain; **Circa**: 1916-1935; **VALUE**: $75.

COVERED DEEP SKILLET-**Size**: No. 9; **Markings**: FAVORITE PIQUA WARE; **Finish**: gray porcelain; **Circa**: 1916-1935; **VALUE**: $75-$100.

No. 1 SKILLETS-Size: No. 1; **Markings**: FAVORITE PIQUA WARE; **Finish**: red, blue, mahogany, cream; **Circa**: 1916-1935; **VALUE: $75-$100.**

REGULAR SKILLET-Size: No. 9; **Markings**: FAVORITE PIQUA WARE; **Finish**: red porcelain; **Circa**: 1916-1935; **VALUE: $75-100**. Red porcelain is rare.

No. 1 SKILLET-Size: No. 1; **Markings**: FAVORITE PIQUA WARE; **Finish**: mahogany pattern porcelain; Circa: 1916-1935; **VALUE: $75-$125**.

DUTCH OVEN-Size: No. 8; **Markings**: FAVORITE PIQUA WARE (cover) 3F8D; **Finish**: blue porcelain; **Circa**: 1916-1935; **VALUE: $75-$125**.

DUTCH OVEN-Size: No. 8; **Markings**: FAVORITE PIQUA WARE
(cover) 3F8D; **Finish**: cream-colored porcelain; **Circa**: 1916-
1935; **VALUE**: **$100-150**. Cream-colored porcelain is rare.

SCOTCH BOWL-Size: No. 2; **Markings**: FAVORITE PIQUA WARE; **Finish**: blue porcelain; **Circa**: 1916-1935; **VALUE**: $60.

HAND TAMPER-Size 13 1/2" long; **Circa**: 1916-1935; **VALUE:** **$100**. This wooden tool was used in the Favorite Piqua Foundry to pack sand around a pattern to create the mold for casting.

WAFFLE IRON-Size: No. 8 Deep; **Markings**: Favorite Piqua Ware logo;
Finish: iron waffle, blue porcelain base; **Circa**: 1916-1935; **VALUE: $75**.

SQUARE WAFFLE IRON-Size: No. 4 Deep; **Markings**: Favorite Piqua Ware logo;
Finish: iron waffle, blue porcelain base; **Circa**: 1916-1935; **VALUE: 125**.

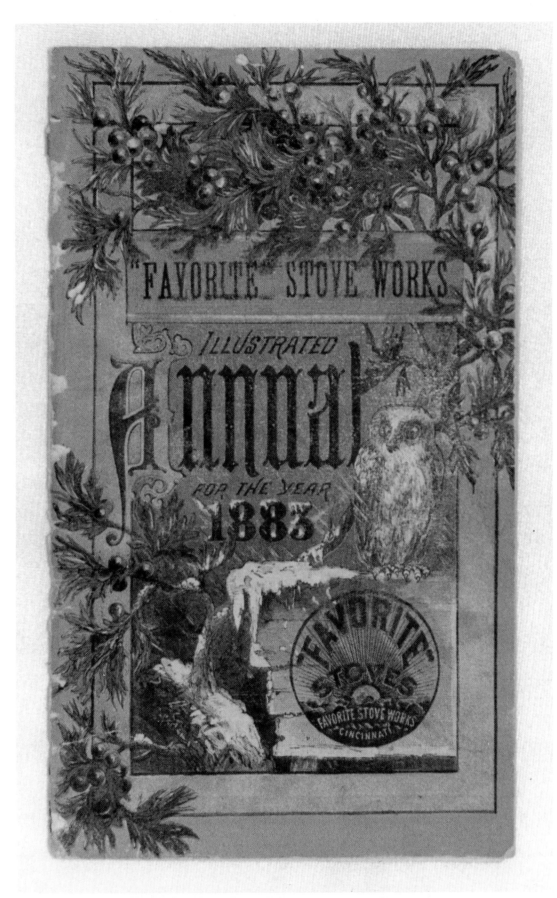

FAVORITE ILLUSTRATED ANNUAL-**Circa**: 1883; **VALUE: $100-
150**. Similar to an almanac, this booklet was apparently used as
a promotional item by the Favorite Stove Works, Cincinnati, Ohio.

"DOLLYS FAVORITE" CHILD'S STOVE-Size: 23 1/2"h x 19"w
x 11"d; **Finish**: blue porcelain with nickel trim; Circa: 1910;
VALUE: $4000-6000.

ADVERTISING CLOCK—**Size:** 8 1/8" dia.; **p/n:** none; **Markings:** WE SELL ERIE HOLLOW WARE, UP TO TIME; **Finish:** nickel; **Circa:** 1900; **VALUE: Rare.**

BANQUET RIBBON—**Size:** approximately 5" x 1 3/4"; **Markings:** Griswold spider, GRISWOLD MFG. COMPANY, No. 332; **Finish:** appears to be silk; **Circa:** unknown; **VALUE: $200.** The slight tear at the top indicates that the ribbon probably hung from a pin or button.

FROM
THE GRISWOLD MFG. CO.
ERIE, PENNA.
ERIE HOLLOW WARE, GAS STOVES

SEARS, ROEBUCK & CO.,
Dept. ◇ 9 ◇   CHICAGO, ILL.

SHIPPING LABEL—**VALUE: $25.** Labels were glued or tacked to barrels packed with skillets, etc.

JELLY CAKE PAN—**Size:** 10 1/8" dia.; **p/n:** A2510; **Markings:** struck (stamped) Griswold logo ; **Finish:** aluminum; **Circa:** 1910-1920; **VALUE: $150**.

ALUMINUM CUP—Size: 2 5/8" dia. x 3" high; **Markings:** struck (stamped) Griswold logo ; **Finish:** aluminum; **Circa:** 1910; **VALUE: $25-$50.**

EMPLOYEE IDENTIFICATION PIN—Markings: THE GRISWOLD MFG. CO. ERIE PA, 596; **Circa:** 1920s; **VALUE: $100-$200.**

ANNIVERSARY EGG SEPARATOR—Size: 3 3/8" dia.; **p/n:** none; **Markings:** 1889 GRISWOLD'S GOLDEN ANNIVERSARY 1939; **Finish:** tinned steel; **Circa:** 1939; **VALUE: $100-$150.** This piece was not made by Griswold, nor does it refer to the Griswold Mfg. Co. of Erie, PA..

ZIPPO CIGARETTE LIGHTER—Markings: Griswold logo, Since 1865; **Circa:** 1950s; **VALUE: $200-$250.**

THE WAGNER MANUFACTURING COMPANY
SIDNEY, OHIO

Mathias Wagner was born in Stundweiller, Germany, on April 8, 1818. When Mathias was twelve years old, he and his parents immigrated to the United States and settled near Pittsburgh, Pennsylvania, where Mathias worked in a tobacco factory. In 1837, at the age of nineteen, Mathias moved to Sidney, Ohio and began working on the construction of the Miami and Erie Canal. Around the same time he began a butchering business, selling the meat to canal workers. With his profits, he bought property around Sidney, which ultimately led him to become Sidney's wealthiest citizen.

In 1846 Mathias Wagner married Anna M. Rauth, who had immigrated from Bavaria with her parents. Their marriage produced eight children.

In 1891, their two sons Milton M. and Bernard P. Wagner organized a partnership, forming the Wagner Manufacturing Company in Sidney, Ohio on July 21. Another son, William H. Wagner, owned hardware stores in Columbus and Sidney, Ohio. William's store in Sidney was located adjacent to the Arcade department store, a family-owned business started by Mathias Wagner. William closed the Columbus store, allowing him to run the hardware store in Sidney while sharing management of the Arcade with his younger brother, Louis R. Wagner.

As the Wagner Manufacturing Company became more successful, William decided he wanted to join the company. To accommodate his move to the company (around 1897), Milton and Bernard decided to put out a second line of skillets to sell to jobbers and distributors. They purchased the Sidney Hollow Ware Foundry from Philip Smith, putting William H. Wagner in charge.

Around 1903, the family realized that the Sidney Hollow Ware Company (managed by William) was undercutting the sales of hollow wares produced by the Wagner parent company. Consequently, Milton and Bernard sold the Sidney Hollow Ware foundry back to Philip Smith, and

brought William H. into the partnership of the Wagner Manufacturing Company. Because William was the oldest brother, he assumed the position of president. Shortly after, Louis "LR" Wagner left the Arcade (in which he had a 50% interest) to join the Wagner Manufacturing Company as Secretary and General Manager. Louis also became a director in the Wagner Hotel Company and the Wagner Realty Company.

In addition to hollow ware, the Wagner Manufacturing Company made brass castings, and installed nickel plating baths for the manufacture of the cash register and calculator they held patents for. Manufacture of these never materialized however, because they sold the patents to the Osgood Cash Register Company of Detroit, Michigan, a buying front for the National Cash Register Company.

The original Wagner shop was small, consisting of two buildings and employing twenty men. R.O. Bingham, who had been a molder and machinist, was hired as their superintendent and was responsible for designing and building the factory.

The company started with the production of cast iron hollow ware, and introduced nickel-plated hollow ware to their line in 1892. This was followed in 1894 by cast aluminum ware.

By 1913 the plant had grown to employ three hundred men. Eighty-three molders worked in the 110' x 450' foundry building, one of the many buildings in the rapidly expanding factory complex.

The Wagner firm made a radical improvement in 'aluminum cookware', as it was known, and braved the market with a line of seamless cast aluminum ware of a heavier weight. Wagner's cast aluminium ware became known throughout the world.

Although Wagner continued to manufacture cast iron ware, they became equally noted for their aluminum utensils. They produced a huge line of aluminum ware, including cake and ice cream

W. H. Wagner
President

B. P. Wagner
Vice-President

M. M. Wagner
Treasurer

L. R. Wagner
Sec'y and Gen'l Mgr.

The founders of the Wagner Manufacturing Company.

molds, spoons, scoops, coffee pots and percolators, tea pots, and pitchers. Wagner's aluminum won honors at the Chicago, Nashville, Paris, Buffalo, and St. Louis Expositions. At the San Francisco Exposition, Wagner Ware captured the Grand Prize, acknowledging it as the finest aluminum ware on the world market.

Bernard P. Wagner died in 1923, leaving his twenty-five percent of the Wagner stock to his wife. His son, Jerome Wagner, Sr., took his position as Vice President. Subsequently, Jerome's mother transferred what had been his father's stock to Jerome.

In 1929, William H. Wagner died at the age of 74. Milton Wagner moved from his position as Treasurer to President. Louis "LR" Wagner advanced from Secretary to Treasurer. Cable Wagner, William's son who had been hired as a teenager, replaced "LR" as Secretary.

Milton M. Wagner died at the age of 78 in 1940, leaving his quarter of the Wagner stock to his sons, Philip and Joseph. Philip Wagner was named as President, replacing his father.

Louis "LR" Wagner left the company in 1946, selling his stock to Philip and Joseph. Joseph Wagner joined his brother Philip in the company, replacing "LR" as Treasurer.

In 1953, Philip Wagner, then President, let it be known that he wanted to retire and sell off his stock in the company. He had been successful in other investments, and was tired of working. He liked Florida, and wanted to move there. Jerome Wagner did not want to invest any more in the company. Joseph wanted to stay but he also didn't want to invest. Cable decided to purchase the Wagner Hotel Company. After considerable financial negotiations, the Wagner Manufacturing Company was acquired by the Randall Company of Cincinnati, Ohio, a company connected with the automotive industry. Un-

der the agreement, Jerome Wagner stayed on as an advisor for six months, and Joseph Wagner remained as General Manager.

Under Randall, in October of 1957 the Wagner Division purchased the Griswold Cookware Line from McGraw Edison, which had purchased all of the assets of the Griswold Manufacturing Company of Erie, Pennsylvania. In the purchase, Wagner acquired the patent and trademark rights, patterns, and existing inventory of the Griswold Cookware line.

In 1959, the Randall Company, including the Wagner Ware division, was acquired by Textron Incorporated of Providence, Rhode Island. Joe Wagner remained as General Manager until December 29, 1965, when he reached his sixty-fifth birthday and mandatory retirement age for Textron. He remained another three years, however, as a consultant.

Under Randall-Division of Textron, the Wagner Division acquired the Durham Manufacturing Company of Muncie, Indiana. They were a manufacturer of casual leisure furniture for household use, such as card tables and chairs, baby highchairs and playpens, and mailboxes.

In September of 1969, Textron Incorporated sold the household line to the General Housewares Corporation, a holding company. With the sale went all patent and trademark rights for both Wagner Ware and Griswold. The Cookware Division of General Housewares Corporation produces cast iron and aluminum cookware in the Wagner Factory today.

Plant of The Wagner Manufacturing Company, at Sidney, Ohio

The Wagner Factory, 1916.

229

Here are reproduced some of the medals won by Wagner Ware "against the field" at various expositions both in this country and abroad. They indicate in a small way the real, rock-bottom merit of this ware. From the expositions now in progress at San Francisco and San Diego, we expect that the Wagner Exhibits will bear off honors as fitting companions for those portrayed above.

From "The Griddle," March 1915.

SKILLETS

"WAGNER," SIDNEY O.
Circa: 1898—1915

No. 5	$25
No. 6	$25
No. 7	$25
No. 8	$30
No. 9	$35
No. 10	$65
No. 11	$110
No. 12	$85

WAGNER WARE, SIDNEY -O-
(stylized logo with size no.)
Circa: 1920-1924

No. 2	$100
No. 3	$15
No. 4	$50
No. 5	$15
No. 6	$20
No. 7	$29
No. 8	$25
No. 9	$30
No. 10	$60
No. 11	$100
No. 12	$75
No. 13	$200
No. 14	$125

WAGNER WARE, SIDNEY -O-
(stylized logo with 4-digit catalog no.)
Circa: 1924-1935

No. 2	$75
No. 3	$10
No. 4	$50
No. 5	$20
No. 6	$20
No. 7	$25
No. 8	$25
No. 9	$35
No. 10	$50
No. 11	$100
No. 12	$75
No. 13	$200-$250
No. 14	$100-$150

WAGNER WARE, SIDNEY -O-
(pie logo)
Circa: 1915-1920

No. 2	$75
No. 3	$10
No. 4	$100
No. 5	$20
No .6	$25
No. 7	$30
No. 8	$30
No. 9	$50
No. 10	$75
No. 11	$200
No. 12	$100
No. 13	$500-$600
No. 14	$350-$400

NATIONAL
Circa: 1895-1914

No. 7	$50
No. 8	$50
No. 9	$50

WAGNER WARE, SIDNEY -O-
(stylized logo with 4-digit catalog no.)
(smooth bottom)
Circa: 1935-1959

No. 2	$60
No. 3	$10
No. 4	$35
No. 5	$15
No. 6	$15
No. 7	$35-$50
No. 8	$20
No. 9	$80-$100
No. 10	$30
No. 11	$75
No. 12	$45
No. 13	$150-$200
No. 14	$75-$100

NATIONAL and STYLIZED LOGO
Circa: 1924-1945

No. 7	$50-$60
No. 8	$50-$60
No. 9	$50-$60

Smooth-bottom skillets manufactured after 1959 were marked with their size in inches and Made in USA or simply USA, in addition to the stylized logo. These skillets are generally regarded as not collectible.

REGULAR SKILLET—Size: No. 13; **Cat. No.:** none; **Markings:** stylized logo, 13A; **Finish:** iron; **Circa:** 1924; **VALUE: $100-$150.**

REGULAR SKILLET—Size: No. 12 (11 3/4" dia.); **Cat. No.:** 1062; **Markings:** stylized logo; **Finish:** iron or nickel; **Circa:** 1924; **VALUE: $75-$100.**

REGULAR SKILLET—Size: No. 2; **Cat. No.:** none; **Markings:** stylized logo, 2; **Finish:** iron; **Circa:** 1924; **VALUE: $100.**

SIDNEY, 2B—Finish: iron; **Circa:** unknown; **VALUE: $100.** It is debatable whether this skillet is Sidney Hollow Ware or Wagner. It is believed that Wagner used this mark after purchasing Sidney Hollow Ware, and this skillet is identical to the Wagner marked skillet.

LONG LIFE REGULAR SKILLET—Size: No. 7; **Cat. No.:** 1757; **Markings:** LONG LIFE SKILLET, 1757B; **Finish:** iron; **Circa:** 1936; **VALUE: $30.**

ADVERTISING SKILLET—Size: No. 2; **Cat. No.:** none; **Markings:** YOU CAN GET IT OF WERTZ AND SINGER CO, MIDDLETOWN, O., 2; **Finish:** iron; **Circa:** unknown; **VALUE: $50-$100.** The style, finish, and (no.) 2 mark indicate that this skillet was made by Wagner.

Above and Right: ANGUS BROILER—Size: No. 9; **Cat. No.:** 1129; **Markings:** stylized logo; **Finish:** iron; **Circa:** 1960s-1970s; **VALUE: $50-$75.**

WARDWAY REGULAR SKILLET—Size: No. 2; **Cat. No.:** 1431; **Markings:** WARDWAY, 1431; **Finish:** iron; **Circa:** 1930s; **VALUE: $20.** "Wardway" was the brand for Montgomery Wards.

CHEF SKILLET—**Size**: 9"; **Cat. No.:** none; **Markings**: 9 inch; **Finish**: iron; **Circa**: 1980s; **VALUE: $15**. Product of General Housewares Corp.

CHEF SKILLETS—**Size**: 11", 10", and 9"; **Cat. No.:** (11") 1390, (10") 1388, (9") 1386; **Markings**: stylized logo, CHEF SKILLET; **Finish**: iron; **Circa**: 1970-1980; **VALUE: 11", $50; 10", $40; and 9", $30**.

CHEF SKILLET—**Size**: No. 11; **Cat. No.:** 1390; **Markings**: stylized logo, CHEF SKILLET, 11 INCH; **Finish**: iron; **Circa**: 1970-1980; **VALUE: $50**.

Above and Left:
FRENCH FRY PAN—**Size**: 6 1/2" dia.; **Cat. No.:** 521; **Markings**: stylized logo; **Finish**: aluminum with steel handle; **Circa**: 1920s; **VALUE: $35**.

235

SQUARE SKILLET—Size: 9 1/2" sq. x 1 1/2" deep; **Cat. No.:** 1218; **Markings:** stylized logo, 1218; **Finish:** iron; **Circa:** 1930s; **VALUE: $35**.

SQUARE CHICKEN FRYER—Size: 9 5/8" sq. x 2 3/4" deep; **Cat. No.:** 1400; **Marking:** stylized logo; **Finish:** iron; **Circa:** 1930s; **VALUE: $100-$125**.

WARM OVER PAN—Size: 9 5/8" sq. x 1 1/2" deep; **Cat. No.:** 1219; **Markings:** stylized logo, WARM OVER PAN, 1219; **Finish:** iron; **Circa:** 1930s-1940s; **VALUE: $100, with Lid $150**.

FLAT BACON FRYER WITH PRESS—Size: 8 3/4" sq.; **Cat. No.:** 1103; **Markings:** stylized logo; **Finish:** iron; **Circa:** 1938; **VALUE: Skillet, $25-$30; Press, $100-$125**.

Left and Above:
5 STAR SKILLET SET—**Size**: 10 1/2" dia.;   **Cat. No.:** 1403;
Markings: stylized logo, 5 STAR SKILLET SET, 1403; **Finish:** iron;
Circa: 1941; **VALUE: $100**.

DOUBLE SKILLET—**Size**: 10 1/4" dia. x
4 7/8"; **Markings**: stylized logo; **Finish:** iron;
Circa: 1941; **VALUE: $125**.

SKILLET OVEN—Size: No. 8; **Cat. No.:** 1275-1, 1275-2; **Markings:** stylized logo, SKILLET OVEN, PAT'D AUG 10, 1920; **Finish:** iron; **Circa:** 1920s; **VALUE: $200 complete with base, $100 without base.** This unit should set on a base or ring. The patent describes this invention as a "portable oven for use on top of stoves... the parts can be readily taken apart and used as skillets in the ordinary manner."

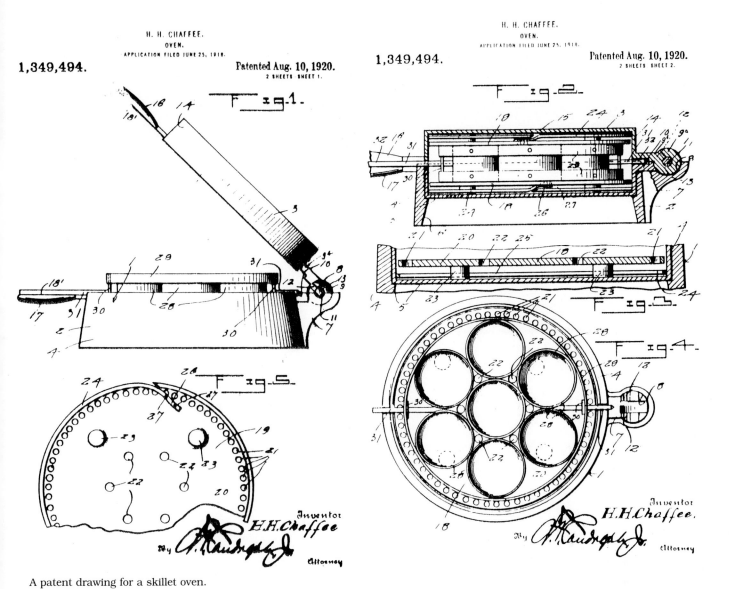

A patent drawing for a skillet oven.

SHALLOW SKILLETS

SHALLOW SKILLET—**Size**: No. 8; **Cat. No.:** none; **Markings**: stylized logo, SHALLOW SKILLET; **Finish:** iron or nickel; **Circa**: 1915-1920s; **VALUE: $65-$85**. Also made sizes No. 7, No. 9, and No. 10.
SHALLOW SKILLET—**Size**: No. 9 (11" dia.); **Cat. No.:** 1099; **Markings**: WAGNER WARE, SIDNEY O; **Finish:** iron or nickel; **Circa**: 1924; **VALUE: No. 7, $90; No. 8, $90; No. 9, $90; No. 10, $100.**

HALF SKILLET—**Size**: No. 7 (8 3/8" dia. x 1" deep); **Cat. No.:** none; **Markings**: stylized logo, HALF SKILLET; **Finish:** iron; **Circa**: 1915-1924; **VALUE: $70-$90**.

SHALLOW SKILLET—**Size**: No. 8; **Cat. No.:** 1098; **Markings**: stylized logo, SHALLOW SKILLET; **Finish:** iron; **Circa**: 1941; **VALUE: No. 7 and No. 8, $90; No. 9, $90; and No. 10, $125.** Note the single hole handle.

Above and Right:
GREASELESS FRYING SKILLET—**Size**: 11 3/4" dia. x 1 1/4"
deep; **Cat. No.:** 1102B; **Markings**: stylized logo, GREASELESS
FRYING PAN, PAT PENDING ; **Finish:** iron; **Circa:** 1938; **VALUE:**
$50-$75.

FAT FREE FRYER—**Size**: 11 1/4" dia. x 1" deep; **Cat. No.:** 1102;
Markings: stylized logo, fat free fryer; **Finish:** iron ; **Circa:** 1970-
1980s; **VALUE:** $45.

Above two photographs:
FAT FREE FRYER—**Size**: 11 1/8" X 7/8";   **Cat. No.:** 1102E;
Markings: stylized logo, FAT FREE FRYER, PAT APPLIED FOR;
Finish: iron; **Circa:** 1940s; **VALUE:** $30-$40.

GRIDDLES

HANDLED GRIDDLE—Size: No. 10; **Cat. No.:** none; **Markings**: "WAGNER", 10 (under handle); **Finish**: iron; **Circa**: 1892-1898; **VALUE**: $60; **No. 7, $30-$35; No. 8, $25-$30, No. 9, $40-$45.**

HANDLED GRIDDLE—Size: No. 8; **Cat. No.:** 1108; **Markings**: stylized logo; **Finish**: iron; **Circa**: 1924-1970; **VALUE**: $20; **No. 6, $60-$65; No. 7, $40-$45; No. 9, $25-$35; No. 10, $35-$45..**

HANDLED GRIDDLE—Size: No. 8 (9 5/8" dia.); **Cat. No.:** none; **Markings**: "WAGNER"; **Finish**: iron; **Circa**: 1892-1898; **VALUE**: $50; **No. 7, $30-$35; No. 9, $40-$45.**

WARDWAY HANDLED GRIDDLE—Size: 9 3/4" dia.; **Cat. No.:** 1435; **Markings**: WARDS CAST IRON, MONTGOMERY WARD; **Finish**: iron; **Circa**: unknown; **VALUE**: $20-$30.

BAIL GRIDDLE—**Size**: No. 10; **Cat. No.:** none; **Markings**: "WAGNER" SIDNEY, O.; **Finish**: iron; **Circa**: 1900; **VALUE: No. 10, $75; No. 12, $65; No. 14, $75; and No. 16, $100.**

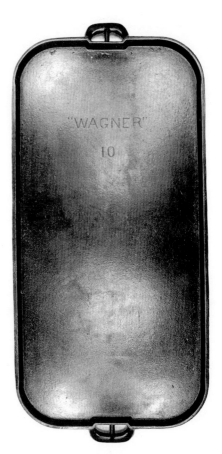

LONG GRIDDLE—**Size**: No. 10 (12 3/8" x 24 2/4"); **Cat. No.:** none; **Markings**: "WAGNER", 10; **Finish**: iron; **Circa**: 1900-1915; **VALUE: $60; No. 8, $35-$45; No. 9, $45-$50.**

BAILED GRIDDLE—**Size**: No. 16 (15 1/4" dia.); **Cat. No.:** 1126; **Markings**: stylized logo; **Finish**: iron; **Circa**: 1924-1940s; **VALUE: No. 10, $50; No. 12, $45; No. 14, $50; and No. 16, $75.**

LONG GRIDDLE—
Size: No. 8 (8 7/8" X 19 3/8"); **Cat. No.:** none; **Markings**: "WAGNER" SIDNEY O; **Finish**: iron; **Circa**: 1910-1920; **VALUE: No. 7 and No. 8, $40; No. 9, $50; No. 10, $60; and No. 11, $100.**

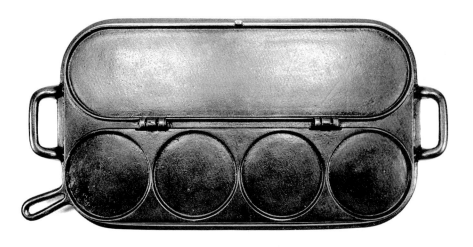

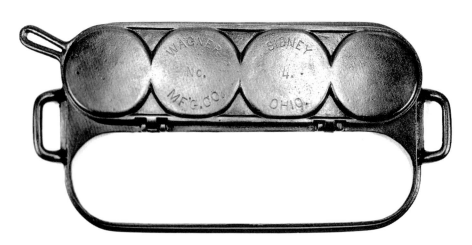

Above and Right:
No. 4 CAKE GRIDDLE—Size: 18 7/8" x
10 1/2"; **Cat. No.:** none; **Markings:**
WAGNER MFG. CO., SIDNEY OHIO, NO.
4; **Finish:** iron; **Circa:** 1900; **VALUE:**
$300-$400, two-section No. 2 griddle
$350-$400.

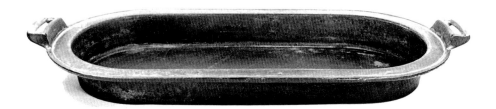

Above and Right:
DEEP LONG PAN—Size: 17" x 7 1/4";
Cat. No.: none; **Markings:** "WAGNER"
SIDNEY O; **Finish:** iron; **Circa:** 1895-
1915; **VALUE:** $75.

DUTCH OVENS & OVAL ROASTERS

Left and Below:
DUTCH OVEN—Size: No. 9; **Cat. No.:** none; **Markings**: "WAGNER", SIDNEY O., 9. (cover) 9; **Finish**: iron; **Circa**: 1895; **VALUE: $50**; No. 8, $40; and No. 10, $100.

ROUND ROASTER—Size: No. 7; **Cat. No.:** none; **Markings**: (bottom) WAGNER WARE SIDNEY O, ROUND ROASTER; (cover, inside) 7; (cover, outside) single knob; **Finish**: iron; **Circa**: 1915; **VALUE: No. 6, $85; No. 7, 45; No. 8, $35; No. 9, $45; No. 10, $75; and No. 11, $100-$150.**

Left and Above:
ROUND ROASTER—Size: No. 6 (8 1/4" dia. x 3 3/4" deep); **Cat. No.:** none; **Markings**: (cover) WAGNER DRIP DROP BASTER, (bottom) WAGNER WARE SIDNEY O, ROUND ROASTER, 6A; **Finish**: iron; **Circa**: 1924; **VALUE: No. 6, $90; No. 7, $50; No. 8, $40; No. 9, $50; No. 10, $80; and No. 11, $100-$150.**

DUTCH OVEN—Size: Nos. 6—11; **Markings**: raised letter cover; **Finish**: iron or chrome; **VALUE: No. 6, $90; No. 7, $50; No. 8, $40; No. 9, $50; No. 10, $80; and No. 11, $100-$150**.

DUTCH OVEN—Size: No. 6 (8 5/8" dia. x 3 3/4" deep, 2 1/2 qts.); **Cat. No.:** 1266; **Markings**: stylized logo, 1266; **Finish**: iron; **Circa**: 1941; **VALUE: No. 6, $100; No. 7, $60; No. 8, $40; No. 9, $60; No. 10, $100; and No. 11, $125**.

DUTCH OVEN—Size: No. 8; **Cat. No.:** none; **Markings**: Wagner stylized logo, & Griswold logo, 5 QT., MADE IN USA; **Finish**: iron with glass cover; **Circa**: 1970-1975; **VALUE: $30**. The Dutch Oven was the last item marked with the double logo to be produced by General Housewares Corp.

Magazine advertisement, 1922

	Size
No. 1	$6\frac{5}{8}$ x $11\frac{1}{8}$
No. 2	$7\frac{1}{2}$ x $11\frac{1}{4}$
No. 3	8 x $12\frac{1}{4}$
No. 4	$8\frac{1}{4}$ x $13\frac{1}{2}$
No. 5	$9\frac{1}{4}$ x $14\frac{1}{4}$
No. 6	$10\frac{1}{4}$ x $14\frac{3}{4}$
No. 7	$10\frac{7}{8}$ x $15\frac{3}{4}$
No. 8	$11\frac{1}{4}$ x 17
No. 9	$12\frac{3}{8}$ x $18\frac{1}{2}$

The Correct Shape for Roast and Fowl

OVAL ROASTERS—**Finish**: iron or chrome; **Circa**: 1930s; **VALUES**: No. 1, $200; No. 2, $200; No. 3, $150-$200; No. 4, $250, No. 5, $150-$200; No. 6, $150-$200; No. 7, $150-$200; No. 8, $250-$300; and No. 9, $250. Add $50-$100 more for roasters with trivets.

KETTLES & TEA KETTLES

Regular Kettle

REGULAR KETTLE—**Size**: Nos. 6, 7, 8, 9; **Circa**: 1890-1940; **VALUE**: No. 6, $75; No. 7, No. 8, and No. 9, $50-$60.

Flat Bottom Kettle

FLAT BOTTOM KETTLE—**Size**: Nos. 6, 7, 8, 9, 10, 12; **Finish**: iron; **Circa**: 1890s-1940; **VALUE**: No. 6, No. 7, No. 8, and No. 9, $50-$60; No. 10, $100; No. 12, $150-$200.

Bottom two photos:
OVAL ROASTER—**Size**: No. 3 (12 1/4" x 8" x 3 7/16"); **Cat. No.:** 1283; **Markings**: stylized logo, OVAL ROASTER, 1283; **Finish**: iron; **Circa**: 1941; **VALUE**: No. 3, $200 No. 1, $200; No. 5, $200-$250; No. 7, $250-$300; No. 9, $250-$300. Add $50 for roasters with trivets.

Flat Bottom Bulged Pot

Eccentric Pot

New England Style

Rimmed Pot

FLAT BOTTOM BULGED POT—**Size**: Nos. 7, 8, 9; **Finish**: iron; **Circa**: 1890s-1920s; **VALUE**: $50-60.

ECCENTRIC POT—**Size**: Nos. 7, 8, 9; **Finish**: iron; **Circa**: 1890s-1920s; **VALUE**: $80-$100.

RIMMED POT—**Size**: Nos. 7, 8, 9; **Finish**: iron; **Circa**: 1890s-1915; **VALUE**: $75-$100.

Low Kettle

Low Bulged Pot

Eccentric Kettle

New England Style

LOW KETTLE—**Size**: Nos. 7, 8, 9; **Finish**: iron; **Circa**: 1890s-1920s; **VALUE**: $75.

REGULAR BULGE POT—**Size**: Nos. 7, 8, 9; **Finish**: iron; **Circa**: 1890s-1920s; **VALUE**: $50-$60.

LOW BULGED POT—**Size**: Nos. 7, 8, 9; **Finish**: iron; **Circa**: 1890s-1915; **VALUE**: $50-$60.

ECCENTRIC KETTLE—**Size**: Nos. 7, 8, 9; **Finish**: iron; **Circa**: 1890s-1915; **VALUE**: $50-$60.

Regular Bulged Pot

Extra Large Eccentric Pot

Style B

EXTRA LARGE ECCENTRIC POT—**Size**: No. 7 (14 qts.) No. 8, (20 qts.), No. 9, (30 qts.); **Finish**: iron; **Circa**: 1890s-1915; **VALUE**: No. 7 and No. 8, $75-$100; No. 9, $150-$200.

Lipped Kettle

LIPPED KETTLE—Size: Nos. 7, 8, 9; **Finish:** iron; **Circa:** 1890s-1915; **VALUE: No. 7 and No. 8, $50-$60; No. 9, $75-$100.**

Right:
REGULAR KETTLE— Size: No. 6 (8 1/4" x 6 1/2" deep); **Cat. No.:** none; **Markings:** WAGNER SIDNEY O, R.N.A. on side; **Finish:** iron; **Circa:** 1900; **VALUE: $150-$200.**

Both photos above:
CONVEX OR BERLIN KETTLE—Size: No. 2 (7"dia. x 5" high); **Cat. No.:** none; **Markings:** "WAGNER SIDNEY O, 2; **Finish:** aluminum; **Circa:** 1898-1915; **VALUE: $40-$50.**

Above and Right:
RIMMED POT—Size: No. 8; **Cat. No.:** none; **Markings:** WAGNER, 8 POT; **Finish:** iron; **Circa:** 1900; **VALUE: $100.** An applied handle was added to this pot, as was a stir mechanism with a blade shaped to fit the contour of the bottom. This may have been done so the pot could be used as a chestnut roaster.

Left and Below Left:
PAUL REVERE SAUCE PAN—Size: 2 pts.; **Cat. No.:** none; **Markings:** stylized logo, The Paul Revere, PAT APL'D FOR, 2 PT.; **Finish:** aluminum with 7 1/2" black enameled wood handle; **Circa:** 1915-1930; **VALUE: $75-$100.**

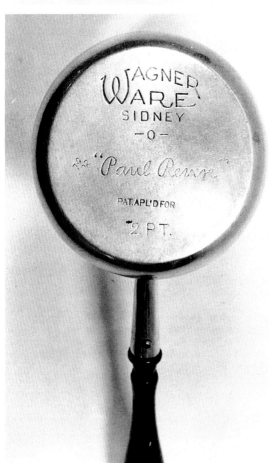

Right and Above Right:
SCOTCH BOWL—Size: No. 2; **Cat. No.:** none; **Markings:** WAGNER WARE SIDNEY O, SCOTCH BOWL, 2; **Finish:** nickel or iron; **Circa:** 1895-1924; **VALUE: No. 2, $40; No. 3, $35; No. 4, $40; and No. 5 $50.**

Above and Right:
TEA KETTLE—Size: No. 8; **Cat. No.:** none; **Markings:** (bottom) large gate mark, (spout) 8, (cover) WAGNER SIDNEY O; **Finish:** plain iron or galvanized; **Circa:** 1895; **VALUE: No. 8, $60; No. 7, $75; and No. 9, $85**.

DISPLAY STANDS

KETTLE DISPLAY STAND—Used for store displays.

A Display Rack of Wagner Cast Iron Ware

DISPLAY STAND FOR ALUMINUM UTENSILS—Size: 50" high; **Cat. No.:** none; **Markings:** stylized logo on nameplate; **Finish:** wood, stained brown, nickel nameplate; **Circa:** 1915-1930s; **VALUE: $250-$300**.

WAFFLE IRONS, WAFTER IRONS & RELATED ITEMS

SQUARE WAFFLE IRON—Size: 6 3/4" square; **Cat. No.:** none; **Markings**: WAGNER MFG. CO. SIDNEY OHIO, PATENTED JULY 26, 1892; **Finish:** iron; **Circa**: 1900; **VALUE: $100.**

SQUARE WAFFLE IRON—Size: 9" sq.; **Cat. No.:** none; **Markings**: THE WAGNER MFG. CO. SIDNEY O, SQUARE WAFFLE IRON, PAT'D FEB 22, 1910; **Circa**: 1920-1930; **VALUE: $75-$100.**

WAFFLE IRON—Size: No. 7, (6 5/8" dia.); **Cat. No.:** none; **Markings**: "WAGNER", WAGNER MFG. CO. SIDNEY O, PAT'D JULY 26, 1892 & PENDING; **Circa**: 1895-1915; **VALUE**: No. 7, No. 8, and No. 9, $50.

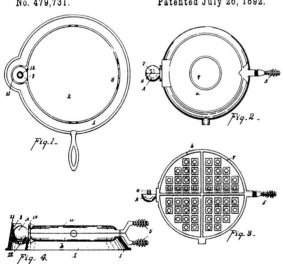

TWIN WAFFLE IRON—Size: 10 3/4" x 11"; **Cat. No.:** none (later was 1421); **Markings**: "SIDNEY", PAT'D JULY 26, 1892 & PENDING; **Finish:** iron; **Circa**: 1900-1910; **VALUE: $400-$500.**

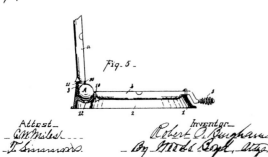

A patent drawing for waffle iron features, from July 26, 1892.

Above and Left:
WAFER IRON—Size: (wafer) 5 3/8"; **Cat. No.:** 1451; **Markings:** WAGNER MFG. CO., SIDNEY O, PAT'D FEB 22, 1910; **Circa:** 1920-1940; **VALUE: $150-$200.** This iron has a drain hole in the base.

Above and Left:
WAFER IRON—Size: (wafer) 5 3/8" dia. **Cat. No.:** 1450; **Markings:** stylized logo, WAFER IRON; **Circa:** 1915-1940; **VALUE: $150-$200.** This iron has Alaskan wire handles; and no drain hole in the base.

Above and Right:
SANDWICH TOASTER—**Size**: 6" sq.; **Cat. No.:** 1455; **Markings**: stylized logo, SAND-WICH TOASTER, PAT NO. 1553741; **Circa**: 1930s; **VALUE: $150**.

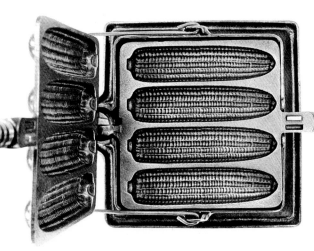

Left, Above, and Above Left:
KRUSTY KORN SAUSAGE PAN—**Size**: 6 3/4" x 6 7/8" x 4 1/2" high; **Cat. No.:** 1426; **Markings**: stylized logo, KRUSTY KORN, REG IN US PAT OFC, SAUSAGE PANS, PATENTED 2-22-10, 7-6-20, 9-15-25; **Circa**: 1927; **VALUE: $250-$300**.

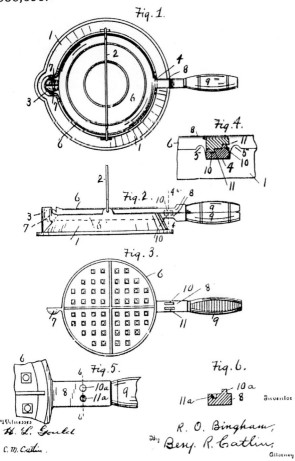

R. O. BINGHAM.
WAFFLE IRON.
APPLICATION FILED JULY 10, 1909.

950,090.   Patented Feb. 22, 1910.

A patent drawing for waffle iron features,
from February 22, 1910

Right:
E-Z ICE CREAM CONE MAKER—Circa: 1920; **VALUE: 300.**
ICY CONE BAKER—Circa: 1920; **VALUE: $300-$400.**

WAGNER WARE

High Grade Cast Iron

E Z Ice Cream Cone Baker

This Cone Baker is the best cheap cone baker on the market. It makes a regulation size cone and is used by persons doing a small ice cream cone business. It is also good for family use or for church fairs, etc.

A wooden cone for rolling the wafers on is furnished with every iron, also a recipe for making the batter.

Price   list, $30.00 per dozen

Icy Cone Baker

This is the heavy regulation Cone Baker used by persons doing an extensive business. Wooden cone and recipe furnished with every baker.

Price...........................list, $7.00 each

For Ice Cream Cone Disher, see page 48

Page Ninety-Three

BAKING PANS & GEM PANS

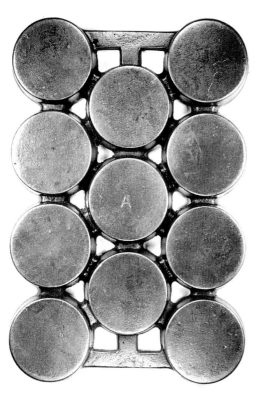

STYLE A GEM PAN—Size: 11 3/16" x 7 5/8"; **Cat. No.:** A; **Markings**: none; **Circa**: 1900-1920; **VALUE: $30**.

STYLE C GEM PAN—Size: 10 1/4" x 7", (cups) 2 1/8" x 3/4"; **Cat. No.:** none; **Markings**: WAGNER WARE; **Finish**: iron; **Circa**: 1895-1940; **VALUE: $100-$125**.

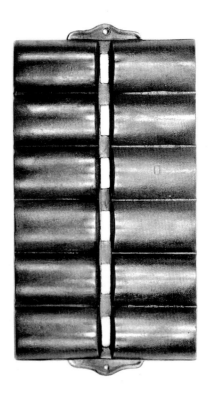

STYLE B POP-OVER PAN—Size: 11 1/4" x 7 5/8"; **Cat. No.:** none; **Markings**: WAGNER WARE, B; **Finish**: iron or nickel; **Circa**: 1920s; **VALUE: $30**.

STYLE D GEM PAN (New England Pattern)—Size: 12 3/4" x 6 7/8"; **Cat. No.:** (1325); **Markings**: D; **Finish**: iron; **Circa**: 1897-1940s; **VALUE: $45**.

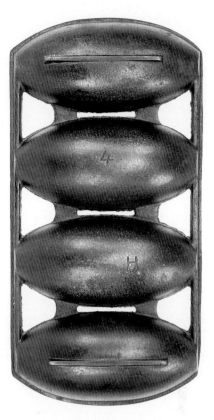

SIZE "H" VIENNA ROLL PAN—Size: 12 1/2" x 6 3/8"; **Cat. No.:** none; **Markings:** 4, H; **Finish:** iron; **Circa:** 1910-1924; **VALUE:** $200-$250.

STYLE 'E' BREAD STICK PAN—Cat. No.: none; **Markings:** E BREAD STICK PAN, WAGNER WARE SIDNEY, OHIO; **Finish:** iron; **Circa:** 1900-1940; **VALUE:** $35.

VIENNA ROLL PAN—Size: 11 1/2" x 6 1/2"; **Cat. No.:** 1331; **Markings:** stylized logo, VIENNA ROLL PAN, 'I', 1331; **Finish:** iron; **Circa:** 1924-1940; **VALUE:** $75-$100.

STYLE 'K' GEM PAN—Size: 7" x 5"; **Cat. No.:** none; **Markings**: K (some are not marked); **Finish:** iron or aluminum; **Circa**: 1915; **VALUE: $400-$600**.

STYLE 'L' GEM PAN—Size: 6 3/4" x 4 1/4"; **Cat. No.:** none; **Markings**: WAGNER WARE, L (most are not marked); **Finish:** iron or aluminum; **Circa**: 1915; **VALUE: marked iron $150, unmarked $75, aluminum $30**

STYLE 'N' GEM PAN—Size: 11 1/8" x 2 3/4"; **Cat. No.:** none; **Markings**: none; **Finish:** iron or aluminum; **Circa**: 1915; **VALUE: $300-$450**.

Above and Right:
STYLE 'O' GEM PAN—Size: 9 1/2" x 3 1/4' x 1 3/4"; **Cat. No.:** none; **Markings**: WAGNER WARE, 0; **Finish:** iron or aluminum; **Circa**: 1915-1940; **VALUE: $100-$150**.

Left:
STYLE 'Q' MUFFIN PAN—**Size:** 7 3/8" x 5 1/2", (cups) 2 3/8" x 1 1/2"; **Cat. No.:** none; **Markings:** WAGNER WARE, Q; **Finish:** iron or aluminum; **Circa:** 1915-1940; **VALUE:** $45.

Below:
STYLE 'T' GEM PAN—**Size:** 12 7/8" x 10 1/8"; **Cat. No.:** 1338; **Markings:** WAGNER WARE, T; **Finish:** iron; **Circa:** 1924-1940; **VALUE: $100-$150.**

STYLE 'R' GEM PAN—**Size:** 7 3/8" x x 8 1/4"; **Cat. No.:** 1336; **Markings:** WAGNER WARE, R; **Finish:** iron or aluminum; **Circa:** 1915-1948; **VALUE: $50.**

STYLE 'U' TURKS HEAD GEM PAN—**Size:** 11 7/8" x 7 7/8", (cups) 3" x 1"; **Cat. No.:** 1339; **Markings:** WAGNER WARE, U; **Finish:** iron; **Circa:** 1924-1940; **VALUE: $50-$75.**

No. 1 HANDLED GEM PAN—Size: (total length) 6 3/8", (cups) 2 1/2" x 1 1/8"; **Cat. No.:** none; **Markings:** none; **Finish:** iron or aluminum; **Circa:** 1915; **VALUE: $450-$650**.

Right:
LITTLE SLAM GEM PAN—Size: 7 5/8" x 10 3/4", (cups) 2 1/2" x 1 1/4"; **Cat. No.:** 1340; **Markings:** WAGNER SARE, SIDNEY O, No 1340, LITTLE SLAM BRIDGE PAN; **Finish:** iron or nickel; **Circa:** 1930s; **VALUE: $125, nickel $100**.

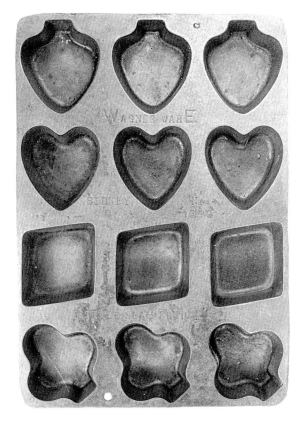

No. 2 HANDLED GEM PAN—Size: (total length) 6 5/8"; (cups) 2 1/2" x 1 5/8" deep, **Cat. No.:** none; **Markings:** WAGNER WARE, 2; **Finish:** iron or aluminum; **Circa:** 1915; **VALUE: $200-$300**. Many are unmarked.

LITTLE GEM—Size: 9 cups, (total size) 7" x 7 1/8", (cups) 1 3/4" x 7/8"; **Cat. No.:** records indicate this pan was designated 1321 even though it is marked 1320; **Markings:** LITTLE GEM, WAGNER WARE, 9 CUPS 1320, PAT PENDING; **Finish:** iron; **Circa:** 1920; **VALUE: $100-$200**. Also made with cut-outs.

Right:
SWEDISH PLETT PAN—
Size: 9 1/4" dia.; **Cat. No.:**
1316; **Markings:** SWEDISH
CAKE PAN (SVENSK
PLETTE PAN), stylized logo;
Finish: iron; **Circa:** 1920-
1940; **VALUE: $45.**

Above:
LITTLE GEM—Size: twelve
cups, 7 1/8" x 9 5/8"; **Cat.
No.:** none; **Markings**:
LITTLE GEM, WAGNER
WARE, PATENT PENDING,
C; **Finish:** iron or alumi-
num; **Circa:** 1920; **VALUE:
iron $150, aluminum $75.**

POP OVER PAN—Size:
11 1/8" x 7 3/4"; **Cat. No.:**
none; **Markings**: Wagner
stylized logo, Griswold block
logo, MADE IN USA; **Finish:**
iron; **Circa:** 1970-1975;
VALUE: $20. Made in the
Wagner plant by General
Housewares Corp.

Above and Left:
DANISH CAKE PAN—Size: 9" dia., (cup) 2 1/2"
dia.; **Cat. No.:** 1312; **Markings**: stylized logo; **Finish:** iron; **Circa:** 1924-1940s; **VALUE: $45-$65.**

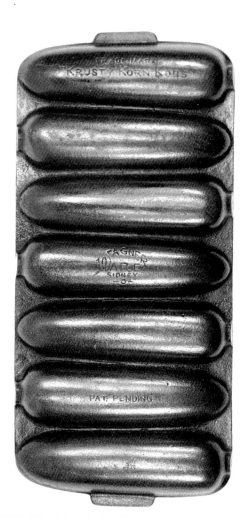

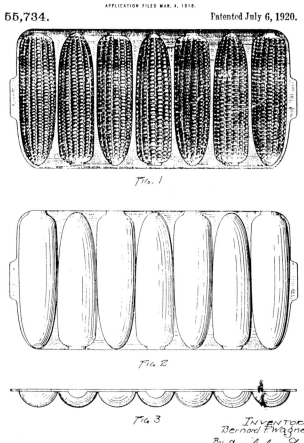

DESIGN.

B. P. WAGNER.
METAL BAKING PAN.
APPLICATION FILED MAR. 4, 1918.

55,734.

Patented July 6, 1920.

Fig. 1

Fig. 2

Fig. 3

INVENTOR
Bernard F. Wagner
By Fay, Oberlin & Fay
ATTORNEYS

CORN STICK PAN (Senior)—Size: 13 3/4" x 6 3/8"; **Cat. No.:** 1319; **Markings**: stylized logo, KRUSTY KORN KOBS, PAT PENDING; **Finish**: iron; **Circa**: 1918-1930s; **VALUE: $75-$100.** Also made in Junior and Tea sizes.

A design patent drawing for a baking pan, from July 6, 1920.

KRUSTY KORN KOB BAKING MOLDS —
Circa: 1940-1960s.
Senior—Cat. No.: 1318;
   Size: 13 3/4" x 6 7/8";
   VALUE: $50.
Junior— Cat. No.: 1319;
   Size: 11 5/8" x 5 7/8";
   VALUE: $20.
Tea Size— Cat. No.: 1317;
   Size: 7 1/8" x 4 1/8";
   VALUE: $60.

REPRODUCTION OF A TEA SIZE MOLD—Poor casting quality and poor detail.

Left and Above:
CORN BREAD PAN—Size: 12 7/8" x 5 1/2"; **Cat. No.:** none; **Markings**: CORN BREAD STICK PAN, B; **Finish:** iron; **Circa**: 1940s; **VALUE: $60.** This wheat pattern was patented by Griswold. The "B" is characteristic of Wagner as is the hole in each end of the pan.

STYLE 'A' CAKE MOLD—Size: 8 3/4" dia.; **Cat. No.:** none; **Markings:** none; **Finish:** iron; **Circa:** 1915; **VALUE: $300-$400.**

Left:
POP-OVER PAN—Size: 11 7/16" x 7 1/4"; **Cat No. :** 1323A; **Marking:** stylized logo in oval, 1323A; **Finish:** iron or aluminum; **Circa:** 1950s; **VALUE: $30.**

Above and Right:
STYLE 'B' CAKE MOLD—**Size**: 10" dia.; **Cat. No.**: 310; **Markings**: WAGNER WARE, B; **Finish**: iron; **Circa**: 1915-1940; **VALUE: $150-$200**.

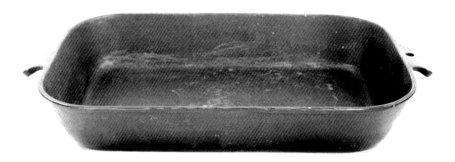

Above and Left:
CAKE PAN—**Size**: 12 3/4" x 18 1/2"; **Cat. No.**: 1510; **Markings**: stylized logo, BAKING PAN, 1510; **Finish**: iron; **Circa**: 1920; **VALUE: $150-$200, No. 1508 $125-$200**.

DOUBLE BREAD PAN—**Size**: 12 1/4" x 6 1/2", 1 1/2 deep; **Cat. No.**: none; **Markings**: stylized logo; **Finish**: iron; **Circa**: 1980s; **VALUE: $20-$30**.

TOYS/MINIATURES

PHOTO OF LITTLE WAGNERS—From "The Griddle", April 1915.

TOY KETTLE—**Size**: 4 1/2" dia.; **Cat. No.:** none; **Markings**: WAGNER, SIDNEY O; **Finish**: iron; **Circa**: 1924; **VALUE**: $60.

TOY SKILLET—**Size**: No. "0"; **Cat. No.:** none; **Markings**: WAGNER MFG CO, SIDNEY, O.; **Finish**: iron; **Circa**: 1910-1915; **VALUE**: $50-$75.

CAST IRON TOY SETS

Wagner Cast Iron Toy Sets are all year round sellers because they are exact replicas of the large utensils. The diameters average four and one-half inches and they are large enough for actual cooking. Children enjoy a set of these toys that are "just like mother's". All toys are plain smooth castings.

TOY SETS—**Circa**: 1930s; **VALUE**: **Toy Set No. 1** $350-$450; **Toy Set No. 2** $450-$550.

	CONTENTS	CODE
Toy Set No. 1	Large Skillet—Cover—Small Skillet—Handled Griddle	OMLET
Toy Set No. 2	Large Skillet—Cover—Lipped Kettle—Small Skillet—Handled Griddle	ONTOG

STYLE 'A' TOY TEA KETTLES—Size: 4 1/2"
dia. x 3 3/4"; **Cat. No.:** none; **Markings:**
stylized logo, A; **Finish:** iron or nickel; **Circa:**
1915-1925; **VALUE: iron $150, nickel $100.**

Above and Left:
TOY WAFFLE IRON—Size: No. "0", 4 1/2" dia.; **Cat. No.:** none;
Markings: "WAGNER" SIDNEY O, PAT'D FEB 22, 1910; **Finish:** iron or
nickel; **Circa:** 1915-1920s; **VALUE: $150-$250.** Note the long, turned
handle with a metal ferrule at the base. Also note the shape of the bail
handle where it connects to the base ring.

Below and Right:
REPRODUCTION—Advertised in 1990
for $10 each, minimum order of three.
Note the shape of the handle and the
shape of the bail ends.

Above Left, and Above Right:
TOY SKILLET WITH COVER—**Size**: No. "0", (1/2" dia.); **Cat. No.:** none; **Markings**: stylized logo, A, (cover) WAGNER TOY SKILLET COVER; **Finish**: iron; **Circa**: 1930s; **VALUE: $200-$300**. This skillet with a cover was sold in toy sets.

Right:
TOY LIPPED KETTLE—**Size**: 2 3/4" dia. x 2 1/4" deep; **Cat. No.:** none; **Markings**: stylized logo; **Finish**: iron; **Circa**: 1930s; **VALUE: $50-$75**.

SMALL TOY SKILLET—**Size**: 3 1/2" dia.; **Cat. No.:** 1367; **Markings**: stylized logo, -O-; **Finish**: iron; **Circa**: 1930s; **VALUE: $100-$200**.

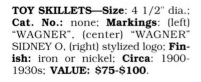

TOY SKILLETS—**Size**: 4 1/2" dia.; **Cat. No.:** none; **Markings**: (left) "WAGNER", (center) "WAGNER" SIDNEY O, (right) stylized logo; **Finish**: iron or nickel; **Circa**: 1900-1930s; **VALUE: $75-$100**.

TEA POT (shown with "0" Tea Kettle)—**Size**: 3 1/4" x 3" dia.; **Cat. No.:** 212; **Markings**: stylized logo, 212; **Finish**: aluminum; **Circa**: unknown; **VALUE**: $75-$125.

ANNIVERSARY TOY SET—**Size**: No. "0"; **Cat. No.:** none; **Markings**: WAGNERS 1891 ORIGINAL, CAST IRON COOKWARE, 100 YEAR ANNIVERSARY, LIMITED EDITION; **Finish:** iron; **Circa**: 1991; **VALUE:** $100. This may be a good investment for the future.

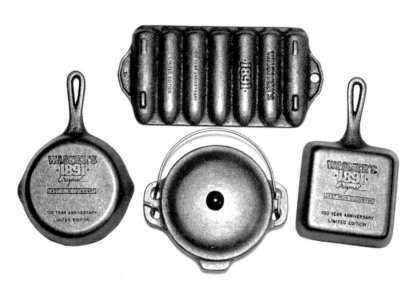

MISCELLANEOUS

HOT POTS—**Size**: (left) 3 9/16" dia. x 2" high, (right) 4 5/16" dia. x 2 1/16" high; **Cat. No.:** (left) 1364, (right) 1368; **Markings**: stylized logo, cover: HOT POT; **Finish:** iron; **Circa**: 1930; **VALUE:** $60-$75.

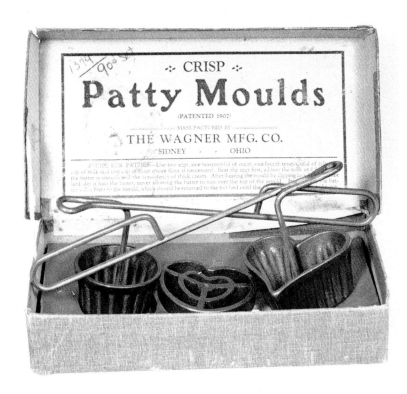

PATTY MOULD SET—**Circa**: 1925; **VALUE: $30.**

PATTY BOWL—**Size**: 5 1/4" dia. x 2 3/4" deep; **Cat. No.:** 1362; **Markings**: stylized logo, 1362D; **Finish**: iron; **Circa**: 1950s; **VALUE: $75-$100.** A bail handle was notched to make this patty mold handle.

Above and Left:
LONG BROILER—**Size**: No. 8 (19" x 9"); **Cat. No.:** none; **Markings**: WAGNER; **Finish**: iron; **Circa**: 1891-1920; **VALUE: No. 7, No. 8, and No. 9, $150.**

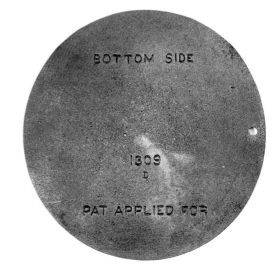

STOVE BROILER—**Size**: 10 5/8" dia.; **Cat. No.:** 1350; **Markings**: WAGNER WARE, SIDNEY O, 1350; **Finish:** iron with a black enameled wood handle; **Circa**: 1915-1940; **VALUE: $50-$75.**

Above and Top Right:
FLAME TAMER (Heat Regulator)—**Size**: 7 3/4" dia.; **Cat. No.:** 1309; **Markings**: stylized logo, PROTECTIVE HOT PLATE; (reverse) BOTTOM SIDE, 1309, PAT APPLIED FOR; **Finish:** iron; **Circa**: 1930-1940; **VALUE: $75-$125.**

FRUIT JUICE EXTRACTOR—**Size**: 6 1/4" dia.; **Cat. No.:** 453; **Markings**: stylized logo, CAST ALUMINUM, 453; **Finish:** aluminum; **Circa**: 1930; **VALUE: $30-$60.**

MAGAZINE ADVERTISEMENT from the 1920s.

Right:
No. 1 COFFEE PERCOLATOR—Size: 2 pts.; **Cat. No.:** none; **Markings**: stylized logo, 1; (glass knob) "WAGNER"; **Finish:** aluminum with "ebonized" handle; **Circa**: 1915; **VALUE: $75-$100**.

CHEESE SLICER—**Cat. No.:** 299; **Markings**: CUT RITE, MULTIPLE CHEESE SLICER, WAGNER WARE SIDNEY O, PATENT PENDING; **Finish:** aluminum; **Circa:** unknown; **VALUE: $100-$200**.

No. 3 LARGE CUP—**Size**: 2 3/8" x 3 3/8"; **Cat. No.:** none; **Markings**: stamped stylized logo; **Finish:** aluminum; **Circa**: 1910-1930s; **VALUE: $30-$50**.

Above and Right:
SHALLOW PAN No. 1- **Size**: 7" dia.; **Cat. No.:** none; **Markings**: stylized logo, 1; **Finish:** aluminum; **Circa**: 1915; **VALUE: $75. TABLE SPOON—Marking**: WAGNER WARE; **Finish:** aluminum; **VALUE: $20-$35**

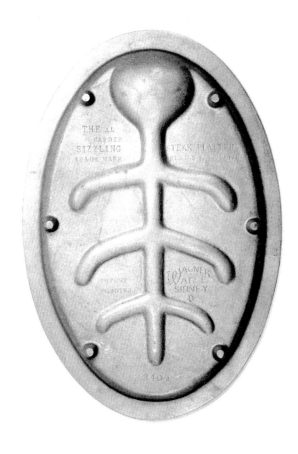

STEAK PLATTER—Size: 12 7/8" x 8 7/8"; **Cat. No.:** 340c; **Markings**: stylized logo, THE AL CARDER SIZ-ZLING TRADE MARK, STEAK PLATTER, PAT PENDING; **Finish**: aluminum; **Circa**: 1940s-1950s; **VALUE: $75.**

THE GRIDDLE   5

The Best in the World

Solid Aluminum Sugar Scoop

Wood Handled Sugar Scoop

Wood Handled Coffee Scoop

Solid Aluminum Coffee Scoop

Solid Aluminum Confectionery Scoop

Wood Handled Confectionery Scoop

Salt Scoop

Flaring Coffee Scoop

Lard Spade   Lard Ladle

Also a Full Line of Drug Scoops

ALUMINUM SCOOPS & LADLES—Circa: 1915; **VALUE: flaring coffee scoop $35-$40; ladles $15; the rest $20-**

SMOKER'S SET— Cat. No.: (kettle) 1051, (ashtray) 1051; **Markings**: stylized logo inside oval; **Finish**: black enamel, with brass wire bail on the kettle; **Circa**: 1960s; **VALUE: kettle $40, ashtray $15.**

WITHOUT STUFFER

STUFFER ATTACHMENT

ADVERTISING ASHTRAY— Cat. No.: none; **Markings:** stylized logo inside oval, SIDNEY O; **Finish:** black enamel; **Circa:** 1980s; **VALUE: $10.**

FRUIT & LARD PRESSES—
Circa: 1910-40s; **VALUE: 2 qts. $75-$100, 4 qts. or 6 qts. $75, 8 qts. $100-$125.**
Circa: 1924-40; **VALUE: 3 qts. $75, 10 qts. $100-$125, 12 qts. $150.**

Wagner Catalog Numbers

Pattern
Number   Piece

ALUMINUM

105	6 pt. Colonial Tea Kettle (automatic cover)		138-B	8 qt Sidney Tea Kettle (with double boiler)
106	8 pt. Colonial Tea Kettle (automatic cover)			
107	10 pt. Colonial Tea Kettle (automatic cover)		144	4 qt. Sidney Tea Kettle (swing lid)
108	12 pt. Colonial Tea Kettle (automatic cover)		145	5 qt. Sidney Tea Kettle (swing lid)
109	16 1/2 pt. Colonial Tea Kettle (automatic cover)		146	6 qt. Sidney Tea Kettle (swing lid)
			148	8 qt. Sidney Tea Kettle (swing lid)
115	6 pt. Colonial Tea Kettle (swing cover)			
116	8 pt. Colonial Tea Kettle (swing cover)		156	7 pt. Grand Prize Tea Kettle (swing lid)
117	10 pt. Colonial Tea Kettle (swing cover)		157	9 1/2 pt. Grand Prize Tea Kettle (swing lid)
118	12 pt. Colonial Tea Kettle (swing cover)		158	12 pt. Grand Prize Tea Kettle (swing lid)
119	16 1/2 pt. Colonial Tea Kettle (swing cover)			
			165	3 pt. or 4 cup Two-Way Coffee Maker
127	10 pt. Puritan Tea Kettle (automatic cover)		166	2 qt. or 6 cup Two-Way Coffee Maker
128	12 pt. Puritan Tea Kettle (automatic cover)		167	3 qt. or 10 cup Two-Way Coffee Maker
			168	4 qt. or 12 cup Two-Way Coffee Maker
132	2 qt. Sidney Tea Kettle (loose lid)		169	6 qt. or 17 cup Two-Way Coffee Maker
133	3 qt. Sidney Tea Kettle (loose lid)		(169 has handle and wire bail)	
134	4 qt. Sidney Tea Kettle (loose lid)			
135	5 qt. Sidney Tea Kettle (loose lid)		171	2 pt. or 5 cup Tall Colonial Coffee Percolator
136	6 qt. Sidney Tea Kettle (loose lid)		172	3 pt. or 7 cup Tall Colonial Coffee Percolator
138	8 qt. Sidney Tea Kettle (loose lid)		173	4 1/2 pt. or 9 cup Tall Colonial Coffee Percolator
134-B	4 qt. Sidney Tea Kettle (with double boiler)		185	3 pt. or 4 cup Low Colonial Coffee Percolator
135-B	5 qt. Sidney Tea Kettle (with double boiler)		186	2 qt. or 6 cup Low Colonial Coffee Percolator
136-B	6 qt. Sidney Tea Kettle (with double boiler)		187	3 qt. or 10 cup Low Colonial Coffee Percolator

188	4 qt. or 12 cup Low Colonial Coffee Percolator
191	3 pt. Colonial Coffee Pot
192	2 qt. Colonial Coffee Pot
193	3 qt. Colonial Coffee Pot
194	4 qt. Colonial Coffee Pot
195	6 qt. Colonial Coffee Pot
202	2 pt. Colonial Tea Pot
203	3 pt. Colonial Tea Pot
204	4 pt. Colonial Tea Pot
211	1 pt. Sidney Tea Pot
212	1/2 pt. Sidney Tea Pot
221	3 pt. Sidney Coffee Pot
222	2 qt. Sidney Coffee Pot
223	3 qt. Sidney Coffee Pot
224	4 qt. Sidney Coffee Pot
228	5 pt. French Style Coffee Pot
229	3 pt. French Style Coffee Pot
232	2 pt. Sidney Tea Pot
233	3 pt. Sidney Tea Pot
234	4 pt. Sidney Tea Pot
236	6 pt. Sidney Tea Pot
246	5 1/2 pt. Drip Drop Round Roaster
247	8 1/2 pt. Drip Drop Round Roaster
248	9 2/3 pt. Drip Drop Round Roaster
248-C	9 2/3 pt. Combination Cooker
249	12 1/2 pt. Drip Drop Round Roaster
250	17 pt. Drip Drop Round Roaster
251	22 1/2 pt. Drip Drop Round Roaster
246-251	Trivets for Roasters with the same numbers.
261	6 5/8" x 11" Drip Drop Oval Roaster
263	8" x 12 1/8" Drip Drop Oval Roaster
265	9 1/4" x 14 1/8" Drip Drop Oval Roaster
265-T	9 1/4" x 14 1/8" Oval Roaster and Baker with tray
267	10 7/8" x 15 5/8" Drip Drop Oval Roaster
269	12 1/4" x 18 3/8" Drip Drop Oval Roaster
261,3,5, 7, & 9	Trivets for Oval Roasters with the same numbers
272	4 1/2" Round Casserole
273	5" Round Casserole
274	6" Round Casserole
275	7 1/16 in Round Casserole
281	6" x 8 1/4" Oval Casserole
282	7" x 9 5/8" Oval Casserole
283	8 3/16" x 11 1/4" Oval Casserole
291	7 3/4" Shallow Round Casserole
292	8 3/4" Shallow Round Casserole
295	8 1/2" Double Casserole
301	6 1/8" x 8 1/4" Shallow Oval Casserole
302	6 7/8" x 9 3/8" Shallow Oval Casserole
303	6 7/8" x 10 7/8" Shallow Oval Casserole
311	4 1/2" Shirred Egg Pan
312	5 1/2" Shirred Egg Pan
321	2 7/8" Custard Cup
322	3 1/4" Custard Cup
331	6 1/2" Casserole Pan
332	7 1/2" Casserole Pan
335	9 3/4" Pie Casserole
343	3 pt. Pudding Pan
344	4 pt. Pudding Pan
345 1/2	5 1/2 pt. Pudding Pan
347	7 pt. Pudding Pan
349	9 pt. Pudding Pan

351	7" Shallow Pan
352	8" Shallow Pan
353	9" Shallow Pan
353 1/2	9 3/4" Shallow Pan
354	10 1/2" Shallow Pan
361	6 5/8" Pie Pan
362	8 1/4" Pie Pan
363	9 7/8" Pie Pan
364	10 5/8" Pie Pan
371	8 1/2" Cake Pan
372	9 1/4" Cake Pan
381	5" x 8 1/4" Bread or Cake Pan
382	5"x 10" Bread or Cake Pan
383	5 3/4" x 11 1/4" Bread or Cake Pan
385	3 3/16" Handled Ramequin
401	2" x 2 3/4" Small Cup
402	2 1/8" x 3 1/4" Small Cup
403	2 3/8" x 3 3/8" Large Cup
404	2 1/2" x 3 7/8" Large Cup
406	3" x 3 3/4" Tall Cup
408	5 1/4 pt. Water Bottle with Cast Cover
409	2 1/2 qt. Water Pitcher
410	4 qt. Water Pitcher
411	5 pt. Water Carrier
421	4 3/4" x 3" Round Jelly Mould
422	6 x 5" Round Jelly Mould
423	7 x 3" Round Jelly Mould
424	5 3/4 x 8 x 2 1/2" Round Jelly Mould
425	9 1/4 x 2 1/4" Round Jelly Mould
426	3 3/4 x 7 x 2 3/4" Square Jelly Mould
432	3 qt. Mixing Bowl
433	4 qt. Mixing Bowl
434	5 qt. Mixing Bowl
435	6 qt. Mixing Bowl
442	3 qt. Oyster Stew Bowl
443	4 qt. Oyster Stew Bowl
444	5 qt. Oyster Stew Bowl
448	10" Bundt Cake Mould
450	3 5/8" Fruit Juice Extractor (without holes)
452	3 5/8" Fruit Juice Extractor (with holes)
453	6 1/4" Fruit Juice Extractor
454	7 1/4" x 7 1/4" x 9 1/4" Sink Strainer
456	6 7/8" x 13 3/4" Corn Bread Mould (senior)
458	5 7/8" x 11 5/8" Corn Bread Mould (junior)
460	7 1/4" x 13 7/8" Bread Stick Mould (EE)
462	7 1/4"x 13 7/8" Bread Stick Mould (E)
464	7 1/8" x 7 3/16" Little Gem Pan (9 cups)
466	7 3/16" x 9 5/8" Little Gem Pan (12 cups)
468	7 5/8" x 11 1/4" Pop-Over Pan (B)
470	7" x 11 3/8" French Roll Pan (D)
472	6 5/8" x 9 7/8" Golfball Pan (F)
474	6 1/2" x 12" Vienna Roll Pan (I)
476	5 1/2" x 7 1/4" Pop-Over Pan (Q)
478	7 3/8" x 8" Pop-Over Pan (R)
480	7 1/4" x 10 1/2" Pop-Over Pan (S)
500	Bacon and Egg Breakfast Skillet (wood handle)
503	6 1/2" Wooden Handled Skillet (3)
504	7" Wooden Handled Skillet (4)
505	7 5/8" Wooden Handled Skillet (5)
506	8 5/8" Wooden Handled Skillet (6)
507	9 1/2" Wooden Handled Skillet (7)
508	10 1/4" Wooden Handled Skillet (8)
509	11" Wooden Handled Skillet (9)
510	11 1/4" Wooden Handled Skillet (10)
515	7 5/8" Buffet Skillet (5)
516	8 5/8" Buffet Skillet (6)

520	6 1/4" French Fry Skillet
521	6 1/2" French Fry Skillet
522	7 1/2" French Fry Skillet
523	9" French Fry Skillet
524	11" French Fry Skillet
537	9 1/2" Flaring Skillet (7)
538	10 1/4" Flaring Skillet (8)
539	11" Flaring Skillet (9)
557	8 5/8" Handled Griddle (7)
558	9 3/4" Handled Griddle (8)
559	10 3/4" Handled Griddle (9)
560	12" Handled Griddle (10)
578	10" National Skillet (8)
600	13" Griddle-Broiler
610	10 5/8" Bailed Griddle (10)
612	12" Bailed Griddle (12)
614	14" Bailed Griddle (14)
616	15 7/8" Bailed Griddle (16)
617	8 5/8" Wood Handled Griddle (7)
618	9 3/4" Wood Handled Griddle (8)
619	10 3/4" Wood Handled Griddle (9)
620	12" Wood Handled Griddle (10)
630	10" Rapid Heating Griddle
631	11" Rapid Heating Griddle
637	7 5/8" x 16 3/4" Long Griddle
638	8 7/8" x 19 1/4" Long Griddle
639	10 x 21 3/8" Long Griddle
640	12 3/8" x 24 1/4" Long Griddle
642	14 3/8" Wood Handled Round Broiler
644	3 egg Egg Poacher
646	6 egg Egg Poacher
648	3/4 pt. Sauce Pan; Paraffin Ladle if the handle is wood
651	2 pt. Sauce Flaring Pan
652	2 1/2 pt. Sauce Flaring Pan
653	3 pt. Sauce Flaring Pan
661	2 1/2 pt. Buffet Sauce Pan
662	3 1/2 pt. Buffet Sauce Pan
672	2 qt. Deep Sauce Pan
673	3 qt. Deep Sauce Pan
674	4 qt. Deep Sauce Pan
682	2 qt. Lipped Sauce Pan
683	3 qt. Lipped Sauce Pan
684	4 qt. Lipped Sauce Pan
685	5 qt. Lipped Sauce Pan
686	6 qt. Lipped Sauce Pan
691	5 pt. Convex Sauce Pan
692	7 pt. Convex Sauce Pan
693	8 1/2 pt. Convex Sauce Pan
695	1 qt. Paul Revere Sauce Pan
697	15 1/8" Egg Whip or Beating Spoon
699	14 1/2" Cake or Egg Beater
701	1 qt. Double boiler
702	2 qt. Double Boiler
703	3 qt. Double Boiler
704	4 qt. Double Boiler
706	14 1/2" Chafing Dish Spoon
708	9 1/2" Soup Ladle
709	11" Flat Spoon
710	13" Flat Spoon
711	15" Flat Spoon

713	11" Spoon with Hook
714	13" Spoon with Hook
716	11 1/2" Preserving Ladle or Tom and Jerry Ladle, without Hook
717	11 1/2" Preserving Ladle or Tom and Jerry Ladle, with Hook
718	10" Spoon (double knobbed handle)
720	Jar Filler
722	3 1/2" x 12" Long Handled Ladle
723	3 3/4" x 15" Long Handled Ladle
724	4 1/8" x 15" Long Handled Ladle
726	3 1/2" x/12" Strainer Ladle
727	3 3/4" x/15" Strainer Ladle
728	4 1/8" x 15" Strainer Ladle
730	7" Fruit or Gravy Ladle
731	7" Fruit Ladle with Hook
732	2 qt. Lipped Kettle
733	3 qt. Lipped Kettle
734	4 qt. Lipped Kettle
736	6 qt. Lipped Kettle
736-C	6 qt. Cooking and Baking Kettle
738	8 qt. Lipped Kettle
740	10 qt. Lipped Kettle
740-C	10 qt. Cooking and Baking Kettle
R-740	Baking Rack
742	12 qt. Lipped Kettle
742-C	12 qt. Cooking and Baking Kettle
744	14 qt. Lipped Kettle
746	16 qt. Lipped Kettle
750	20 qt. Lipped Kettle
754	24 qt. Lipped Kettle
767	6 qt. Flat-Bottom Kettle
768	7 qt. Flat-Bottom Kettle
769	9 qt. Flat-Bottom Kettle
772	2 qt Scotch Bowl
773	3 qt. Scotch Bowl
774	4 qt. Scotch Bowl
775	5 qt. Scotch Bowl
781	5 pt. Convex Kettle
782	7 pt. Convex Kettle
783	8 1/2 pt. Convex Kettle
784	10 pt. Convex Kettle
791	5 pt. Convex Pot
792	7 pt. Convex Pot
793	8 1/2 pt. Convex Pot
794	10 pt. Convex Pot
796	12 1/4" Wood-Handled Dipper (2 1/2" x 3 7/8" bowl)
798	15 1/2" Wood-Handled Ladle (2 1/2" x 4 1/2" bowl)
800	9 1/2" Cover
801	10 1/2" Cover
802	11 1/2" Cover
803	6 qt. Steam Cooker
804	3 qt. (each) Triplicate Sauce Pan Set
805	2 qt. (each) Triplicate Sauce Pan Set
820	9 1/4" Double Fry Pan
821	12" Double Fry Pan
827	6 5/8" Round Waffle Mould (low base) (7)
828	7 9/16" Round Waffle Mould (low base) (8)
829	8 5/8" Round Waffle Mould (low base) (9)
837	6 5/8" Round Waffle Mould (high base) (7)
838	7 9/16" Round Waffle Mould (high base) (8)
839	8 5/8" Round Waffle Mould (high base) (9)

840	6 3/4 x 6 3/4" Square Waffle Mould (high base)
841	7 1/2" Cake or Omelette Baker
843	(heart, hexagon, round) Boxed Swedish Cake and Patty Moulds
844	(heart, hexagon) Boxed Swedish Cake and Patty Moulds
845	(hexagon, round) Boxed Swedish Cake and Patty Moulds
846	(four card shapes) Crisp Card Moulds
848	(deep heart, round) Crisp Patty Moulds
850	Toy Skillet
851	Toy Bailed Griddle
852	Toy Waffle Mould
853	Toy Kettle
854	Toy Handled Griddle
861	10 qt. Steam Pressure Cooker
862	15 qt. Steam Pressure Cooker
863	20 qt. Steam Pressure Cooker
864	25 qt. Steam Pressure Cooker

The complete cooker includes two insert pans, a meat rack, a lifting hook, a canning trivet, and a cookbook.

900	3" x 8 1/2" Sugar Scoop
901	4" x 10" Sugar Scoop
901 1/2	4 x 11" Sugar Scoop
902	5" x 12" Sugar Scoop
903	5 1/2" x 14" Sugar Scoop
904	6 1/4" x 15 1/4" Sugar Scoop
906	4 1/2" x 12" Salt Scoop
907	8 3/4" x 15 7/8" Flaring Coffee Scoop
908	2 3/4" x 9" Narrow Scoop
911	3" x 8 1/2" Solid Coffee Scoop
911 1/2	3 1/2" x 9 1/2" Solid Coffee Scoop
912	4" x 10" Solid Coffee Scoop
913	4 1/2" x 11" Solid Coffee Scoop
914	5" x 13 3/4" Solid Coffee Scoop
915	6" x 14" Solid Coffee Scoop
921	3" x 8 1/2" Wood Handled Coffee Scoop
921 1/2	3 1/2" x 9 1/2" Wood Handled Coffee Scoop
922	4" x 10" Wood-Handled Coffee Scoop
923	4 1/2" x 11 1/8" Wood-Handled Coffee Scoop
924	5 1/8" x 13 3/4" Wood-Handled Coffee Scoop
925	6" x 14 1/2" Wood-Handled Coffee Scoop
926	2 3/4" x 8 3/8" Solid Confectionery Scoop
928	2 1/2" x 8" Wood-Handled Confectionery Scoop
930	3" x 7 1/4" Thumb Scoop
932	3" x 10 1/4" Solid Ice Scoop
934	3" x 9 3/4" Wood-Handled Ice Scoop
936	2 1/2" x 4 1/2" Drug Scoop
937	3" x 4 7/8" Drug Scoop
938	3 1/4" x 5 3/8" Drug Scoop
939	3 5/8" x 5 3/4" Drug Scoop
940	11 3/4" Solid Ice Cream Spade
942	10 1/2" Wood-Handled Ice Cream Spade
944	1 pt. Ice Cream Pail (Sefton Wire Bail)
945	1 qt. Ice Cream Pail (Sefton Wire Bail)
946	1 pt. Ice Cream Pail (Yale and Northland)
946-1	1/2 pt. Ice Cream Pail (Yale and Northland)
947	1 qt. Ice Cream Pail (Yale and Northland)
948	1 pt. Ice Cream Pail (Tall or Regular)
948-1	1/2 pt. Ice Cream Pail (Tall or Regular)
949	1 qt. Ice Cream Pail (Tall or Regular)
950	1 pt. Ice Cream Pail (Crunden)
951	1 qt. Ice Cream Pail (Crunden)

960	1 1/2 pt. Mixing Cup
962	7 3/4" x 9 x 1" Candy Tray
963	7 3/4" x 11 x 1" Candy Tray
964	7 3/4" x 13 x 1" Candy Tray
965	7 3/4" x 19 x 1" Candy Tray
966	7 3/4" x 9 x 1 1/2" Candy Tray
967	7 3/4" x 9 x 2 3/8" Candy Tray
968	8" x 21" x 2 1/2" Candy Tray
968-1	8" x 24" x 2 1/2" Candy Tray
968-2	8" x 20" x 2 1/2" Candy Tray
972	3 1/2" x 10 1/2" Solid Lard Spade
973	3 1/8" x 12 3/8" Wood-Handled Lard Spade, also a Cake or Meat Turner
974	6 3/8" x 9 1/2" Transfer Ladle
975	3 1/4" x 9" Lard Ladle
976	4" x 10" Lard Ladle
978	1 pt. Small Dipper
979	1 qt. Small Dipper
980	2 qt. Large Dipper
981	4 qt. Large Dipper
982	5 1/2 qt. Large Dipper
984	1 pt. Measure
985	1 qt. Measure
986	2 qt. Measure
987	4 qt. Measure
988	1 pt. Funnel
989	1 qt. Funnel
990	2 qt. Funnel
991	4 qt. Funnel
992	1 pt. Pickle Dipper
998	1 qt. Measure (Canadian)
999	2 qt. Measure (Canadian)
1001	6" x 12" Baker's Peel
1002	9" x 18" Baker's Peel
1003	7" x 30" Baker's Peel
1004	8" x 36" Baker's Peel
1005	2 1/4" x 9 3/4" x 13 3/4" Counter Pan
1006	2 1/4" x 10 3/4" x 14 1/2" Counter Pan
1007	2 1/4" x 11 1/2" x 16 1/2" Counter Pan
1008	2 1/4" x 12 3/4" x 18 1/4" Counter Pan
1009	Lamb Cake Mould (aluminum)

NICKEL-PLATED CAST IRON

1012	Regular Skillet (2)
1013	Regular Skillet (3)
1014	Regular Skillet (4)
1015	Regular Skillet (5)
1016	Regular Skillet (6)
1017	Regular Skillet (7)
1018	Regular Skillet (8)
1019	Regular Skillet (9)
1020	Regular Skillet (10)
1021	Regular Skillet (11)
1022	Regular Skillet (12)
1025	Skillet, Wood Handle (5)
1026	Skillet, Wood Handle (6)
1027	Skillet, Wood Handle (7)
1028	Skillet, Wood Handle (8)
1029	Skillet, Wood Handle (9)
1030	Skillet, Wood Handle (10)
1036	Handled Griddle (6)
1037	Handled Griddle (7)
1038	Handled Griddle (8)
1039	Handled Griddle (9)
1040	Handled Griddle (10)

CHROME-PLATED CAST IRON
(SILVERLITE)

S-1053	Regular Skillet (3)
S-1054	Regular Skillet (4)
S-1055	Regular Skillet (5)
S-1056	Regular Skillet (6)
S-1057	Regular Skillet (7)
S-1058	Regular Skillet (8)
S-1059	Regular Skillet (9)
S-1060	Regular Skillet (10)
S-1061	Regular Skillet (11)
S-1062	Regular Skillet (12)
S-1063	Regular Skillet (13)
S-1064	Regular Skillet (14)
S-1065	Skillet Cover (5)
S-1067	Skillet Cover (7)
S-1068	Skillet Cover (8)
S-1069	Skillet Cover (9)
S-1070	Skillet Cover (10)
S-1071	Skillet Cover (11)
S-1072	Skillet Cover (12)
S-1073	Skillet Cover (14)
S-1074	Wood-Handled Skillet (4)
S-1075	Wood-Handled Skillet (5)
S-1076	Wood-Handled Skillet (6)
S-1077	Wood-Handled Skillet (7)
S-1078	Wood-Handled Skillet (8)
S-1079	Wood-Handled Skillet (9)
S-1080	Wood-Handled Skillet (10)
S-1081	Skillet Cover (deep skillet) (8)
S-1082	Skillet Cover (deep skillet) (9)
S-1088	Deep Skillet (8)
S-1089	Deep Skillet (9)
S-1090	Deep Skillet (10)
S-1103	Flat Bacon Fryer with press
S-1107	Handled Griddle (7)
S-1108	Handled Griddle (8)
S-1109	Handled Griddle (9)
S-1110	Handled Griddle (10)
S-1120	Bailed Griddle (10)
S-1122	Bailed Griddle (12)
S-1124	Bailed Griddle (14)
S-1126	Bailed Griddle (16)
S-1147	Long Griddle (7)
S-1148	Long griddle (8)
S-1149	Long Griddle (9)
S-1150	Long Griddle (10)
S-1151	Long Griddle (11)
S-1317	Krusty Korn Kob (tea size)
S-1318	Krusty Korn Kob (senior size)
S-1319	Krusty Korn Kob (junior size)
S-1323	Pop-Over Pan (style B)
S-1326	Bread Stick Pan (style E)
S-1327	Small Stick Pan (style EE)
S-1335	5 cup Pop-Over Pan (style Q)
S-1336	8 cup Pop-Over Pan (style R)
S-1337	11 cup Pop-Over Pan (style S)
S-1390	Lamb Cake Mould
S-1401	Top Skillet for Combination Fryer-Roaster
S-1402	Deep Skillet for Combination Fryer-Roaster

CAST IRON

1050	Skillet Ashtray
1051	Kettle, Cigarette Holder
1052	Regular Skillet (2)
1053	Regular Skillet (3)
1054	Regular Skillet (4)
1055	Regular Skillet (5)
1056	Regular Skillet (6)
1057	Regular Skillet (7)
1058	Regular Skillet (8)

1059	Regular Skillet (9)
1060	Regular Skillet (10)
1061	Regular Skillet (11)
1062	Regular Skillet (12)
1063	Regular Skillet (13)
1064	Regular Skillet (14)

Nos. 13 and 14 skillets have opposite side handles.

1065	Skillet Cover, Drip-Drop (5)
1067	Skillet Cover, Drip-Drop (7)
1068	Skillet Cover, Drip-Drop (8)
1069	Skillet Cover, Drip-Drop (9)
1070	Skillet Cover, Drip-Drop (10)
1071	Skillet Cover, Drip-Drop (11)
1072	Skillet Cover, Drip-Drop (12)
1073	Skillet Cover, Drip-Drop (14)
1075	Skillet, Wood Handle (5)
1076	Skillet, Wood Handle (6)
1077	Skillet, Wood Handle (7)
1078	Skillet, Wood Handle (8)
1079	Skillet, Wood Handle (9)
1080	Skillet, Wood Handle (10)
1081	Skillet Cover, Drip-Drop (8) (fits skillet 1088)
1082	Skillet Cover, Drip-Drop (9) (fits skillet 1089)
1088	Skillet, Extra Deep (8)
1088-C	Skillet Roaster (8)
1089	Skillet, Extra Deep (9)
1089-C	Skillet Roaster (9)
1090	Skillet, Extra Deep (10)
1097	Skillet-Griddle (7)
1098	Skillet-Griddle (8)
1099	Skillet-Griddle (9)
1100	Skillet-Griddle (10)
1101	Bacon and Egg Skillet
1102	Greaseless Frying Skillet
1106	Handled Griddle (6)
1107	Handled Griddle (7)
1108	Handled Griddle (8)
1109	Handled Griddle (9)
1110	Handled Griddle (10)
1120	Bailed Griddle (10)
1122	Bailed Griddle (12)
1124	Bailed Griddle (14)
1126	Bailed Griddle (16)
1126-V	Skillet Grill 9" dia. (6)
1129-V	Skillet Grill 10 1/2" dia. (9)
1137	Griddle, Wood Handle (7)
1138	Griddle, Wood Handle (8)
1139	Griddle, Wood Handle (9)
1140	Griddle, Wood Handle (10)
1147	Griddle, Long (7)
1148	Griddle, Long (8)
1149	Griddle, Long (9)
1150	Griddle, Long (10)
1151	Griddle, Long (11)
1157	Griddle, Long (bailed) (7)
1158	Griddle, Long (bailed) (8)
1159	Griddle, Long (bailed) (9)
1160	Griddle, Long (bailed) (10)
1168	Griddle, Long (flat bottom) (8)
1169	Griddle, Long (flat bottom) (9)
1172	Scotch Bowl, 3 qts. (2)
1173	Scotch Bowl, 4 qts. (3)
1174	Scotch Bowl, 5 qts. (4)
1175	Scotch Bowl, 6 qts. (5)
1182	Yankee Bowl, 4 qts. (2)
1183	Yankee Bowl, 6 qts. (3)

1184	Yankee Bowl, 7 qts. (4)
1185	Yankee Bowl, 9 qts. (5)
1194	Maslin Kettle, 4 qts. (4)
1196	Maslin Kettle, 6 qts. (6)
1198	Maslin Kettle, 8 qts. (8)
1202	Maslin Kettle, 12 qts. (12)
1206	Regular Kettle, 4 qts. (6)
1207	Regular Kettle, 6 qts. (7)
1208	Regular Kettle, 8 qts. (8)
1209	Regular Kettle, 10 qts. (9)
1217	Low Kettle, 5 qts. (7)
1218	Low Kettle, 6 qts. (8) (LATE: Square Skillet)
1219	Low Kettle, 8 qts. (9) (LATE: Square Warm-Over pan, 9 5/8")
1220	Square Skillet 11 1/4"
1226	Kettle, Flat Bottom, 4 qts. (6)
1227	Kettle, Flat Bottom, 6 qts. (7)
1228	Kettle, Flat Bottom, 7 qts. (8)
1229	Kettle, Flat Bottom, 9 qts. (9)
1230	Kettle, Flat Bottom, 12 qts. (10)
1232	Kettle, Flat Bottom, 16 qts. (12)
1237	Pot, Flat Bottom, Bulged, 6 qts. (7)
1238	Pot, Flat Bottom, Bulged, 8 qts. (8)
1239	Pot, Flat Bottom, Bulged, 11 qts. (9)
1247	Pot, Regular Bulged, 7 qts. (7)
1248	Pot, Regular Bulged, 9 qts. (8)
1249	Pot, Regular Bulged, 12 qts. (9)
1257	Pot, Eccentric (New England Style) 8 qts. (7)
1258	Pot, Eccentric (New England Style) 12 qts. (8)
1259	Pot, Eccentric (New England Style) 15 qts. (9)
1266	Round Roaster, Drip-Drop, 2 1/2 qts. (6)
1267	Round Roaster, Drip-Drop, 3 1/2 qts. (7)
1268	Round Roaster, Drip-Drop, 5 qts. (8)
1269	Round Roaster, Drip-Drop, 6 qts. (9)
1270	Round Roaster, Drip-Drop, 8 qts. (10)
1271	Round Roaster, Drip-Drop, 12 qts. (11)

Cast aluminum trivets were furnished with the Iron Round Roasters. Lids were match numbered to the pot section of the roasters. Cast iron trivets were provided later.

1275-1	Skillet Oven (top)
1275-2	Skillet Oven (bottom)
1276-1	Skillet Oven (top)
1276-2	Skillet Oven (bottom)
1281	Oval Roaster, Drip-Drop 6 5/8" x 11 1/8" 2 7/8 qts. (1)
1283	Oval Roaster, Drip-Drop 8" x 121/4" 4 qts. (3)
1285	Oval Roaster, Drip-Drop 9 1/4" x 14 1/4" 5 1/3 qts. (5)
1287	Oval Roaster, Drip-Drop 10 7/8" x 15 3/4" 9 qts. (7)
1289	Oval Roaster, Drip-Drop 12 3/8" x 18 1/2" 14 1/2 qts. (9)

Cast aluminum trivets were furnished with the Iron Oval Roasters. Lids were match-numbered to the pot section of the roasters. Cast iron trivets were provided later.

1298	Dutch Oven, with Legs 5 qts. (8)
1299	Dutch Oven, with Legs 6 qt (9)
1300	Dutch Oven, with Legs 8 qts. (10)
1301	Dutch Oven, with Legs 12 qts. (11)

Trivets were not furnished with the Dutch Ovens. Lids were match numbered to the pot sections.

1305	Square Iron Heater (polished or plain) 11 x 11"
1308	Round Iron Heater (polished or plain) 10 1/2"
1309	Flame Tamer
1310	Cake Mould (bundt) 10 in dia.

1312	Danish Cake Pan (aebleskiver), 9" (no rim)
1314	Danish Cake Pan (aebleskiver), 9 3/8" (rimmed)
1316	Swedish Plett Pan (swedish pancake pan), 9 1/4"
1317	Krusty Korn Kob Mould (tea size)
1318	Krusty Korn Kob Mould (senior size)
1319	Krusty Korn Kob Mould (junior size)
1320	Little Gem Pan 7 3/16" x 9 5/8" (9 cups)
1320	Little Gem Pan 7 3/16" x 9 5/8" (12 cups
1321	Little Gem Pan 7 1/8" x 7 3/16" (9 cups)
1322	Gem Pan (Style A) (11 cups, flat)
1323	Gem Pan (Style B) (11 cups, pop-over)
1324	Gem Pan (Style C) (11 cups, turk head without rim)
1325	Gem Pan (Style D) (12 cups, french roll)
1326	Gem Pan (Style E) (11 cups, bread stick)
1327	Gem Pan (Style EE) (22 cups, bread stick)
1328	Gem Pan (Style F) (12 cups, golfball)
1329	Gem Pan (Style G) (8 cups, rectangular)
1330	Gem Pan (Style H) (4 cups, french bread)
1331	Gem Pan (Style I) (6 cups, vienna roll)
1334	Gem Pan (Style O) (5 cups, large french roll)
1335	Gem Pan (Style Q) (5 cups, pop-over with lid lifter handle)
1336	Gem Pan (Style R) (8 cups, pop-over with lid lifter handle)
1337	Gem Pan (Style S) (11 cups, pop-over with lid lifter handle)
1338	Gem Pan (Style T) (12 cups, turk head with rim)
1339	Gem Pan (Style U) (6 cups, turk head with rim)
1340	Little Slam Gem Pan

With the exception of 1326,1327,1334, and 1340, all pans came with and without cut-outs.

1350	Broiler, Improved, with tin lid, 10 1/2" dia.
1357	Skillet, National (7)
1358	Skillet, National (8)
1359	Skillet, National (9)

National Skillet Covers are match-numbered to the skillets.

1362	Lipped Pot (bailed)
1363	Hot Pot with lid, 4 1/4" dia.
1364	Hot Pot with lid, 3 1/2" dia.
1365	Skillet (toy)
1366	Griddle, bailed (toy) (LATE: Toy Skillet Cover)
1367	Waffle Iron (toy) (LATE: Toy Skillet, small, 3 1/2" dia.)
1368	Kettle (toy) (LATE: Toy Lipped Kettle, smooth bottom)
1369	Tea Kettle (toy)
1370	Handled Griddle (toy)

All toys are 4 1/2" dia.

1374	Patty Mould Set (round, rosette)
1375	Patty Mould Set (heart, hexagon, round)
1376	Patty Mould Set (heart, hexagon)
1377	Patty Mould Set (hexagon, round)
1378	Patty Mould Set (heart, spade, club, diamond)
1379	Patty Mould Set (deep heart, deep round)
1380	Timbale Iron, (patty iron) plain round
1381	Timbale Iron, (patty iron) fluted round
1382	Timbale Iron, (patty iron) fluted oval
1383	Timbale Iron, (patty iron) fluted heart
1384	Timbale Iron, (patty iron) fluted club (LATE: Chef Skillet 71/2" dia.)
1385	Timbale Iron, (patty iron) fluted diamond
1386	Timbale Iron, (patty iron) fluted spade (LATE: Chef Skillet 9" dia.)
1388	Chef Skillet, 10" dia.
1390	Lamb Cake Mould, 11 3/4" x 7 3/4" x 7 1/2"
1400	Square Chicken Fryer with cover
1402-T	Combination Fryer-Roaster (double skillet)

1407	Waffle Iron, 6 5/8" pans (low base) (7)
1408	Waffle Iron, 7 9/16" pans (low base) (8)
1409	Waffle Iron, 8 5/8" pans (low base) (9)

Pans available with either wood or wire handles.

1417	Waffle Iron, 6 5/8" pans (high base) (7)
1418	Waffle Iron, 7 9/16" pans (high base) (8)
1419	Waffle Iron, 8 5/8" pans (high base) (9)
1420	Waffle Iron, square pans, 6 3/4" x 6 3/4" (high base)
1421	Waffle Iron, twin pattern with square pans (high base)
1422	Waffle Iron, double twin pattern with square pans (high base)
1423	Waffle Iron, Hotel with gas stove, double twin pattern (square pans)
1425	Griddle, Hotel with gas stove, 12" x 22 1/2"
1426	Krusty Korn Kob corn dog maker (domestic size)
1427	Krusty Korn Kob corn dog maker, two pans (restaurant size)
1430	Krusty Korn Kob corn dog and sandwich maker (two restaurant size corn dog pans, one sandwich fryer pan)
1431	Same as 1430, with gas stove included. (LATE: No. 3 Wardway Skillet)
1450	Wafer Iron with Wood Handles, 5 1/4" pans (low base) (No. 1)
1451	Wafer Iron with Long Steel Handles, 5 1/4" pans (low base) (No. 2)
1455	Minute Sandwich Toaster, 6" x 6" pans
1458	Cake and Omelette Baker, 7 9/16" pans
1508	Ham Boiler, 12" x 22" x 10 3/4"
1512	Sealing Wax Ladle with Wooden Handle
1514	Sealing Wax Ladle with Iron Handle
1522	Fruit and Lard Press, 2 qts.
1523	Fruit and Lard Press, 3 qts.
1524	Fruit and Lard Press, 4 qts.
1526	Fruit and Lard Press, 6 qts.
1528	Fruit and Lard Press, 8 qts.
1530	Fruit and Lard Press, 10 qts.
1532	Fruit and Lard Press, 12 qts.
1541	Lard Press, 2 3/4 gal.
1542	Lard Press, 5 3/4 gal.

Lard press 1541 was available with or without a sausage stuffer attachment.

1551	Sugar Kettle, New Style (10 gal.)
1552	Sugar Kettle, New Style (15 gal.)
1553	Sugar Kettle, New Style (20 gal.)
1554	Sugar Kettle, New Style (22 gal.)
1555	Sugar Kettle, New Style (25 gal.)
1556	Sugar Kettle, New Style (30 gal.)
1557	Sugar Kettle, New Style (35 gal.)
1558	Sugar Kettle, New Style (40 gal.)

New style sugar kettles have three short legs.

1561	Sugar Kettle, Old Style (35 gal.) (Furnace Kettle)
1562	Sugar Kettle, Old Style (48 gal.) (Furnace Kettle)
1563	Sugar Kettle, Old Style (55 gal.) (Furnace Kettle)
1564	Sugar Kettle, Old Style (60 gal.) (Furnace Kettle)
1565	Sugar Kettle, Old Style (70 gal.) (Furnace Kettle)
1566	Sugar Kettle, Old Style (85 gal.) (Furnace Kettle)

Old style sugar kettles have no legs.

1581	Boiler and Feed Cooker (15 gal.)
1582	Boiler and Feed Cooker (25 gal.)
1583	Boiler and Feed Cooker (30 gal.)
1584	Boiler and Feed Cooker (35 gal.)
1585	Boiler and Feed Cooker (40 gal.)
1586	Boiler and Feed Cooker (50 gal.)
1587	Boiler and Feed Cooker (55 gal.)
1590	Fire Pot for Cookers

1600	Tamper, 7" x 7"
1601	Tamper, 8" x 8"
1602	Tamper, 9" x 9"
1603	Tamper, 10" x 10"
1605	Maul with wooden block, 8 lbs.
1606	Maul with wooden block, 10 lbs.
1607	Maul with wooden block, 12 lbs.
1608	Maul with wooden block, 14 lbs.
1609	Maul with wooden block, 16 lbs.
1610	Maul, Solid, 8 lbs.
1611	Maul, Solid, 10 lbs.
1612	Maul, Solid, 12 lbs.
1613	Maul, Solid, 14 lbs.
1614	Maul, Solid, 16 lbs.
1819	Pot, 34 qts. (cast aluminum)

HAMMERED ALUMINUM

2127	5 qt. Tea Kettle
3248	Round Roaster (No. 8)
3249	Round Roaster (No. 9)
3341	Sizzling Steak Platter
3342	Sizzling Steak Platter
3682	2 qt. Lipped Kettle with lid
3683	3 qt. Lipped Kettle with lid
3684	4 qt. Lipped Kettle with lid
3685	5 qt. Lipped Kettle with lid
3686	6 qt. Lipped Kettle with lid

MAGNALITE

4005	Deep Roaster Pan, 9 5/8" x 15 3/8"
4007	Bake and Roast Pan, 12 7/8" x 13 3/8"
4052	Salad Bowl
4054	2 qt. Round Casserole
4056	Round Casserole with glass lid
4133	Tea Kettle
4248	Round Roaster (8)
4249	Round Roaster (9)
4263	Oval Roaster (3)
4265	Oval Roaster (5)
4267	Oval Roaster (7)
4269	Oval Roaster (9)
4341	Sizzling Steak Platter
4342	Sizzling Steak Platter
4506	8" Covered Skillet (6)
4507	8" Chef Skillet
4508	10" Covered Skillet (8)
4509	10" Chef Skillet
4509-C	10" Chef Skillet Cover
4510	Square Skillet with lid
4512	12" Covered Skillet
4569	10 1/2" Covered Chicken Fryer
4570	12" Covered Chicken Fryer
4602	12" x 12 1/2" Broiler-Griddle
4672	2 qt. Covered Gourmet Pan
4680	1 qt. Covered Petite Gourmet Pan
4681	1 1/2 qt. Covered Sauce Pan
4682	2 qt. Covered Sauce Pan
4683	3 qt. Covered Sauce Pan
4684	4 qt. Covered Sauce Pan
4738	7 1/2 qt. Deep Kettle Dutch Oven

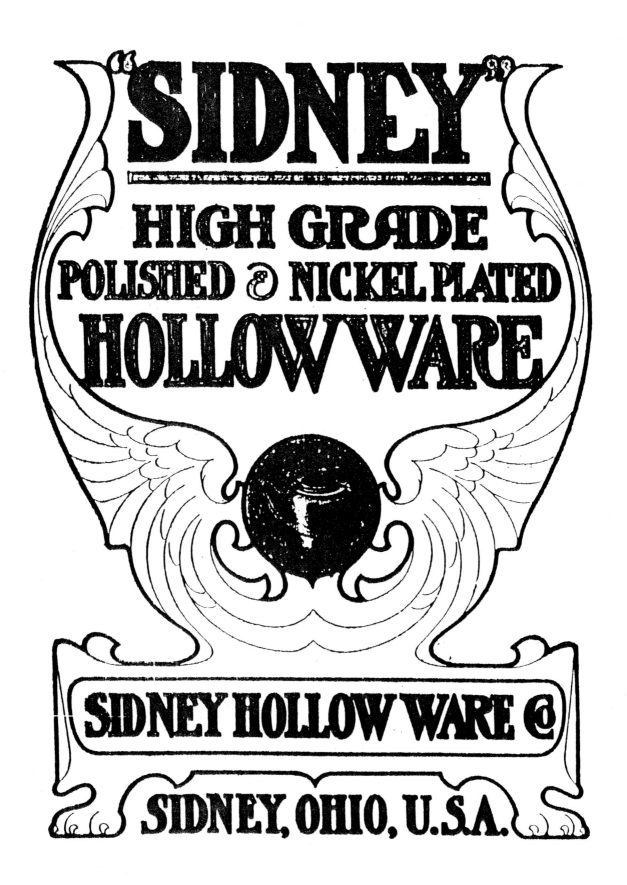

THE SIDNEY HOLLOW WARE COMPANY
SIDNEY, OHIO

The Sidney Hollow Ware Company was founded by Philip Smith in Sidney, Ohio.

Phillip Smith was born in 1839, the son of a foundryman who had emigrated from Germany in 1834. The boy learned the molders' trade at the age of fourteen in a foundry in Dayton, Ohio. When he was twenty-one he moved to Sidney, Ohio, and started out in business for himself. With his twenty-five dollars of capital, he was able to purchase the site of an old foundry which had been destroyed by fire, and in 1859 he put up his first shop. He was soon joined by his brother, and the P. Smith, Bro. & Co. was formed.

The company was quite diversified, manufacturing bells, lard presses, kettles, and stoves in their foundries. They also manufactured grain warehouse and elevator machinery, as well as hub, spoke, and bending machinery. By 1886 they were manufacturing a general assortment of hollow ware.

Demand for their retort coal stoves, invented by F.J. Gould, became greater than the company's facilities could handle, so in 1888, they accepted propositions to move the stove foundry to Marion, Indiana. In March of 1888, after moving the stove works to Marion, Philip Smith built an addition to his Sidney foundry, expressly for the purpose of manufacturing hollow ware. He employed twenty-four workers to operate his new company: The Sidney Hollow Ware Company. For ten years, the Sidney Hollow Ware Company produced the finest quality polished hollow ware.

In 1897, Philip Smith sold the hollow ware business to his competitor, the Wagner Manufacturing Company, also of Sidney, Ohio.

SIDNEY HOLLOWWARE Co., SIDNEY O
Circa: 1887-1898;

No. 6	$30	No. 10	$75
No. 7	$30	No. 11	$150
No. 8	$50	No. 12	$85
No. 9	$50		

REGULAR SKILLETS

Sidney O (script)
Circa: 1887

No. 6	$30
No. 7	$35
No. 8	$35
No. 9	$50
No. 10	$60
No. 11	$100

SHALLOW SKILLET—Size: No. 8; **Markings**: SIDNEY HOLLOW WARE Co., SIDNEY O; **Finish**: polished or nickel; **Circa**: 1887-1898; **VALUE**: Nos. 7, 8, 9, and 10, $100-$150.

HANDLED GRIDDLE—Size: No. 9; **Markings**: Sidney O (script); **Finish**: polished or nickel; **Circa**: 1887-1890; **VALUE**: $75.

Above and Right:
SCOTCH BOWL—Size: No. 2; **Markings**: Sidney O (script); **Finish**: iron or nickel; **Circa**: 1887-1890; **VALUE**: No. 2, $50-$75; No. 3, No. 4, and No. 5, $40-$60.

Left and Below:
"SIDNEY" WAFFLE IRON—Size: No. 8; **Markings**: SIDNEY HOLLOW WARE Co., PAT'D OCT 18, 1896; **Finish**: polished iron or nickle; **Circa**: 1895-1898; **VALUE: No. 7 and No. 8, $125**.

(No Model.)

E. F. NUTT, Dec'd.
J. N. Nutt, Administrator.
WAFFLE IRON.

No. 569,227.   Patented Oct. 13, 1896.

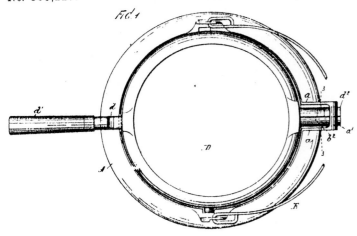

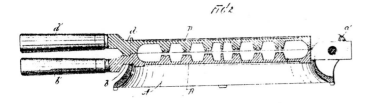

WITNESSES:

ATTORNEYS.

A patent drawing for a waffle iron, October 18, 1896.

283

TOY(?) TEA KETTLE & TOY SKILLET

TOY SKILLET— **Size**: No. "0"; **Markings**: SIDNEY HOLLOW WARE Co., SIDNEY O; **Finish**: polished iron; **Circa**: 1887-1898; **VALUE**: $100-$150.

Left and Above Left:
TOY(?) TEA KETTLE—Size: 4 1/4" dia. x 5" high; **Markings**: (cover) SIDNEY HOLLOWARE Co. **Finish**: polished iron; **Circa**: 1887-1898; **VALUE**: $300-$500.

THE FAVORITE STOVE & RANGE COMPANY
PIQUA, OHIO

The works of the Favorite Stove and Range Co. in Piqua, OH.

In 1848, William C. Davis started the W.C. Davis Company, located at Main and Ninth Streets in Cincinnati, Ohio. The company manufactured cast iron heating stoves and cast iron cookware (hollow ware). After the Civil War, the factory relocated to East Front Street and became known as the Great Western Stove Works.

In 1872, local businessman William King Boal purchased part ownership in the firm. From 1875 to 1888, Boal sought capital to expand the firm. During this same period, he gradually acquired controlling interest in the company. This change of control led to the retirement of W.C. Davis.

By 1880, the Great Western Stove Works had expanded into a new plant in a new location in Cincinnati. With this expansion came reorganization, and the name was changed to "The Favorite Stove Works."

In 1888, unable to secure funding for modernization of their manufacturing facilities, William Boal began looking outside Cincinnati for opportunities. After successful negotiations with the Citizens Committee and the City Council of Piqua, Ohio, William Boal and the City of Piqua signed a contract to bring the Favorite Stove Works to Piqua. The Cincinnati plant closed down its operation on December 22, 1888.

The Favorite Stove and Range Company officially opened on February 25, 1889 in Piqua Ohio, employing over two hundred and sixty men, including a hundred and twenty molders. By 1900 they employed four hundred, and their products were being shipped worldwide. The Favorite Stove and Range Company had such a huge financial impact on Piqua that it gradually became known as the "Favorite City." The name "Favorite" was used everywhere.

The founder of the Favorite Stove and Range Company, William King Boal, died in 1916 at the age of eighty four. His son, William S. Boal, took over the company as President. The new management made several changes, including an increased emphasis on hollow ware.

The Favorite Stove and Range Company had produced hollow ware as early as the 1890s, and prior to that as the W.C. Davis Company in Cincinnati, but after 1916 the product line was expanded and more heavily promoted. Hollow ware became one of the company's best sellers, particularly during the 1920s. Their line included kettles, griddles, skillets, and gem pans. They also did extensive porcelainizing, the most popular color being blue.

The depression of the 1930s hit the company hard, and sales plummeted. When William S. Boal died in December of 1933, the Favorite Stove and Range Company was facing economic ruin. By fall of 1934, an announcement was made that the firm was to be sold and shut down. By January of 1935 the firm had been liquidated and the plant facilities sold to a Cincinnati investment group. The factory buildings were then sold or leased.

FAVORITE

Thirty-eight Sizes For Wood.

Thirty-two Sizes For Coal and Wood.

"FAVORITE" STOVES

W.C. DAVIS & Co. CINCINNATI.

STOVES,

"THE BEST IN THE WORLD!"

Nearly 170,000 now in daily use!

ALL PRICES!   FROM $18 to $70.

Manufactured and Warranted by

W. C. DAVIS & CO.,

150 to 180 E. Front St., Cincinnati, O.

FOR SALE BY

W. W. WELCH,

HARVEYSBURG, - OHIO.

An advertisement for Favorite stoves, circa 1880.

REGULAR SKILLETS

FAVORITE PIQUA WARE
Circa: 1916-1934

No. 1	$60
No. 2	$100
No. 3	$15
No. 4	$75
No. 5	$20
No. 6	$20
No. 7	$30
No. 8	$30
No. 9	$40
No. 10	$75
No. 11	$150-$200
No. 12	$100

MIAMI
Circa: 1916-1935

No. 7 $30
No. 8 $30
No. 9 $30

REGULAR SKILLET—Size: No. 8; **Markings**: FAVORITE PIQUA WARE, THE BEST TO COOK IN; **Finish**: polished iron; **Circa**: 1916-1935; **VALUE: No. 8, $35; No. 9, $45; and No. 10, $60.**

SALESMAN'S SAMPLE SKILLET—Size: No. 4; **Markings**: Favorite logo; **Finish**: half blue, half gray porcelain; **Circa**: 1916-1935; **VALUE: $150-$200.**

WOOD HANDLE SKILLET—Size: No. 7; **Markings**: Favorite logo, MIAMI; **Finish**: nickel; **Circa**: 1930s; **VALUE: $75.**

SKILLET DISPLAY STAND—Markings: FAVORITE CAST IRON COOKWARE; **Finish**: wood with metal nameplate; **Circa**: 1900; **VALUE: $250-$300.**

Above and Right:
BROILER SKILLET—Size: 12 1/4" dia. x 2" deep; **Markings**:
FAVORITE PIQUA WARE; **Finish**: iron; **Circa**: 1920s; **VALUE**:
$100-$125.

SHALLOW SKILLET—Size: No. 7 (8 7/8" dia.); **Markings**: Favorite
logo; **Finish**: polished iron; **Circa**: 1916-1935; **VALUE**: No. 7, No.
8, and No. 9, $30; No. 10, $50.

HANDLED GRIDDLE—Size: No. 8; **Markings**: Favorite
logo; **Finish**: blue porcelain, iron; **Circa**: 1930s; **VALUE**:
$30.

IRON HANDLE GRIDDLE—Size: No. 9
(10 1/4" dia.); **Markings**: FAVORITE PIQUA
WARE; **Finish**: nickel or iron; **Circa**: 1916-
1930; **VALUE**: No. 9, $30; No. 7, $30; No.
8, $30; and No. 10, $50.

Above and Above Right:
COMBINATION GRIDDLE—Size: 9 7/8" dia.;
Markings: COMBINATION GRIDDLE 10, FAVOR-
ITE PIQUA WARE; **Finish:** polished iron; **Circa:**
1920s; **VALUE: $100-$125**. This griddle can be
used on either side.

LONG GRIDDLE—Size: No. 8 (19" x 9 1/2");
Markings: FAVORITE PIQUA WARE; **Finish:** iron;
Circa: 1916-1935; **VALUE: No. 7, No. 8, and No.
9, $50.**

SAD IRON HEATER OR LONG PAN—
Size: No. 9; **Markings:** FAVORITE PIQUA
WARE; **Finish:** iron; **Circa:** 1916-1935;
VALUE: $75.

DUTCH OVEN—Size: No. 8 (10" dia.); **Markings:** Favorite logo;
Finish: iron or porcelain; **Circa:** 1916-1935; **VALUE: No. 7,
$50; No. 8, $40; No. 9, $60; and No. 10, $75-$100.**

Above and Right:
SCOTCH BOWL—**Size:** No. 5 (11 3/4" dia. x 5" deep); **Markings:** FAVORITE PIQUA WARE; **Finish:** iron; **Circa:** 1900; **VALUE:** No. 2, No. 3, No. 4, and No. 5, $40.

SCOTCH BOWL—**Size:** No. 2; **Markings:** Favorite logo; **Finish:** blue porcelain; **Circa:** 1916-1935; **VALUE:** No. 2, No. 3, No. 4, and No. 5, $50.

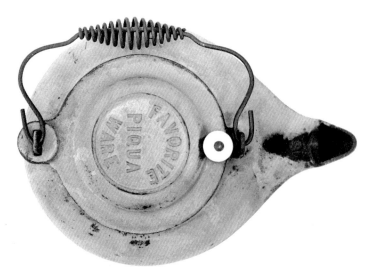

FLAT BOTTOM TEA KETTLE—**Size:** No. 9 (8 qts.); **Markings:** FAVORITE PIQUA WARE; **Finish:** blue porcelain, iron; **Circa:** 1916-1935; **VALUE: $75.** Also made sizes 7 & 8.

FRENCH BOWL—**Size:** No. 2 (9 1/2" dia. x 3 3/4" deep); **Markings:** Favorite logo; **Finish:** blue porcelain, iron; **Circa:** 1916-1935; **VALUE:** No. 2, No. 3, No. 4 and No. 5, $40.

WC DAVIS GEM PAN—Size: 10 cups (14 1/2" x 9 1/8"); **Markings**: W.C. DAVIS, CIN'TI; **Finish**: iron; **Circa**: 1860s; **VALUE: $200**. This pan was also made with 13 sections.

WAFFLE IRON—Size: No. 8 (7 1/2" dia.); **Markings**: Favorite stove logo, FAVORITE PIQUA WARE, No. 8; **Finish**: iron, japanned base; **Circa**: 1916-1935; **VALUE: $75-$100**.

HANDLED GEM PAN—Size: 7 cup (10" dia.); **Markings**: WC. DAVIS, CIN'TI; **Finish**: iron; **Circa**: 1880s; **VALUE: $150**.

Above and Right:
POP-OVER PAN—Size: 10 1/2" x 10 1/2", (cups) 2 5/8" deep; **Markings**: FAVORITE PIQUA WARE; **Finish**: iron; **Circa**: 1920s; **VALUE: Solid, $200-$300; with cut outs, $300-$400**. This pan is available solid and with cut-outs. The solid pan weighs 8 lbs., 12 ozs and is the largest of the gem pans (with the possible exception of the G.F. Filley No. 15, which is believed to have been a commercial size).

No. 4 GEM PAN—**Size**: 11 1/8" x 7 1/2"; **Markings**: FAVORITE PIQUA WARE, 4; **Finish**: iron; **Circa**: 1916-1935; **VALUE: $75-$90**.

No. 2 GEM PAN—**Size**: 13" x 6 5/8"; **Markings**: FAVORITE PIQUA WARE; **Finish**: iron; **Circa**: 1916-1935; **VALUE: $60**.

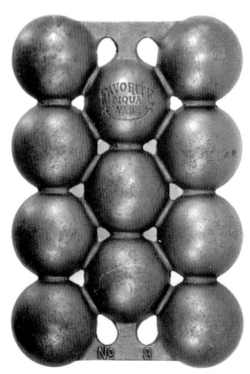

No. 3 GEM PAN—**Size**: 12 1/2" x 8 1/2"; **Markings**: FAVORITE PIQUA WARE; **Finish**: iron; **Circa**: 1916-1935; **VALUE: $150**.

EGG SPIDER & APPLE CAKE PAN—**Size**: 9 1/2" dia.; **Markings**: FAVORITE PIQUA WARE; **Finish**: iron; **Circa**: 1916-1935; **VALUE: $75**.

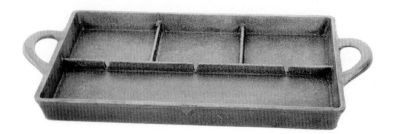

Above and Right:
BACON & EGG PAN—Size: 7 3/8" x 10 7/8"; **Markings**: Favorite logo, BAK-N-EGG, PAT APPLD FOR; **Finish:**; **Circa**: 1916-1935; **VALUE: $200-$300**.

FAVORITE PIQUA TOYS: Bailed Griddle, No. 1 Skillet, Dutch Oven, Handled Griddle, and Waffle Iron; **VALUE: $1700-$2500 for the set.**

TOY WAFFLE IRON—Size: No. 1; **Markings**: Favorite stove logo, FAVORITE PIQUA WARE, WE GUARANTEE FAVORITE STOVES & RANGES, THE BEST IN THE WORLD; **Finish**: iron, japanned base; **Circa**: 1916; **VALUE: $600-$1000**.

Below:
TOY SKILLET—**Size**: No. 1; **Markings**: Favorite logo; **Finish**: iron, nickel, porcelain; **Circa**: 1916-1935; **VALUE**: $75-$1255.

Above:
TOY DUTCH OVEN—**Size**: No. 1; **Markings**: Favorite logo; **Finish**: iron; **Circa**: 1916; **VALUE**: $200-$300.

Left:
TOY HANDLED GRIDDLE—**Size**: No. 1; **Markings**: Favorite logo, 1; **Finish**: iron; **Circa**: 1916-1935; **VALUE**: $150-$250.

TOY SKILLETS—**Size**: No. 1; **Markings**: (left) FAVORITE PIQUA WARE, (right) FAVORITE PIQUA; **Finish**: iron; **Circa**: 1916-1935; **VALUE**: $75-$125.

TOY BAIL GRIDDLE—**Size**: No. 1; **Markings**: Favorite logo, 1; **Finish**: iron; **Circa**: 1916-1935; **VALUE**: $150-$200.

MINI ADVERTISING SKILLETS—Size: 2 3/8" dia.; **Finish:** iron or nickel; **Circa:** 1916-1935; **VALUE: $100-$150.**

ADVERTISING ITEMS—Circa: 1916-1935: **VALUES:** tape measure $100, cigarette lighter $100, pins $50.

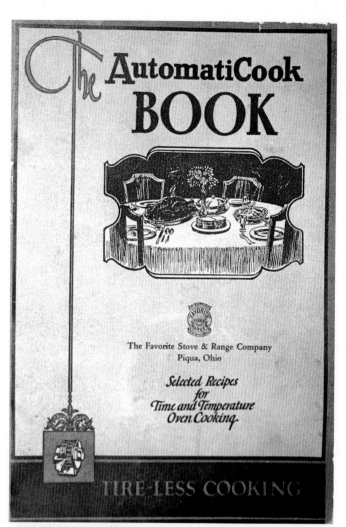

COOKBOOK—Markings: The AutomatiCook Book; **Circa:** unknown; **VALUE: $100.**

Left and Above:
CHILD STOVE—Size: 23 1/2" h x 19" w x 11" d; **Markings:** DOLLYS FAVORITE, THE FAVORITE STOVE & RANGE CO. PIQUA OHIO; **Finish:** blue porcelain with nickel trim; also available in black with nickel; **Circa:**1910; **VALUE: $4000-$6000 (blue porcelain).** This is a functional coal cook stove.

The Wapak molding room, circa 1910. *Reprinted with the permission of Glenn Miller, Wapakoneta, Ohio.*

THE WAPAK HOLLOW WARE COMPANY
WAPAKONETA, OHIO

The Wapak Hollow Ware Company commenced business on July 9, 1903 in the city of Wapakoneta, in Auglaize County, Ohio. Wapakoneta is rich with Indian history, so it is not surprising that the Wapak Hollow Ware Company included an Indian Head in their trademark.

A listing in the 1905 *History of Western Ohio and Auglaize County* states that "the buildings of this company are located in the southern part of Wapakoneta. The main building is one hundred and eighty feet in length by sixty feet in width. The firm is composed of the following members: Milton Bennett, President; Marion Stephenson, Secretary; Harry Bennet, Treasurer; Charles Stephenson, and S.P Hick."

The Hollow Ware Company's location directly on the Baltimore and Ohio railroad system, with access to the Western Ohio Railroad and the New York Central System, was ideal for shipping their products to all areas of the country.

Even though the Wapak Hollow Ware Co. boasted that it was the largest exclusive cast hollow ware manufactory in the world, and the largest and most important employer of labor in Wapakoneta, there is little recorded history of its existence. In fact, other than the listing in *History of Western Ohio and Auglaize County* there is almost no published history of this company. County records indicate, however, that the Wapak Hollow Ware Company ended in bankruptcy in 1926.

During the company's twenty-three years of production, they manufactured a complete line of hollow ware including skillets, kettles, griddles, pots, gem pans, and waffle irons, They also produced a complete line of sad irons, tailor's irons and pressing irons. They also made catch basins, manhole covers, and stove and furnace accessories.

As collectibles, pieces with the Wapak Indian Medallion are the most desirable. These skillets were of high quality and uniquely styled, particularly the handles. Many of their other products seem to copy other manufacturers' ideas, or patterns. For example, the cylinder-type hinges on early Wapak waffle irons and the accompanying base are nearly identical to the hinge patented by the Sidney Hollow Ware Company. The single ball hinge on another style is similar to the Wagner Ball Bearing hinge. The front hinge on the waffle iron with the double hinge is identical to the style Wager use on their skillet oven. It is also not uncommon to find Wapak skillets or kettles with Griswold pattern numbers or even ERIE markings faintly visible, both evidence that Griswold patterns were used.

Although little is known about the Wapak Hollow Ware Company, their products attract much interest.

Left:
WAPAK (Early logo)
Circa: 1903-1910

No. 6	$40
No. 7	$50
No. 8	$50
No. 9	$60
No. 10	$75
No. 11	$100-$150
No. 12	$75

Right:
WAPAK ('Z' Mark)
Circa: 1903-1926

No. 3	$20	No. 9	$60
No. 4	$60	No. 10	$75
No. 5	$40	No. 11	$100-$150
No. 6	$40	No. 12	$75
No. 7	$50	No. 13	$200-$300
No. 8	$50	No. 14	$125

INDIAN HEAD MEDALLION
Circa: 1903-1926

No. 2	$250-$300
No. 3	$100
No. 4	$400-$600
No. 5	$125
No. 6	$125
No. 7	$125
No. 8	$75-$100
No. 9	$100
No. 10	$150
No. 11	$250
No. 12	$200
No. 13	$700-$1000
No. 14	$500

Left:
WAPAK (Tapered)
Circa: 1912-1926

No. 3	$20	No. 9	$60
No. 4	$60	No. 10	$75
No. 5	$40	No. 11	$100-$150
No. 6	$40	No. 12	$75
No. 7	$50	No. 13	$200-$250
No. 8	$50	No. 14	$125

Right:
WOOD HANDLE SKILLET
Circa: 1903-1926

No. 5	$50	No. 9	$40
No. 6	$50	No. 10	$50
No. 7	$40	No. 11	$100
No. 8	$40	No. 12	$75

BEWARE OF REPRODUCTIONS—The Indian head medallion skillets are being reproduced. Original (right): clear, smooth casting, and fine, clear detail. Fake (left): poor casting, and rough, poor detail. Note difference the in the handle!

"ONETA" SKILLET OR SPIDER—Size: No. 7; **Markings**: ONETA, 7; **Finish:** iron or nickel; **Circa:** 1912-1926; **VALUE: No. 7, No. 8, and No. 9, $30**. Oneta was the economy line of Wapak Skillets. The ONETA line was known as "C" Grade prior to 1912.

REGULAR SKILLET—Size: No. 10; **Markings**: WAPAK (center mark); **Finish:** iron; **Circa:** 1905; **VALUE: $50**.

Left:
REGULAR SKILLET—Size: No. 5; **Markings**: WAPAK, 5; **Finish**:
iron or nickel; **Circa**: 1903-1926; **VALUE**: $30.

Above and Above Right:
EXTRA DEEP SKILLET OR DOUGHNUT FRYER—Size: No. 8 (9" dia.);
Markings: WAPAK, 8; **Finish**: nickel or iron; **Circa**: 1903-1926; **VALUE**: No.
8 and No. 9, $60; No. 10, $75.

Above and Right:
SHALLOW SKILLET OR SPIDER—Size: No. 9; **Markings**: WAPAK, 9;
Finish: iron or nickel; **Circa**: 1903-1926; **VALUE: No. 7, No. 8, and No. 9,
$40, No. 10, $50**.

REGULAR SKILLET—Size: No. 3; **Markings**: AA with arrow, WAPAKONETA OHIO, CAST IRON SKILLET (with Griswold logo undermark); **Finish**: iron; **Circa**: unknown; **VALUE: $40**. This is not Wapak. It was allegedly made by a small foundry, Ahrens and Arnold, probably using a Griswold skillet for a pattern.

SHALLOW SKILLET—Size: No. 8; **Markings**: WAPAK; **Finish**: nickel or iron; **Circa**: 1903-1926; **VALUE: $50-$100**. Note one-hole handle.

Above and Right:
SHALLOW SKILLET OR SPIDER—Size: No. 9; **Markings**: WAPAK, 9; **Finish**: nickel or iron; **Circa**: 1903-1926; **VALUE: No. 7, No. 8, $45-$55; No. 9, $50-$60, No. 10, $75-$85**. Note the three-hole handle.

IRON-HANDLE GRIDDLE—Size: No. 8 (9 3/4"); **Markings**: WAPAK 'Z' mark, 8; **Finish**: iron or nickel; **Circa**: 1903-1926; **VALUE: No. 6, $60, No. 7, No. 8, No. 9, and No. 10, $30-$40.**

IRON-HANDLED GRIDDLE—Size: No. 8; **Markings**: Indian head medallion, WAPAK; **Finish**: iron; **Circa**: unknown. This is a crude casting, not typical of Medallion castings. The medallion is not recessed, and is accompanied by the tapered WAPAK marking; again, not consistent with Wapak Hollowware markings. Is it possible this piece is not legitimate?

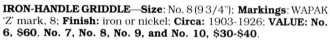

Above and Above Right:
WOOD-HANDLED GRIDDLE—Size: No. 7 (8 5/8" dia.); **Markings**: WAPAK, 7; **Finish**: iron or nickel; **Circa**: 1903-1926; **VALUE: No. 6, $50; No. 7, $40; No. 8, $40; No. 9, $60; and No. 10, $60.**

Right:
BAILED GRIDDLE—Size: No. 12; **Markings**: WAPAK 'Z' mark; **Finish**: iron or nickel; **Circa**: 1903-1926; **VALUE: No. 12, $50; No. 14 and No. 16, $60.**

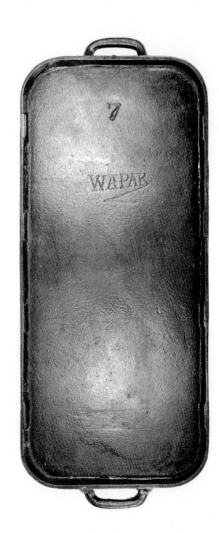

LONG GRIDDLE—Size: No. 7 (16 3/4" x 7 5/8"); **Markings:** WAPAK 'Z' mark; **Finish:** iron; **Circa:** 1903-1926; **VALUE:** No. 7, $40; No. 8, $50; No. 9, $60; and No. 10, $75.

LONG GRIDDLE—**Size:** No. 9 (21 1/2" x 10 1/8"); **Markings:** WAPAK, 9; **Finish:** iron; **Circa:** 1903-1926; **VALUE: $40.**

Above and Left:
LONG GRIDDLE-NEW ENGLAND STYLE—**Size:** No. 9 (20 1/2" x 10 1/4"); **Markings:** WAPAK, 9; **Finish:** iron; **Circa:** 1903-1926; **VALUE:** No. 7, $60; No. 8, $60; No. 9, $75; and No. 10, $100.

Right:
DUTCH OVEN-FLAT COVER—**Size:** No. 8; **Markings:** (cover) WAPAK, 8, (inside) 8; **Finish:** iron; **Circa:** 1903-1926; **VALUE:** No. 6, $75; No. 7, $50; No. 8, $50, No. 9, $50; No. 10, $75, No. 11, $100; and No. 12, $125.

Left and Below:
DUTCH OVEN WITH A DOME-SHAPED COVER—Size: No. 7;
Markings: (cover) WAPAK, 7, (outside) plain, (inside) WAPAK HOL-
LOW WARE CO COOKING UTENSILS, WAPAKONETA, OHIO, CAST
IRON, No. 7, (undermark) 1604; **Finish:** iron; **Circa:** 1903-1926;
**VALUE: No. 6, $100; No. 7, $75; No. 8, $75; No. 9, $75; No. 10,
$100; No. 11, $125; and No. 12, $150**.

Above and Right:
SELF BASTER DUTCH OVEN—Size: No. 8; **Markings**: (cover) WAPAK, 8; WAPAK
No 8, SELF BASTER DUTCH OVEN; broken basting rings inside; **Finish:** iron;
Circa: 1915-1926; **VALUE: $75-$150**. It appears that a later cover is matched with
an earlier bottom. Also, the cover has characteristics very similar to Griswold
pieces.

Above, Left, and Above Left:
DUTCH OVEN-DOME TOP—Size: No. 8; **Markings**: Indian head medallion, 8; (cover) fully marked interior; **Finish**: iron; **Circa**: 1903-1926; **VALUE**: **$100-$150**.

Left and Above:
OVAL ROASTER—Size: No. 3; **Markings**: (cover) WAPAK tapered mark, 3; (inside) 3; **Finish**: iron; **Circa**: 1903-1926; **VALUE: No. 3, $100; No. 5, $200; and No. 7, $250.**

SCOTCH BOWL—Size: No. 3; **Markings**: WAPAK, 3; **Finish:** iron or nickel; **Circa:** 1903-1926; **VALUE: No. 3, $45; No. 4, No. 5, and No. 6, $45.** Note the early kettle ear design.

YANKEE BOWL—Size: No. 3 (4 qts.); **Markings**: WAPAK, 3; **Finish:** iron; **Circa:** 1903-1926; **VALUE: No. 2, No. 3, No. 4, and No. 5, $40.** Note the early kettle ear.

Above and Right:
MASLIN KETTLE—Size: No. 6; **Markings**: WAPAK tapered mark, faint 937 (arrow); **Finish:** iron; **Circa:** 1903-1926; **VALUE: No. 4, No. 6, and No. 8, $60; No. 12, $100.** Griswold's pattern number for the No. 6 Maslin Kettle was No. 937.

Left:
MASLIN KETTLE—**Size:** 12; **Markings:** WAPAK, 12; **Finish:** iron;' **Circa:** 1903-1926; **VALUE: $100.** This is the largest of the Maslin kettles.

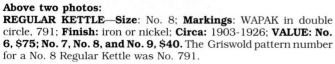

Above two photos:
REGULAR KETTLE—**Size:** No. 8; **Markings:** WAPAK in double circle, 791; **Finish:** iron or nickel; **Circa:** 1903-1926; **VALUE: No. 6, $75; No. 7, No. 8, and No. 9, $40.** The Griswold pattern number for a No. 8 Regular Kettle was No. 791.

Above two photos:
RIMMED KETTLE—**Size:** No. 8; **Markings:** WAPAK, 8, 804; **Finish:** iron or nickel; **Circa:** 1903-1926; **VALUE: No. 7, No. 8, and No. 9, $60.** The Griswold pattern number for a No. 8 Rimmed Kettle was No. 804.

FLAT BOTTOM KETTLES—Size: No. 6; **Markings**: WAPAK, 6; **Finish:** (left) iron, or (right) nickel; **Circa:** 1903-1926; **VALUE: No. 6, $100; No. 7, No. 8, and No. 9, $40; No. 10, $50; and No. 12, $75.**

LOW KETTLE—Size: No. 8, (6 qts.); **Markings**: WAPAK, 8; **Finish:** iron or nickel; **Circa:** 1903-1926; **VALUE: $45.**

Left and Above:
WAFFLE IRON—Size: No. 8; **Markings**: WAPAK, 'A' (one side), 'O' (other side); **Hinge:** Cylinder; **Finish:** iron; **Circa:** 1903-1926; **VALUE: $85.** Note the unique wire handles.

Left and Above:
WAFFLE IRON—Size: No. 8; **Markings**: WAPAK, 'A' (one side), 'O' (other side); **Hinge**: Cylinder; **Finish**: iron; **Circa**: 1910; **VALUE: $75-$100**. The wooden handles are flattened where they meet.

WAFFLE IRON—Size: No. 8; **Markings**: WAPAK, 'A' (one side), 'O' (other side); **Hinge**: Cylinder; **Finish**: iron; **Circa**: 1903-1926; **VALUE: $60-$75**. Note the grease-catching base.

Above and Right:
WAFFLE IRON—Size: No. 8; **Markings**: WAPAK; **Hinge**: Cylinder; **Finish**: iron; **Circa**: 1903-1926; **VALUE: $75**.

WAFFLE IRON—Size: No. 8; **Markings**: WAPAK 'Z' mark; **Hinge**: Cylinder**; Finish**: iron; **Circa**: 1903-1926; **VALUE: $50**. Note the grease-catching base.

WAFFLE IRON—Size: No. 8; **Markings**: WAPAK 'Z' mark; **Hinge**: ball; **Finish**: iron; **Circa**: 1903-1926; **VALUE: $50**. Also available with a high base. **No. 7, $50-$60; No. 9, $50-$60.**

Left and Below:
WAFFLE IRON—**Size**: No. 7; **Markings**: Indian head medallion; **Hinge**: ball; **Finish**: iron with contoured wooden handle; **Circa**: 1903-1926; **VALUE: $100**.

WAFFLE IRON—Size: No. 8; **Markings**: 8 (handle); Indian head medallion; **Hinge**: ball; **Finish**: iron with tapered handles; **Circa**: 1903-1926; **VALUE: $100**.

Above and Left:
WAFFLE IRON—Size: No. 8; **Markings**: Indian head medallion; **Hinge**: double ball; **Finish**: iron; **Circa**: 1925; **VALUE: $150.**

WAFFLE IRON—Size—Size: No. 8; **Markings**: Indian head medallion; **Hinge**: double ball; **Finish**: iron with contoured wood handles; **Circa**: 1925; **VALUE: $125.**

WAFFLE IRON—Size: No. 8; **Markings**: Indian head medallion; **Hinge**: double ball; **Finish**: iron with Alaskan handle; **Circa**: 1920s; **VALUE: $125-$150.**

WAFFLE IRON—Size: No. 9; **Markings**: Indian head medallion; **Hinge**: double ball; **Finish**: iron with a variation of Alaskan wire handle.; **Circa**: 1920s; **VALUE**: $125-$150.

SMALL SAD IRONS—Size: 1 lb. to 2 lbs.; **Markings**: WAPAK (handle); **Finish**: iron or nickel; **Circa**: 1903-1926; **VALUE**: No. 1, $100; No. 2, $75; No. 3, $60; No. 4 and No. 5, $35.

MEDIUM SAD IRONS—Size: 6 lbs. to 9 lbs.; **Markings**: WAPAK on handle; **Finish**: iron or nickel; tops painted aluminum or black; **Circa**: 1903-1926; **VALUE**: No. 6, $35; No. 7, No. 8, and No. 9, $60-$90; No. 10, $100; and No. 11, $100.

PRESSING IRON—Size: 18 lbs.; **Markings**: WAPAK, 18; **Finish**: iron or nickel; **Circa**: 1903-1926; **VALUE**: $100-$150.

SLEEVE IRON—**Size**: only size made; **Finish**: iron or nickel; **Circa**: 1903-1926; **VALUE**: $50.

No. 1 CEMENT TAMPER—**Size**: 6" x 8" x 4" high; **Markings**: WAPAK; **Finish**: iron; **Circa**: 1903-1926; **VALUE**: $50. Also made sizes No. 1 1/2 and No. 2. The tamper came with a wood handle.

MRS. POTTS IRONS—**Size**: No. 1 and No. 2; **Markings**: WAPAK; **Finish**: iron or nickel; **Circa**: 1903-1926; **VALUE**: $35. Note the removable handle.

Above and Right:
HITCHING WEIGHT—**Size**: 25 lbs.; **Markings**: WAPAK; **Finish**: iron; **Circa**: 1903-1926; **VALUE**: $75-$100.

BIBLIOGRAPHY

Albertson, Don, "1865 Griswold-Erie 1957," *The Erie Story*, Vol. 35, No. 8, December 1987

Principles of Metal Casting, McGraw Hill, 1955

Beers, W. H., *History of the Miami County, Ohio*, 1880

Campbell, *Casting and Forming Process in Manufacturing*, n.p.,1950

Favorite Stove & Range Company, *Catalog c.1923*

Griswold, George T., "History of the Griswold Manufacturing Co.," 1989

Griswold Manufacturing Co., *Catalog, c. 1891; Catalog No. 40, Catalog No. 45, Catalog No. 49 Catalog No. 50, Catalog No. 52, Catalog No. 55, Catalog c. 1934, Bulletin E, Bulletin E-11, and Bulletin W.*

Griswold Cast Iron. Gas City, Indiana: L-W Book Sales, 1993

Harned, Bill & Denise, *Griswold Cast Collectibles History & Values*, n.p., 1985

History Of Erie County, Warner Beers Co., 1884

History of Ohio and Auglaize County, Wm. Linn & Sons, 1905

Hitchcock, A.B.C, *History of Shelby County and Representative Citizens*, Ohio: n.p., 1913.

Hover, John C., et al, *Memoirs of the Miami Valley, Vol. 1*. Chicago:, Robert O. Law, 1919.

Hover, John C., et al, *Memoirs of the Miami Valley, Vol. 3*, Robert O. Law, Chicago, 1920.

Lowman, Les, "Griswold Becoming Memory," *Erie Times News*, 19 December, 1957.

Neuman, Geo. C., *Antique Country Furnishings*, L W Book Sales, 1984

Oda, James, *Favorite Stove & Range Co.— A History*, n.p.,1989

Sidney Journal,The, Ohio, 7 August, 1891

Sidney Hollow Ware Co., *Catalog No. 15*

Tate and Stone, *Foundry Practice*, n.p.,1910

United States Trademark Office records

Wagner Manufacturing Company, *Catalog c. 1997, Catalog No. 20, Catalog No. 30, Catalog c. 1934, Catalog No. 50, Catalog No. 58.*

Wapak Hollow Ware Company, *Catalog c.1912*; reprint. Ohio: Combs Publishing Co., 1991

GRISWOLD PATTERN NUMBERS

Pattern Number	Piece
20C	No.20 Skillet Cover, aluminum
30	Griswold Pup
31	Cowboy Hat Ashtray
32	Wind Proof Ashtray
32	No.32 Gas Hot Plate
33	Wind Proof Ashtray
35	Coffee Grinder Drawer Front
40	Base for No.2 Fruit & Lard Press
41	2 Stainer Plate for No.2 Fruit and Lard Press
42	2 Plunger Plate for No.2 Fruit and Lard Press
42	Snack Skillet
43	2 Cross Bar for No 2 Fruit and Lard Press
43	Chef Skillet
45	2 Lever Handle for No 2 Fruit and Lard Press
47	Base for 4 Qt. Fruit and Lard Press
48	Strainer Plate for4 Qt. Fruit and Lard Press
49	Plunger plate for 4 Qt. Fruit and Lard Press
50	Cross Bar for 4 Qt. Fruit and Lard Press
52	Lever Handle for 4 & 6 Qt.Fruit and Lard Press
52	16 inch American Damper
54	Base for No.10 Fruit and Lard Press
55	Strainer Plate for No10 Fruit and Lard Press
56	Plunger Plate for No10 Fruit and Lard Press
57	Cross Bar for No10 Fruit and Lard Press
59	Lever Handle for No.10 Fruit and Lard Press
63	Table Service Pot
65	Round Casserole
67	Casserole dish
68	Cover for Casserole Dish
69	Casserole Dish
71	Deep Patty Bowl
72	Deep Patty Bowl
77	Base for No. 6 Fruit and Lard Press
78	Strainer Plate for No. 6Fruit and Lard Press
79	Plunger Plate for No. 6Fruit and Lard Press
80	Cross Bar for No. 6Fruit and Lard Press
82	Oval Service Dish
83	Service Casserole Dish
84	Sauce Pan
87	Fish Service Dish
89	Casserole Dish
90	Oval Casserole, Cover 90C
91	Oval Casserole Dish
93	Oval Bean Pot
100	Base for No.110 Fruit and Lard Press
100	Gas Heater Base
101	Strainer Plate for No. 110 Fruit and Lard Press
102	Plunger Plate for No. 110 Fruit and Lard Press
103	Cross Bar for No. 110 Fruit and Lard Press
103	3 qt. Coffee Pot, aluminum
104	Lever Handle for No. 110 Fruit and Lard Press
105	No 3 Mailbox Lid
106	No.3 Mailbox Door
107	No.3 Mailbox Body
109	"0" Table Service Dutch Oven
111	603
111	3 Pt. Casserole
112	Casserole Lid for p/n 111
114	Fire Pot for Gas Heaters, No.s 100 and 200
115	Coffee Mill, wall mounted
123	3 pt. Coffee Pot
125	Coal and/or Wood Oven
128	Skillet w/wood handle, aluminum
129	Square Egg Skillet
130	Stove for No.13 Waffle Iron
133	2 pt. Tea Kettle
135	Ring surrounding valve at end of burner on has hot plate
141	No.6 Waffle Iron
142	No.6 Waffle Iron Frame, low w/bail handle
143	No.6 Waffle Iron Frame, low w/side handle
145	Coffee Mill, wall mounted
146	No.7 Waffle Iron
147	No.7 Waffle Iron Frame, low w/bail handle
148	No.77 Waffle Iron Frame, high w/bail handle
149	No.7 Waffle Iron Frame, low w/side handles
150	No.77 Waffle Iron Frame, high w/side handles
151	No.8 Waffle Iron
152	No.8 Waffle Iron Frame, low w/bail handle
153	No.88 Waffle Iron Frame, high w/bail handle
154	No.8 Waffle Iron Frame< low w/side handles
155	No.88 Waffle Iron Frame, High w/side handles
156	No.9 Waffle Iron
157	Waffle Iron Frame, low w/bail handle
158	No.99 Waffle Iron Frame, high w/bail handle
159	No.9 Waffle Iron Frame, low w/side handles
160	No.99 Waffle Iron Frame, high w/side handles
161	No.11 Square Waffle Iron
162	No.111 Sq. Waffle Iron Frame, low w/bail handle
164	Waffle Iron, rectangular, three section
166	Base for No. 13 Waffle Iron
171	Size 8 Waffle Iron, hammered surface
172	Size 8 Waffle Iron, hammered surface
173	Size 8 Waffle Iron Frame, hammered, low w/side handles
176	6 cup Coffe Percolator, aluminum
180	No.10 Dutch Oven, w/legs
180C	Insert for Lemon Squeezer<aluminum
185	No.201 Gas Hot Plate, single burner
187	No.203 Gas Hot Plate, three burner
188	size 8 Trivet for Dutch Oven
189	No. 9 "Puritan" Dutch Oven Trivet
191	Burner for Gas Hot Plate
200	Base for No. 40 Kerosene Heater
200	No.107 Skillet Griddle
201	No.108 Skillet Griddle
202	No.109 Skillet Griddle
203	No.110Skillet Griddle
204	No. 6 Dutch Oven Trivet
205	Top for No. 40 Kerosene Heater
205	No.7 Dutch Oven Trivet
206	No.8 Dutch Oven Trivet
207	No.9 Dutch Oven Trivet
208	No.10 Dutch Oven Trivet
209	No.11 Dutch Oven Trivet
210	No.12 Dutch Oven Trivet
211	No.13 Dutch Oven Trivet
212	Sausage Griddle for use on commercial stove
214	Griddle for No. 130 Stove
217N	No.7 Cast Aluminum Skillet w/ Alaskan handle
218	No.3 Oval Roaster
230	Gas Griddle
233	Grate for use on commercial stove
234	No.8 Waffle Iron, CLOWS; both sides are same p/n
235	No.8 Waffle Iron Base, low w/ bail handle, no notches for leveling pins
236	No.9 Waffle Iron, CLOWS; both sides are same p/n
237	No.9 Waffle Iron Base, low w/ bail handle, no notches for leveling pins
238	Clamp tabs for wire supports on 5-Tier Dutch Oven Display Stand.
239	Feet for Dutch Oven Display Stand
241 1/2	Oyster Bowl, aluminum
241 1/2	Utility Bowl
245	5 Qt. Colonial Tea Kettle, Iron
250	Lemon Squeezer
251	Lemon Squeezer
257	No.1 Classic Ice Shave body
258	No.1 Classic Ice Shave top
259	Classic Ice Shave, blade clamp
260	7 Burner Hotel/Resturaunt Gas Stove
274	No.3 Oval Roaster Trivet
275	No.5 Oval Roaster Trivet
276	No.7 Oval Roaster Trivet
277	No.9 Oval Roaster Trivet
297	The Erie Fluter fluting iron bottom
298	The Erie Fluter, top
299	Skillet Grill
300	Heat Regulator
301	Stove Lid Lifter
302	Double Gas Hot Plate
305	No.6 Waffle Iron
306	No.6 Waffle Iron
307	No.6 Waffle Iron Base, low w/ bail handle
308	No.7 Waffle Iron
309	No.7 Waffle Iron
310	No.7 Waffle Iron Base, low w/ bail handle
310	No.10 Dutch Oven w/three legs, bail handle
311	No.7 Waffle Iron Base, high w/ bail handle
312	No.8 Waffle Iron
313	No.8 Waffle Iron
314	No.8 Waffle Iron
314	No.8 Cake or Omlet Baker Iron
315	No.8 Cake or Omlet Baker Iron
315	No.8 waffle Iron
316	No.9 Waffle Iron
317	No.9 Waffel Iron

3 inset rings

716	No.10 Skillet
717	No.11 Skillet
718	No.14 Skillet
719	No.12 Skillet
720	No.13 Skillet
721	No.7 Victor Skillet
722	No.8 Victor Sillet
723	No.9 Victor Skillet
724	No 5 Skillet
724A	No 5 Skillet, aluminum
725	No.7 Wood Handle Skillet
726	No.8 Wood Handle Skillet
727	No.9 Wood Handle Skillet
728	No.20 Hotel Skillet
728	No.7 Shallow Skillet w/three hole handle
729	No 8 Shallow Skillet w/three hole handle
730	No.9 Shallow Skillet
731	No.10 Shallow Skillet w/three hole handle
732	No 8 Deep Skillet
733	No.9 Deep Skillet
734	No.10 Deep Skillet
735	No.2 Wood Handle Skillet
736	No.6 Regular Griddle
737	No.7 Regular Griddle
738	No.8 Regular Griddle
739	No.9 Regular Griddle
740	No.10 Regular Griddle
741	No.12 Bail Griddle
742	No.14 Bail Griddle
743	No.16 Bail Griddle
744	No.12 Gas or Vapor Griddle Base
744	No.7 Long Griddle
745	No.8 Long Griddle
746	No.9 Long Griddle
749	No.8 Deep Long Pan
752	No.8 Shallow Long Pan
753	No.3 Wood Handle Skillet
754	No.7 Skillet, unmarked
755	No.8 Skillet, unmarked
758	No.4 Wood Handle Skillet
763	Side Handled Griddle, 11 inch, (export ware)
768	Center Hinge Parts for early Flop Griddle
768	No. 8 Chicken Pan, block logo, w/heat ring
768	Square Fry Skillet
769	Square Fry Skillet Cover
769	Center Hinge Parts for early Flop Griddle
769	No. 18 Long Griddle, trough around perimeter
770	Square Ashtray w/matchbook holder
771	No. 8 Long Griddle
771	'00'Size Skillet Ash Tray (smoke set)
771	Folding Griddle, end section
772	Folding Griddle, end section
772	'00' Size Handled Kettle (smoke set)
773	'00' Size Bailed Kettle (smoke set)
773	folding Griddle, center section
774	No.12 Erie Gas Griddle, btm. part
775	Square Toy Skillet
776	No.10 Bail Griddle
777	No.8 Extra Deep Skillet or Chicken Pan
778	No.9 Extra Deep Skillet
779	No.10 Extra Deep Skillet
780	No.2 Scotch Bowl
781	No.3 Scotch Bowl
782	No.4 Scotch Bowl
783	No.5 Scotch Bowl
784	No.2 Yankee Bowl
785	No.3 Yankee Bowl
786	No.4 Yankee Bowl
788	No.6 Regular Kettle
789	No.7 Regular Kettle
791	No.8 Regular Kettle
792	No.9 Regular Kettle
794	No.7 Buldge Pot
795	No.8 Buldge Pot

796	No.9 Buldge Pot
797	No.7 Low Kettle
798	No.8 Low Kettle
803	No.7 Rimmed Pot
804	No.8 Rimmed Kettle
808	No.8 Muffin Pan, aluminum
809	No.9 Golf Ball Muffin Pan, aluminum
809	No.6 Flat Bottom Kettle
810	No.7 Flat Bottom Kettle
811	No.8 Flat Bottom Kettle
812	No.9 Flat Bottom Kettle
813	No.7 Flat Bottom Buldge Pot
814	No.8 Flat Bottom Buldge Pot
815	No.9 flat Bottom Buldge Pot
816	No.7 Eccentric Kettle
817	No.8 Eccentric Kettle
820	Barbecue Grill Coal Tray
821	Barbecue Grill
824	No.8 Low Eccentric Kettle
827	No.8 extra Large Eccentric Pot, style B
833	No.8 Dutch Oven
834	No.9 Dutch Oven
835	No.10 Dutch Oven
836	No.11 Dutch Oven
837	No.8 Dutch Oven Cover, early flat type
837	No.2 Scotch Bowl w/flat bottom
838	No.3 Scotch bowl w/flat bottom
838	No.9 Dutch Oven Cover, early flat type
839	No.10 Dutch Oven Cover
840	No.11 Dutch Oven Cover
841	No.8 Flanged Dutch Oven Cover
842	No.9 Flanged Dutch Oven Cover
843	No.10 Flanged Dutch Oven Cover
844	No.11 Flanged Dutch Oven Cover
845	Table Service Caserole
846	No.7 Erie Tea Kettle
847	No.12 Bail Griddle (part of ERIE Gas Griddle)
848	Steak Platter
849	Steak Platter
850	No.9 Hot Service Plate
851	Steak Platter
851	No.7 Flat Bottom Tea Kettle
853	Table Service Casserole
854	Cover for Table Service Casserole
855	No.7 1/2 Hot Service Plate
856	Steak Platter
856	Cover for Tea Kettle
858	No.8 Safety Cooker, flat bottom
859	Loaf Pan Cover for p/n877
860	No.10 Flat Bottom Kettle
861	No.9 Safety Kettle, three legs, round bottom
862	Rabbit Cake Mold, front
863	Rabbit Cake Mold, back
863	Safety Kettle, round bottom
865	Lamb Cake Mold (early)
866	Lamb cake Mold (early)
867	No.6 Flat Bottom Kettle Cover
868	No.7 Flat Bottom Kettle Cover
870	Junior Patty Bowl
871	Patty Bowl
872	Hinge part of Wafer Iron p/n895
873	Nut Cracker
875	No.7 Long Broiler
875	Double Broiler, bottom
876	Double Broiler, top grate
877	Loaf Pan
878	Erie Double Broiler, bottom
880	Erie Double Broiler, top
881	No 8 Flat Bottom Kettle Cover
882	No.9 Flat Bottom Kettle Cover
883	No.10 Flat Bottom Kettle
883	No 7 Waffle Iron Base, low w/ side handle
884	No.8 Waffle Iron Base, low w/ side handle
885	Wafer Iron
885	No.8 Waffle Iron, female joint
886	No.8 Waffle Iron, male joint
888	No.7&8 Waffle Iron w/finger hinge
889	No.8 Waffle Iron, 1880 & 1893

	patents
889	No.7 Waffle Iron half
890	No.8 Waffle Iron, 1880 & 1893 patents
890	No.7 Waffle Iron half
891	Waffle Iron Paddles, rectangular, two section
892	Waffle Iron Paddles, rectangular, two section
894	Wafer Iron Base
895	Wafer Iron Half
897	Santa Cake Mold, front
898	Santa Cake Mold, back
900	No.2 Waffle Iron Base
901	No.1 Waffle Iron Base
902	No.0 Waffle Iron Base
903	No.00 Waffle Iron Base
903A	No.8 Long Griddle, aluminum
904	No.2 Waffle Iron, 3 cakes
905	No.2 Waffle Iron, 3 cakes
906	No.1 Waffle Iron, 3 cakes
907	No.1 Waffle Iron, 3 cakes
908	No.8 Long Griddle, small logo
908	No.0 waffle Iron, 4 cakes
909	No.0 Waffle Iron, 4 cakes
909	No.9 Long Griddle, small logo
910	No.00 Waffle Iron, 6 cakes
911	No.00 Waffle Iron, 6 cakes
913	No.8 Waffle Iron Base, low w/ bail handle
915	No.8 Waffle Iron Base, High w/ bail handle
916	No.7 Ovl Waffle Iron Base
917	No.8 Oval Waffle Iron Base
918	Flat Bottom Kettle w/side handles
919	No.18 Heart Star Waffle Iron, 1920 patent, size 8
920	No.19 Heart Star Waffle Iron, 1920 patent, size 9
921	No.7 Oval Waffle Iron
921	No.866 Lamb Cake Mold, back
922	No.866 Lamb Cake Mold, front
922	No.7Oval Waffle Iron
923	No.8 Oval Waffle Iron
924	No.8 Oval Waffle Iron
925	No.9 Oval Waffle Iron
926	No.9 Oval Waffle Iron
928	No.18 Heart Star Waffle Iron, 1922 patent, size 8
929	No.19 Heart Star Waffle Iron, 1922 patent, size 9
930	No.273 Corn Stick Pan
931	No.283 Corn stick Pan
932	No.19 Heart Star Waffle Iron, size 9
933	No.19 Heart Star Waffle Iron, size 9
934	French Waffle Iron w/three waffles
935	French waffle iron w/three waffles
936	4 Qt. Maslin Kettle
937	6 Qt. Maslin Kettle
938	8 Qt. Maslin Kettle
939	12 qt. Maslin Kettle
940	No.1 Muffin Pan, 11 cups
941	No.2 Muffin Pan, 11 cups
942	No.3 Muffin Pan, 11 cups
943	No.5 Muffin Pan, 8 cups
944	No.6 Muffin Pan, 11 cups
945	No.7 Muffin Pan, 8 cups
946	No.8 Muffin Pan, 8 cups
947	No.9 Golf Ball or Brownie Cake Pan, 10 or 12 cups
947	Lamb Cake Mold, early, large w/legs out front
948	Lamb Cake Mold, early, large w/legs out front
948	No.10 Popover Pan, several variations
949	No.10 Popover Pan
950	No.11 Muffin Pan, 12 cups
951	No.12 Muffin Pan, 11 cups
952	No.14 Erie era Muffin Pan, 12 retangular cups
953	No.20 Turk Head or Queen Cake Pan, 11 cups
954	No.22 Corn Bread Pan (bread stick pan)

955	No.23 Bread Stick Pan, 22 half sticks
956	No.2 Vienna Roll Bread Pan, 2 loaves
957	No.4 Vienna Roll Bread Pan, 4 sections
957	No.24 Corn Bread Pan (identical to p/n 961 but unmarked)
958	No.26 Vienna Bread Roll Pan
959	No.24 Bread Pan, 6 section
959	No 50 Hearts Star Gem Pan
960	No.26 Bread Pan, 2 section
960	No.100 Hearts Star Gem Pan
961	No.No. 21 Corn Bread Pan (bread stick pan), 7 sticks
962	No 32 Apple Cake Pan or Egg Poacher
963	No 31 Danish Cake Pan
964	Erie Wax Ladle
965	Cake Mold or Bundt Pan
966	No.19 Golfball Pan, 6 cups
967	No 6 Waffle Iron
968	No.7 Waffle Iron
969	Plett Pan (marked GRI SW OLD on bottom)
970	No.6 Waffle Iron Base, low w/side handle
971	No.6 Waffle Iron
972	No.7 Waffle Iron Base, low w/side handle
973	No.7 Waffle Iron
975	No.8 Waffle Iron Base, low w/side handle
976	No.8 Waffle Iron
977	No.8 Waffle Iron
978	No.9 Waffle Iron Base, low w/side handle
979	No.9 Waffle Iron
980	No.9 Waffle Iron
981	Alfred Andresen Heart Design Waffle Iron
981	Western Importing Co. Heart Design Waffle Iron
982	No.8 Victor Waffle Iron Base, low, early
983	No.8 Victor Waffle Iron
984	No.8 Victor Waffle Iron
985	No.8 Waffle Iron Base, high w/side handles
986	No.11 Square Waffle Iron Base, low w/side handle
987	No.11 Square Waffle Iron Base, high w/bail handle
988	No.11 Square Waffle Iron, 1901 patent
989	No.11 Square Waffle Iron, 1901 patent
990	No.12 Square Waffle Iron Base, for two rectangular irons
991	No.13 Rectangular Waffle Base, for three rectangular irons
992	No.14 Rectangular Waffle Base, for four rectangular irons
993	Waffle Iron Paddle, rectangular, 3 section
994	Waffle Iron Paddle, rectangular, 3 section
995	Wafer Iron
999	Alfred Andresen Heart Shaped Design Waffle Iron
999	Western Importing Co. Heart Shaped Waffle Iron
1003	Deep Fat Fryer
1004	Deep Fat Fryer Cover
1008	All-In-One Dinner Skillet, size 8
1012	No.13 Oval Skillet
1013	No.15 Oval Skillet
1015	No.16 1/2 Oval Skillet
1018	Skillet Diveder Insert; for No. 8 Skillet
1021	No.90 Double Skillet Bottom
1022	No.90 Double Skillet Top
1029	No.4 Skillet, unmarked (Iron Mountain)
1030	No.5 Skillet, unmarked (Iron Mountain)
1031	No.3 Skillet, unmarked (Iron Mountain)
1032	No.7 Skillet, unmarked (Iron Mountain)
1033	No.8 Skillet, unmarked (Iron Mountain)
1034	No.8 Deep Skillet, unmarked (Iron Mounain)
1035	No.8 Skillet Cover, unmarked
1036	No.8 Dutch Oven, unmarked
1037	No.8 Dutch Oven Cover, unmarked
1038	No.9 Dutch Oven, unmarked
1039	No.9 Dutch Oven Cover, unmarked
1040	No.10 Dutch Oven, unmarked
1041	No.10 Dutch Oven cover, unmarked
1047	No.7 Self Basting Skillet Cover, high
1048	No.8 Self Basting Skillet Cover, high
1049	No.9 Self Basting Skillet Cover, high
1050	No.10 Self Basting Skillet Cover, high
1056	8 inch Steak Plate
1064	"Griswold" name plate for display stands
1065	Dutch Oven Display Stand, top castings
1066	Name Plate for Wood Skillet Display Stand
1068	Name Plate for Skillet Display Stand
1069	5-Tier Dutch Oven Sisplay Stand, top casting w/Logo
1077	No.7 Long Griddle
1078	No.8 Long Griddle, unmarked
1081	No.6 Skillet, unmarked (Iron Mountain)
1082	No.9 Skillet, unmarkded (Iron Mountain)
1083	No.10 Skillet, unmarked (Iron Mountain>
1085	No.14 Skillet, unmarked (IronMountain)
1088	No.8 Skillet Cover,low, unmarked
1093	No.3 Skillet Cover, high, smooth
1094	No.4 Skillet Cover, hign, smooth
1095	No.5 Skillet Cover, high, smooth
1096	No.6 Skillet Cover, high, smooth
1097	No.7 Skillet Cover, high, smooth
1098	No.8 Skillet Cover, high, smooth
1099	No.9 Skillet Cover, high, smooth
1100	No.10 Skillet Cover, high, smooth
1102	No.80 Double Skillet, bottom
1103	No.80 Double Skillet, top
1108	No.18 Cast Iron Grill
1124	No.2020 Elevated Gas Hot PLate, 2-burner
1131	No.31 Single Gas Hot Plate
1160	Star Burner for Gas Hot Plate
1161	Drilled Buner for Gas Hot Plates
1168	No.401 Single Gas Hot Plate
1169	No.402 Double Gas Hot Plate
1171	No.32 Double Gas Hot Plate
1172	Legs for Gas Hot plate 502
1173	Legs for Gas Hot PLate No.s 501 & 502
1178	No.501 Single Gast Hot Plate
1180	Loose Cap Burner for Gas Hot Plate
1181	No.502 Gas Hot Plate
1182	No.503 Triple Gas Hot Plate
1183	Legs for Gas Hot Plate No. 503, wishbone style
1206	Skillet w/wood handle, aluminum
1208	Skillet w/wood handle, aluminum
1224	No.101 Electric Hot Plate
1226	No.101 Electric Hot Plate
1233	No.3 Skillet, Best Made S.R. and Co. (for Sears)
1235	No.5 Skillet, Best Made S.R. and Co. (for Sears)
1236	No.6 Skillet, Best Made S.R. and Co. (for Sears)
1238	No.8 Skillet, Best Made S.R. and Co. (for Sears)
1239	No.9 Skillet, Best Made S.R. and Co. (for Sears)
1240	No.10 Skillet, Best Make S.R. and Co. (for Sears)
1243	No.9 Self basting Skillet Cover, Best Made S.R. and Co.
1250	Waffle Iron, Best Made S.R. & Co.
1251	Waffle Iron Base, low w/side handle
1253	No.10 Popover Pan, Best Made S.R. and Co.
1257	Bacon and Egg Fryer, Best Made S.R. and Co.; variation of p/n 666
1258	No.8 Dutch Oven, Best Made S.R. and Co.
1259	No.9 Dutch Oven, Best Made S.R. and Co.
1261	No.8 Dutch Oven Cover for p/n1258
1262	No.9 Dutch Oven Cover for p.n 1259
1265	No.9 Dutch Oven Trivet
1270	Wheat & Corn Stick Pan, Best Made S.R. and Co.
1277	No.7 Tite-Top Dutch Oven
1278	No.8 Tite-Top Dutch Oven
1279	No.9 Tite-Top Dutch Oven
1288	No.8 Cover for Dutch Oven
1289	No.9 Cover for Dutch Oven
1295	No.8 Dutch Oven, no bail handle, small holes in handles
1298	No.8 Deep Tite-Top Dutch Oven
1305	Griddle for Hotel/Restaurant Gas Stove (p/n 260)
1308	Size 3 Sad Iron
1313	Classic Sad Iron Heater, round
1314	Dome Sad Iron Heater
1329	No.1001 Single Gas Hot Plate
1332	Loose CapBurner for Gas Hot Plate
1335	Food Chopper Stand
1423	3 inch Damper
1424	4 inch Damper
1425	5 inch Damper
1426	6 inch Damper
1428	8 inch Damper
1437	4 1/2 inch New American Damper
1457	Stove Burner for Stoves No.s 130 &140
1462	Stove Burner for Stoves No.s 230,250,260, and 270
1482	Lard or grease Pot, square w/ wire bail handle
1487	7 inch Oval New American Damper
1501	No.3 Merit Skillet
1502	No.5 Merit Skillet
1503	No.7 Merit Skillet
1504	No.8 Puritan Skillet
1507	No.8 Puritan Randle Griddle
1508	No.9 Puritan Regular Griddle
1512	No.10 Popover Pan, Puritan
1513	No.1270 Wheat Stick Pan, Merit or Puritan
1521	No.9 Puritan Dutch Oven Cover
1522	No.10 Merit Dutch Oven Cover
1528	Rarebit Dish
1529	Rarebit Dish
1556	No.2 Eldurado Charcoal Furnace
1602	Classic Sad Iron Stand
1605	No.702 Electric Hot Plate
1618	Removable grate for Gas Hot Plate No.703
1679	No.703 Three Burner Hot Plate
1688	Leg for Gas Hot Plate
1689	Grate for Hotel/Restaurant Gas Stove (p/n 260)
1691	Drilled Twin Burner for Gas Hot Plate
1701	Leg for Gas Hot Plate
1707	Clamp Screw for food chopper No.s 1,2,3,4
1708	Wing Nut for Food Choppers
1711	Body for Food Chopper No.1
1712	Body for Food Chopper No.2
1713	Body for Food Chopper No.3
1714	Body for Food Chopper No.4
1721	Ring for Food Chopper No.1

Part No.	Description
1722	Ring for Food Chopper No.s 2,3
1724	Ring for Food Chopper No.4
1725	Decorative Flat Iron Trivet, large
1726	Decorative Tree Trivet, large
1727	Decorative Round Design Trivet
1728	Decorative Tassel and Grain Design Trivet
1729	Decorative Grape Design Trivet
1730	Decorative Eagle Design Trivet
1731	Scroll for Food Chopper No.1
1732	Scroll for Food Chopper No.s 2,3
1733	Decorative Flat Iron Trivet, small
1734	Scroll for Food Chopper No.4
1735	Decorative Tree Trivet, small
1736	Decorative Wreath and Eagel Trivet, small
1737	Decorative Grape Design Trivet, small
1738	Coffee Pot Trivet, small
1739	Coffee Pot Trivet, large
1740	Star Trivet
1741	Crank for Food Chopper No.1
1742	Crank for Food Chopper No.2,3
1744	Crand for Food Chopper No 4
1832	No.203 Double Gas Hot Plate
1834	Legs for Gas Hot Plate No.s 201,202,203
1837	Burner for Gas Hot Plate No 202
1900	Decorative Flat Iron Trivet, large
1901	Decorative Tree Trivet< large
1902	Decorative Round Design Trivet
1903	Decorative Tassel and Grain Design Trivet, large
1904	Decorative Grape Design Trivet, large
1905	Decorative Eagle Design Trivet, large
1906	Decorative Flat Iron Trivet< small
1907	Decorative Tree Trivet, small
1908	Decorative Wreath and Eagle Trivet, small
1909	DecorativeGrape Design Trivet, small
1916	Burner for Gas Hot Plate No.502
2003	No.3 Hammered Skillet
2005	No.5 Hammered Skillet
2008	No.8 Hammered Skillet
2013	No.3 Hinged Skillet, Hammered
2015	No.5 Hinged Skillet, Hammered
2020	Elevated Hot Plate
2028	No.8 Hinged Skillet, Hammered
2039	No.9 Hinged Skillet, Hammered
2040	No.8 Hinged Double Skillet Top, Hammered
2058	No.8 Hinged Double Skillet Bottom, Hammered
2070	No.10 Hammered Popover
2073	No.273 Hammered Crispy Corn Stick Pan
2093	No.3 Hammered Self Basting Skillet Cover
2095	No.5 Hammered Self Basting Skillet Cover
2098	No.8 Hammered Self Basting Skillet Cover
2103	No.3 Square Fry Skillet
2106	No.6 Square Fry Skillet
2108	No.8 Square Fry Skillet
2148	No.11 Square Waffle Iron
2149	No.11 Square Waffle Iron
2165	No.8 Dutch Oven, hammered
2185	No.5 Oval Roaster
2298	Scroll for Food Chopper No.s 2,3
2301	Scroll for Food Chopper No.1
2306	Scroll for Food Chopper No.4
2352	Clamp Screw for Food Choppers
2358	Crank for Food Choppers No.s 0,1,2,3
2361	Clamp Screw for Food Chopper No.4
2363	No.8 Ham Boiler
2367	Thumb Nut for Food Chopper No.0
2383	Ham Boiler
2400	Folding Pancake Griddle, 3 cakes; both sides are solid
2402	No.21 Waffle Iron, American French Pattern
2403	No.21 Waffle Iron, American French Pattern
2404	No.21 Waffle Iron Base
2405	Folding Pancake Griddle, 2 cakes, solid side
2406	Folding Pancake Griddle, 3 cakes, solid side
2408	Folding Pancake Griddle, separate pans for p/n 2405 & 2406
2423	Alfred Andresen Krum Cake Pan (wafer)
2424	Alfred Andresen Krum Cake Pan(wafer)
2428	No.77 Waffle Iron Base, high w/ side handles
2429	No.9 Waffle Iron Base, high w/ side handles
2434	No.11 Long Griddle
2458	Food Chopper Crank
2459	Food Chopper Scroll
2460	No.10 Food Chopper body
2462	Top Casting for 6 lb. Sad Iron
2463	Top Casting for 4 lb. Sad Iron
2469	Scroll for Puritan Food Chopper No.11
2470	Crank for Food Chopper NO.s 2,3, and Puritan No.11
2474	Crank for Food Chopper No.4
2485	Square Sad Iron Heater
2488	Body for Puritan No.11 Food Chopper
2494	Tobacco Cutter Base
2497	Tobacco Cutter Blade Clamp
2498	Tobacco Cutter Lever Arm
2500	Tobacco Cutter Handle
2503	No.3 Hinged Skillet
2505	No.5 Hinged Skillet
2506	No.6 Hinged Skillet
2507	No.7 Hinged Skillet
2508	No.8 Hinged Skillet
2509	No.9 Hinged Skillet
2528	No.8 Hinged Chicken Fryer
2547	Wishbone Leg for Gas Hot Plate No.703
2551	Cover for No.8 Dutch Oven
2552	Cover for No.9 Dutch Oven
2553	Cover for No.10 Dutch Oven
2553A	No.10 Tite-Top Dutch Oven, aluminum
2554	Cover for No.11 Dutch Oven
2568	No.8 Hinged Dutch Oven
2585	Base for No 2511 Reflector Heater
2593	No.3 Self Basting Hinged Skillet Cover
2595	No.5 Self Basting Hinged Skillet Cover
2598	No.8 Self Basting Hinged Skillet Cover
2603	No.7 Dutch Oven
2604	No.7 Dutch Oven Cover
2605	No.6 Dutch Oven
2606	No.6 Dutch Oven Cover
2608	No.12 Hotel Waffle Iron
2609	No.12 Hotel Waffle Iron
2611	No.2 Fruit & Lard Press & cross bar
2627	No.3 Oval Roaster
2628	No.3 Oval Roaster Cover
2629	No.5 Oval Roaster
2630	No.5 Oval Roaster Cover
2631	No.7 Oval Roaster
2632	No.7 Oval Roaster Cover
2634	No.12 Dutch Oven
2635	No.13 Dutch Oven
2636	No.12 Dutch Oven Cover
2637	No.13 Dutch Oven Cover
2703	No.3 Chefs Skillet w/bakelite handle
2705	No.5 Chefs Skillet w/bakelite handle
2708	No.8 Chefs Skillet w/bakelite handle
2849	No.9 regular Griddle
2980	No.34 Plett Pan
2980A	No.34 Plett Pan, small logo
2992	No.33 Monk Pan
2992	Andresen Monk Pan
2992	Western Importing Co. Munk Pan
3010	Popover Pan, aluminum, single hanging hole
3269	No.11 Square Waffle Iron, male ball joint
3270	No.11 Square Waffle Iron, female ball joint
3365	No.8 Handle Griddle, aluminum
6138	No.15 Muffin Pan, 12 cups
6139	No.16 Muffin Pan, 6 cups
6140	No.17 Muffin Pan, 6 cups
6141	No.18 Popover Pan, 6 cups
6667	No.601 Gas Hot Plate
6669	No.603 Triple Hot Plate
6806	5 Qt Tea Kettle
7032	Elevated Hot Plate
8010	No.10 Popover Pan, aluminum
8022	No.22 Bread Stick Pan, aluminum
A4-0	Toy Sauce Pan, aluminum
A16	Coffee Pot w/base
A20	Miniature Skillet
A40	Sauce Pan
A42	7 qt. Berlin Kettle
A51	Tea Kettle, aluminum
A54L	Omlet Pan
A54R	Omlet Pan
A65	Bundt Pan, aluminum
A105	Coffee Pot w/base
A116	Coffee Pot or Pitcher, 5 pt.
A118A	Aristocraft All Purpose Grill
A124	4 pt. Colonial Coffee Pot
A128	Deep Skillet, aluminum
A134	4 pt. ColonialPercolator
A136	6 pt. Colonial Percolator
A142	2 pt. Gooseneck Tea Pot
A152 1/2	2 1/2 qt. Double Casserole or Baking Dish
A152 1/2C	Cover for 2 1/2 qt. Casserole Dish
A172	Bailed Water Pitcher
A184	4 pt. Casserole Dish
A200	Miniature Aluminum Skillet
A202	No. 2 Wood Handle Skillet
A203	No. 3 Wood Handle Skillet
A208C	No. 8 Skillet Cover, aluminum
A213	5 qt. Hammered Aluminum Tea Kettle
A236	Triplecate Sauce Pans
A240C	Cover(s) for Triplicate Sauce Pans
241 1/2	Oyster Bowl
A250	Skillet Grill
A266	6 Cup Drip Coffee Pot
A270	Miniature Bail Handle Kettle
A303	Miniature Handle Griddle
A308	No.8 Griddle w/wood handle
A327	No.7 Long Griddle
A339	No.9 Flat Bottom Griddle
A412	No.426 6 qt. pot
A412C	Cover
A424C	Cover for 4 qt. Sauce Pan
A458	No.8 Maslin Kettle
A458C	No.8 Maslin Kettle Cover
A565	Round Breakfast Skillet
A470	Toy Kettle w/bail
A483	No.3 Oval Roaster
A485	No.5 Oval Roaster
A487	No.7 Oval Roaster
A489	No.9 Oval Roaster
A502	No.5 Tea Kettle
A508	No 8 Flat bottom Tea Kettle
AA516	2 qt. Tea Kettle
A544	4 qt. Safety Fill Tea Kettle
A545	5 qt. Safety Fill Tea Kettle
A566A	Colonial Breakfast Skillet w/ wood handle
A702	2 qt. Double Boiler
A709	Ladle
A710	Slotted Spoon
A713	13 inch Serving Spoon
A715	15 inch Serving Spoon
A801	No.50 Hearts Star Gem Pan
A802	No.100 Hearts Star Gem Pan
A980L&R	Bread Slicer
A1055	7 inch Steak Platter
A1082	Oval Tree Platter
A1208C	Deep Skillet Cover
A1309	No. Handle Griddle w/wood handle

A1485   No.5 Aristocraft Oval Roaster
A1485T   Trivet for No. 5 Arostcraft Oval Roaster
A1511   Sauce Pan w/square wood handle
A1512   Sauce Pan w/square wood handle
A1513   Sauce Pan w/square wood handle
A1534   Aristocraft Tea Kettle
A1602   Aristocraft Coffee Pot
A2082   Aristocraft Venison Platter w/ wood holder
A2083   Aristocraft Deer Platter
A2092   Aristocraft Venison Platter w/ side dishes
A2103   No. 3 Skillet w/wood handle, hammered aluminum

A2135   5 qt. Tea Kettle
A2141   1 qt. Sauce Pan, hammered finish
A2143   3 qt. Sauce Pan, hammered finish
A2190   Small Family Tree Platter
A2191   Family Tree Platter
A2192   Large Tree Platter
A2510   Jelly Cake Pan
A8011   No. 11 French Roll Pan
A8018   Popover Pan, 6 section
A8027   No.27 Whole Wheat Stick Pan
A8030   Wheat and Corn Stick Pan (2700)
A8040   Wheat and Corn Stick Pan (2800)
A8262   Tea Size Cornstick Pan
A8272   Corn or Wheat Stick Pan
A8273   No.273 Corn Stick Pan
A8280   No.280 Wheat Stick Pan, aluminum
A8282   Large Corn Stick Pan

INDEX

For ease of use this index is divided by manufacturer, in the order of their appearance in this book.